Scotland's Science Next

Stories of pioneering science, technology and medicine (1850–2022)

John Mellis

First published in paperback 2021.
Previously published as Scotland's Science Next – Stories of pioneering
science, technology and medicine (1850-2021) by John Mellis
This edition published October 2022

About the author

John Mellis is the author of *Scotland's Science – stories of pioneering science, engineering and medicine (1550-1900)*, which is effectively the 'prequel' to this book. As a professional physicist, John has authored many technical papers and some not-so-technical articles in various journals and periodicals. He was born in Glasgow, where he studied Applied Physics, Logic and Semantics, and the Philosophy of Science at the University of Strathclyde. His PhD, from the University of St Andrews, was awarded for experimental and computational research on the physics of CO_2 lasers. Most of his career has been with the BT Research Laboratories near Ipswich, working on various aspects of optical communications networks and advanced software algorithms, on tech-based spinout ventures, and in global project management; he still lives in Suffolk. For many years he was a Visiting Professor in the School of Computing and Technology at the University of Sunderland. He is a member of the British Society for the History of Science and is a Fellow of both the Institution of Engineering and Technology, and the Institution of Engineers in Scotland.

For all my family and friends

Contents

Preface to the second edition

The need for a second edition of *Scotland's Science Next* was apparent almost immediately after the first publication of the book, in early October 2021. In the middle of that month, the Royal Swedish Academy of Sciences announced that a co-recipient of the Nobel Prize in Chemistry would be David MacMillan, for his ground-breaking work in a new field of research that he has pioneered, called organocatalysis. Thus Professor MacMillan, born in Bellshill near Motherwell, became the fifth Scots-born Nobel laureate in chemistry, an achievement that (as you will read) understandably gives him great pride and satisfaction, but which was inconveniently timed for the author of this book. Thanks to David's support and approval, that omission has been corrected with a new chapter, 'Cat man', which tells the marvellous story behind his Nobel award.

Beside a few minor corrections, one other update to this edition should be noted. The work of Iain Cameron and his colleagues in monitoring the extent of patches of snow in the Scottish mountains has continued. Their latest report, published in April 2022, recorded that only a single snow patch, on Aonach Beag near Glen Nevis, survived the summer into the winter of 2021/2022. This observation, and the record high UK temperatures recorded in summer 2022, remind us of the crucial importance of carrying through the international commitments to greenhouse gas reduction, agreed at COP 26 in Glasgow.

John Mellis
Suffolk
October 2022

Foreword

Scotland's Science Next (1850-2021) is the sequel to *Scotland's Science (1550-1900)* and brings us up to date with stories of Scotland's pioneering science, engineering, technology and medicine. The contribution of those connected to Scotland, through birth or by choice, to our understanding of our world and the translation of that knowledge into applications as diverse as new drugs and medical diagnostics to criminology is quite breath-taking.

John Mellis is an outstanding storyteller, and he draws us in and introduces each of his subjects both as a person, and as someone who has made a significant contribution to our world of knowledge. We get to know a little about their backgrounds, their family and life as well as what drew them to their area of science, technology or medicine. In a very welcome and accessible way, John has presented these pioneers as real people, just with very special gifts which the world has benefited from.

This book is for everyone who is curious, and offers up many unexpected gems, such as the origin of the saying "the real McCoy" (for you to uncover as you read the book). There were for me wonderful discoveries such as being introduced to Maria Ogilvie Gordon who dipped into music and zoology before becoming captivated by the geology of the Dolomites. Not only did she excel in her research on how the Dolomites were formed, but she found time to marry, have four children and be an active supporter of women's rights, becoming the president of the National Council for Women of Great Britain and Ireland from 1916-1920. I wish I could have met her! There are the unexpected Scottish connections such as Neil Armstrong and Alan Bean, the American astronauts, both of whom were born in the US but were inordinately proud of their Scottish heritage. So much so that Alan Bean, the fourth astronaut to walk on the moon, took a piece of the

McBean tartan with him to the moon and back. And then there are the well-known Scots such as Alexander Fleming of penicillin fame and Ian Wilmut whose name we always link with Dolly the sheep, the first mammal cloned from an adult cell. It was great too to find out more about the life of Richard Henderson who used novel microscopy based on electrons to show the beautiful structures within our cells, and incidentally, was also one of my PhD examiners.

This book is written with care, a great sense of history and liberal good humour. The lives and achievements of these Scots are a compelling read. I feel indebted to John Mellis for making it so easy to learn about them, to share in the adventure of their discoveries, and be inspired by their stories. Scotland truly is a great science nation.

Professor Dame Anne Glover FRS FRSE
Edinburgh
October 2021

Introduction

Whereas *Scotland's Science* described the exploits and achievements of its subjects in the period from roughly 1550 to 1900, this book concentrates on the 20th and 21st centuries. The focus is not quite exclusive, partly because any investigation into the scientific 'discovery' or the engineering 'invention' of just about anything will uncover a chain of events that is more extended and complicated than first thought. A large part of the excitement of science, and the fascination of its history, stem from the interaction of ideas and insights played out over extensive periods of time, and wide ranges of geography. As the regions of the world have become increasingly interconnected, scientific progress has become more of an international affair.

In tracing Scotland's contributions, a global perspective is certainly needed. The legacies of the Industrial Revolution, and the expansion of Britain's Empire, resulted in a large worldwide population of Scots emigrants and people of Scottish descent. Invariably the migrants took advantage of their new opportunities, and they usually brought with them the benefits of a liberal, broad education. The first section of the book is devoted to some of the notable members of that Scottish diaspora whose accomplishments were largely achieved in 'foreign' lands. Dr James Niven's struggle in northwest England to contain the Spanish Flu, while combating initial government complacency, has resonance with our own pandemic a hundred years later. The heroics of doctors in the Scottish Women's Hospitals for Foreign Service deserve more widespread recognition. And at the risk of stretching the definition a little, I have included the stories of those famous 'Scots', Neil Armstrong and Alan Bean, who were proud of their Scottish antecedents and were prominent among the brave cadre of Apollo astronauts who made the first moonlandings – the most impressive and courageous technical achievement of their century.

Any historian of the 20th century cannot fail to realise and be saddened by the devastating impact of the two World Wars. Yet as has often been the case through history, military conflict was a catalyst for urgent innovation in science and engineering. Much of our modern capability in space and electronic technology sprang from the wartime developments of radar, rocket-powered planes and missiles, and early computers. Even the discovery of penicillin by the prepared mind of Alexander Fleming was prompted by his experiences on the battlefields of the First World War. Some of the medical, technical and scientific triumphs of the last century form the middle section of the book.

Most modern scientific endeavours depend as never before on external funding. Certainly 'big' science is a costly business, though to paraphrase Benjamin Franklin, the only thing more expensive than knowledge is ignorance. Huge projects, such as the searches for elementary particles and gravity waves, demand enormous amounts of money and multinational collaborations. In each of those fields, the contributions of researchers in Scotland, Peter Higgs at the University of Edinburgh and Sheila Rowan at Glasgow, have been of fundamental importance. Nevertheless, there is still room for individuals to make a difference. Examples include the radical proposals of Alexander Graham Cairns-Smith on the origin of biochemistry, the record-breaking supernova discoveries of Tom Boles, made from his back-garden observatory, and the diligent work of Iain Cameron in monitoring the effect of climate change on the summer survival – or not – of snow patches in the high Scottish mountains. All those and more are described as 'work in progress' in the final section of the book.

Lastly, the reader may notice that a theme running through some of the stories concerns the rivalries, jealousies, precedence disputes and patent wrangles that are part of the competitive nature of science. I hope that readers will not be surprised or disillusioned by the discovery of those facets. After all, scientists are only human too.

Part One: The Scottish diaspora

1 The Scottish diaspora

Many of Scotland's exports have contributed to wellbeing and progress in the wider world. Poetry and song, dance, a rich literature, malt whisky, and the rules of golf might feature among them. But by many reckonings, it is in the migration of people that we see Scotland's most significant and fundamental global impacts. Since well before the union of the Scottish and English parliaments in 1707, doctors, scholars and soldiers left Scotland to live, learn, teach or work abroad. Since then, successive waves of emigration have taken many Scots to their favourite adopted homelands, including of course, England.

Over the course of the 19th and 20th centuries, an estimated three and a quarter million people left Scotland, principally to work in the nations of the British Empire and Commonwealth, or to that other most favoured destination, the United States of America. Many European countries, as well as Great Britain, experienced high levels of emigration to the 'new world'. Yet in most years from 1850 to 1930, annual emigration from Scotland was proportionally higher than the equivalent rate from England and Wales, and often proportionately exceeded emigrations from the more agrarian economies of Ireland, Italy, Spain and Portugal.

Much has been studied, written, and speculated about the causes underlying the statistics. It seems clear that the influences were many and various. Crop failures, famines, and then the notorious clearances of the Scottish Highlands and islands, initiated in the late 18th century by landlords eager to make agricultural improvements and space for sheep farming, resulted in the forced and voluntary departure of some 70,000 people, mainly to North America.

Industrial revolution in Great Britain was another driver, providing employment in the cities, but with terrible over-crowding and sometimes squalor. For example, by 1840, a third of Scotland's manufacturing labourers lived in the single county of Lanark. The population of Glasgow had surged to around a third of a million, and the city was said to be the worst in Europe for health and housing, with Edinburgh not far behind. Pressure on urban space prompted upward development, but not upward mobility. When tenement buildings became common, outbreaks of disease often followed. Tenements were a ubiquitous phenomenon of Scottish cities. They were initially owned by the middle classes, who then moved farther out of town to newly built houses. Factory workers moved into the old homes which were sub-divided again and again, and new cheaply built tenements, accessed through narrow closes, were erected in what had been back gardens. The census of 1841 showed that a million people – more than a third of Scotland's families – lived in one room accommodation, known as 'single-ends'. In Edinburgh, one tenement of 59 rooms, without water supply, housed 250 people. Typhus, tuberculosis, whooping cough and scarlet fever found ready breeding grounds. Remedial actions were required. Glasgow's cholera epidemic of 1847-9 prompted an Act of Parliament to commission state-of-the-art works to draw water from Loch Katrine, soon giving the city the best public supply in the UK. The twin pressures of agricultural reform and the health hazards of rapid urbanisation explain much of Scottish (and English) emigration of the late 18th, 19th, and early 20th centuries.

Of course, opportunity knocked too. Scotland's universities continued to produce scientists, engineers and medical doctors in quantities that arguably far exceeded the demand in the local economy. From the roots of William Symington's development of the 57-foot-long steam-powered *Charlotte Dundas*, launched on the Forth and Clyde canal in 1802, and Henry Bell's Clyde paddle-steamer *Comet*, which provided Europe's first commercial steamboat service, sprang world leadership in marine and locomotive steam engineering. Skilled workers from the shipyards and iron- and steelworks often followed in the wake of their exported products. By the early 1900s, Clydeside shipyards were constructing around a fifth of all ships launched worldwide, and the North British Company in Springburn was one of the largest global manufacturers of steam railway locomotives, creating a large pool of well-trained craftsmen. For the professional classes too, the burgeoning British Empire stimulated strong overseas demand for administrators, doctors, and engineers, while aggressive colonial expansion continued to require the services of Scottish soldiers and sailors. After the Second World War, yet another stimulus to emigration was presented by the Assisted Passage Migration Schemes established by Australia and New Zealand, which offered Britons the chance to migrate to the Antipodes for ten pounds sterling for adults, and free passage for children.

Over many decades, enterprising Scots exported and invested their talents and money too. Scottish-owned tobacco and sugar plantations in Virginia and the Caribbean provided much of the wealth of Glasgow's merchant class. The bequest of John McGill, a successful merchant in Quebec, enabled the foundation of the distinguished university that bears his name. Robert Fleming, born near Dundee, visited the USA in 1870, to evaluate economic opportunities. He founded the first Scottish American Investment Trust which spawned the wider investment trust movement, and enabled the financing of railways, land, and cattle ranching. Before the First World War, Scottish capital investments in North America exceeded 200 million pounds, with similar amounts invested in developments in Australasia and Asia. The company founded in Guangzhou and Hong Kong by Edinburgh's William Jardine and James Matheson had its origins in the Chinese opium trade, alongside the East India Company that drove much of the expansion of the British Empire. Jardine, Matheson & Co became a behemoth corporate conglomerate spanning shipping, railways, insurance and engineering. Perhaps most famously of all, Andrew Carnegie, born in a one-room weaver's cottage in Dunfermline, emigrated with his parents to the USA at the age of 12, and became one of the richest Americans in history. His investments in oil, railroads and bridges enabled him to donate around 350 million dollars to various institutions and charities by the end of his life in 1919, and still fund the awards of the coveted Carnegie Scholarships.

The result of these diverse historical pressures and opportunities is a present-day Scottish diaspora – albeit loosely defined – of emigrants and their descendants, numbering perhaps 50 million people worldwide, concentrated in the USA, Canada, Australia, New Zealand, Northern Ireland, and England. Scottish universities continue to export their graduates as well as attracting talented students, scientists, technologists and physicians from abroad. And as they always have, many Scots choose to live and work further afield. Currently, at least 20% of the people born in Scotland live elsewhere in the UK or overseas, and of those, around 70% dwell in the land south of the border.

.

2   All the tea in China: Robert Fortune

When you next sip a cup of tea, spare a thought for the Scottish botanist who made two daring undercover expeditions into China, and spirited out the secrets, seeds and seedlings which founded the world's tea production industry. In 1848, botanist Robert Fortune was approached by John Forbes Royle, a professor of *materia medica*, and horticultural adviser to the British East India Company. He asked Fortune to undertake a dangerous mission as an agent – some would say a spy – in the pay of 'The Honourable Company', and offered tempting rewards. Royle, an 'East Indian' Scot, explained the objective, which was clear but difficult to achieve. It was to travel surreptitiously to China, to discover and smuggle out the plants and techniques which gave the country its near-monopoly of tea production.

Fortune, aged 36, curator of the Physic Garden in Chelsea, was an experienced horticulturalist who had made his name by travelling in China for three years and bringing home many exotic plant species. This time the mission would be even more hazardous, since Chinese tea cultivators were jealous of their expertise, and China's 'tea countries' were strictly out-of-bounds for foreigners. Fortune would have to travel illegally and in disguise.

The history of tea is a long one, especially in China where the beverage has been consumed for thousands of years. By the 17th century, exports of processed tea leaves were a major source of China's income, alongside porcelain and silk. In return, British traders paid in silver, and in the form of the East India Company, plied the Chinese with opium, produced mainly in the Indian territories of the British Empire. Prized as a pain-killer, the addictive properties of the drug wreaked havoc on Chinese society. The Emperors of China banned the

Illustration 1: Professor John Forbes Royle FRS, c.1851, botanist and East Indian Commissioner

import of opium – repeatedly and without much impact – in 1729, 1799, 1814, and 1831. When the East India Company continued to sell opium to Chinese smugglers through the free-port of Canton, troubled brewed. In 1839, the Chinese authorities published an open letter to Queen Victoria, pleading for an end to the odious 'China trade'. Chinese soldiers blockaded the opium warehouses and shut down the drug 'factories' in Canton, destroying 1,300 tons of narcotic belonging to British traders. Britain responded with overwhelming military force, and the First Opium War concluded in 1842 after the Royal Navy inflicted a series of crushing defeats on the Chinese Empire. The Treaty of Nanjing forced China to cede Hong Kong in perpetuity to Great Britain, with an additional punitive payment to the British government of 21 million dollars, and agreement to the establishment of five 'treaty ports' in Canton (Guangzhou), Shanghai, Foochow (Fuzhou), Ningbo and Amoy (Xiamen), so that the sales of opium could continue.

This was some of the historical backdrop against which John Forbes Royle approached Robert Fortune on behalf of the East India Company, which had fixed its sights on seizing entirely for itself the increasingly lucrative profits of Chinese tea production. Demand had grown enormously. Tea, particularly black tea, had become the favourite drink of all social classes in Great Britain, and taxation of tea sales accounted for around 10% of all British government income. The opium trade was equally important for the British economy, and its profits financed the management of British India, over which the East India Company was the *de facto* government. Known variously as 'The Honourable Company', and 'John Company', it was a phenomenon.

Founded in 1600 as 'The United Company of Merchants of England Trading to the East Indies', by the Royal Charter of Queen Elizabeth I, it became a monopolistic multinational corporation, and an instrument of British imperial power, signing treaties, acquiring territory, minting money, making shareholder fortunes and waging war with its own army.

Despite Britain's victory in the First Opium War, there was anxiety about the security of tea and opium revenues. Viscount Henry Hardinge, Governor-General of India, and a veteran of the Napoleonic Wars, encapsulated the fears. *"It is...by no means improbable that...the Government of Pekin, by legalising the cultivation of Opium in China, where the soil has already proved equally well adapted with India to the growth of the plant, may deprive this Government of one of its chief sources of revenue...I deem it most desirable to afford every encouragement to the cultivation of Tea in India, in my opinion the latter is likely in the course of time to prove an equally prolific and more safe source of revenue to the state than that now derived from the monopoly on Opium."*

To implement that plan, break the Chinese monopoly on the cultivation of high-quality tea, and secure the revenues of 'John Company' and the British government, Robert Fortune was a natural choice. Born in Berwickshire in 1812, he served as an apprentice gardener at Moredun House in Edinburgh before working in the city's Royal Botanic Garden. At the age of 28 he was appointed as superintendent of the indoor plant department of the Horticultural Society's gardens in Chiswick, London, and moved there with his wife, Jane Penny. A few years later, after the Treaty of Nanjing was signed, the Society sent him to China, charged with collecting ornamental and useful plants, and gathering information on the country's climate, vegetation, and methods of horticulture. He spent several adventurous years in parts of China that were closed to foreigners, disguised in Chinese clothes, and learning enough of the language to pass himself off as a native from a distant province. Somehow he survived shipwreck, fever, and attacks by robbers and pirates. When he returned to London in 1846, he brought anemones, azaleas, and buddleias;

Illustration 2: An example of a Wardian Case

camellias, and chrysanthemums; orchids and rhododendrons. His discoveries included a rose, now known as 'Fortune's Double Yellow', found growing in the garden of a wealthy mandarin in Ningbo, and the fan palm *Chamaerops fortunei*. A year after his return, he published a lively account of his travels, *'Three years' wanderings in the northern provinces of China, including a visit to the tea, silk, and cotton countries, with an account of the agriculture and horticulture of the Chinese'.* For the Honourable Company, Fortune was clearly the man for their China job.

The proposition explained by Royle was tempting. Fortune would return to China to gather tea plants and seeds, which would be shipped back for cultivation in the Company's gardens at Calcutta and Saharanpur in the Himalayas. All travel expenses would be paid, and Robert would receive £500 per year, five times his salary at the Physic Garden. Moreover, he would retain the property rights to all other plants and seedlings he collected – useful or ornamental – potentially making him huge profits when sold at auction in Britain. The plants, as before, would be transported in 'Wardian cases', effectively sealed glass terrariums, which retained soil and moisture, admitted sunlight, and afforded protection from salty sea air during the long voyages. Of course, Fortune would be away from home for years. Having discussed the opportunities and risks with his wife Jane, who would be left alone with their two children, Fortune accepted the Company's offer of employment, and resigned his role at the Horticultural Society.

By strange coincidences, a succession of Scotsmen played crucial roles in the development of the worldwide tea industry. The first to note India's potential for the cultivation of tea was a Scottish ex-Army gentleman traveller who had the evocative name of Robert Bruce. In

1823, while in Assam, he discovered groves of indigenous *Camellia sinensis* plants which were used by the local Singhpo tribe to produce tea. He was allowed to take away samples of plants and seeds, and died soon thereafter, but not before communicating his discovery to his brother, Charles Alexander Bruce, who was a soldier in the employment of the East India Company. Charles in turn reported the finding, and was assigned to develop tea nurseries, and then a plantation, at Sadiya in Upper Assam. Some Chinese workers and tea plants were imported, but cross-pollination with the indigenous specimens failed to produce healthy plants. A nursery consisting only of the native variety was successful, and black tea of reasonable quality was produced. Bruce published his findings and methods in 1838 as '*An account of the manufacture of the black teas now practised at Suddeya in Upper Assam by the Chinamen sent thither for that purpose*'. The Assam tea industry grew from Bruce's plantation, and he was later awarded the Gold Medal of the Royal Society of Arts for his discoveries and initiatives. Tea from China was still considered superior and more desirable, but Bruce's techniques, including his astute importation of skilled Chinese workers, were examples for Robert Fortune to follow.

When Fortune arrived in Shanghai in the September of 1848, he adopted the same approach that had served him well in his previous botanical expedition. He initially hired two Chinese servants. One, known as Wang, was a clever man in his early twenties from a family of tea growers, well familiar with the routes from Shanghai to the tea countries in the interior of China, and employed to act as guide, translator, and transaction manager. The other was hired as a 'coolie' – a luggage carrier, body-guard, and assistant plant-picker. Fortune assumed the guise and clothing of a mandarin from a distant region, with a high shaved hairline and a long 'queue' of pony-tail woven into his own hair, intended as a sign that despite his strange features, he was nevertheless a subject of the Emperor of China.

In his first expedition five years before, Fortune had made an important discovery. The Linnaean Society, and Linnaeus himself, had assumed that processed green tea and black tea came from different taxa of plants, respectively named *Thea viridis* and *Thea bohea*. In fact, Fortune found that the plants in the Chinese gardens that produced black tea were the same as those in the green tea regions. The difference was only in the processing of the harvested leaves, with those intended for black tea being 'fermented', cured for longer in the sun and roasted in cast-iron pans. The Linnaean classification was changed – the tea plant was renamed *Thea sinensis*, and later *Camellia sinensis* as its taxonomy was understood. Fortune had also made a more controversial and troubling finding, by confirming the suspicion that Chinese green tea destined for export was adulterated by dyeing with Prussian Blue (iron ferrocyanide) and gypsum (calcium sulphate dihydrate) to make the tea greener, and thus more appealing to foreign eyes.

Now, Fortune's plan consisted of two phases. First, a trip to the tea gardens in Zhejiang province, fairly easily accessible to the south-west of Shanghai. Next, a more difficult journey to the inland black tea regions to the south, the sub-tropical 'Bohea' or Wuyi mountains in Fujian. They were three hundred miles distant and unvisited by Europeans, but yet the source of the finest black tea, Oolong and Pekoe, which had become the British teas of choice. In phase one, travelling in his disguise as 'Sing-Wa' by boat, sedan chair and on foot, and equipped with two rusty pistols, Fortune passed through the city of Hangzhou and up the Qiantang River where he began the collection of tea plant seedlings and ornamental plants, cuttings and seeds. By November 1848, the expedition party had reached the green tea gardens of Wang's family near the Huangshan mountains of Anhui province, reputed to be the birthplace of green tea. Having made more collections of fine tea seeds and ornamental shrubs, Fortune returned to Shanghai by the Chinese New Year of 1849, with some 10,000 tea plant seeds – about five gallons in volume – and 13,000 young plants.

Illustration 3: Dr Hugh Falconer FRS, Director of the Calcutta Botanic Garden

The hoard was shipped first to the botanic garden in Calcutta, for transport onward to Saharanpur in the Himalayan foothills where the climate was suited to commercial tea production. In March 1849, Fortune's treasure arrived in Calcutta, the seeds in carefully packed sacks and the plants in eleven large Wardian cases. They were received by another Scotsman, Hugh Falconer, Director of the Calcutta Botanic Garden, an accomplished botanist and naturalist, a Fellow of the Royal Society, protégé of John Forbes Royle, and a life-long employee of the East India Company. Despite a complicated voyage from Shanghai via Hong Kong and Ceylon, Fortune's plants and seeds had survived in good condition. Falconer was well aware of the importance of keeping the Wardian cases sealed, and left them undisturbed for the few days before they were loaded on a steamer bound up the River Ganges to Allahabad, halfway to the Company gardens in the Himalayas. In Allahabad an un-named colonial official made the mistake of opening the cases, some of which were now broken, to check the contents. He reported that the seedlings were in good condition, but the cargo was delayed by a month due to low water in the Ganges, before moving onward by ship and ox-cart. It was received at the Company's botanical station at Saharanpur by its manager, yet another Scot, the surgeon and naturalist, William Jameson, who discovered the damage that had been done. Of the 13,000 seedlings, only 1,000 remained alive. Of the seeds, most were rotten and not a single seed had germinated. Jameson was not adept in plant cultivation and his attempts to salvage the surviving tea plants ended in failure. To Falconer's fury, he misunderstood the science of the Wardian cases and attempted to blame the calamity on inadequate care in Calcutta.

Back in China, Fortune continued his expedition, unaware of the disastrous outcome of his first shipment of plants. He dismissed his coolie, dispatched Wang to his family's green tea plantation to gather more seeds, and embarked on a trip to the unmapped province of Fujian, location of the Wuyi hills, the source of the best black tea. No Westerner had travelled there, and he spoke none of the provincial language, Fukienese. He hired more coolies, and a new translator and guide, Sing Hoo, born in Fujian. In May 1849, he set out again from Shanghai by boat and sedan chair, disguised as a Chinese noble. By travelling south through Zhejiang and Jiangxi, Fortune was heading into more danger than he knew. Civil war in China was imminent, fomented by the Taiping rebel leader, Hong Xiquan, self-proclaimed younger brother of Jesus Christ, with the twin aims of overthrowing the Manchu Qing emperors, and establishing a bizarre and intolerant form of Christianity across a new Han Empire. Anti-Manchu sentiment was strongest in the south, and the Taiping 'Heavenly Kingdom' had its stronghold in the black tea provinces. By 1850, Hong had around 20,000 followers, and in the course of the ensuing 14 years of vicious conflict, an estimated 40 million people died before the Taiping Rebellion was quenched. It was the bloodiest civil war in world history.

Despite the obstacles of the terrain and the restless local peasantry, Fortune's party succeeded in carrying him, and his increasingly loaded collection cases, up into the grandeur of the Wuyi mountains, almost 500 miles by river and road from Shanghai. Hosted as a noble guest in monasteries and inns, Fortune studied the practices of tea cultivation and black tea production. He learned of the existence of three sacred tea trees – the Da Hong Pao, or Big Red Robe bushes, 200 years old, growing in the lee of a rock face, yielding the very finest tea leaves and protected by armed guards. But he knew that tea plants are easily cloned by propagating cuttings, and realised that clones of the three trees had been planted throughout the Wuyi mountains. He collected thousands of cuttings, seeds and saplings, and together with exotic plants gifted by

Buddhist monks, he returned slowly and with difficulty to Shanghai, arriving in the autumn of 1849.

Illustration 4: Robert Fortune in later life

A package of documents from Calcutta awaited him. It detailed the calamitous fate of his first shipment of tea plants to India. A whole year of collecting in China had been wasted. To his credit, Fortune was not interested in apportioning blame, but in working out how to improve the safety of his next shipment. This time he planted not only cuttings and seedlings in the sealed cases, but also the seeds, remembering that Nathaniel Ward had observed germination of seeds in the cases which bore his name. Fourteen glazed cases, each 4 feet wide by 8 feet long, were planted with layers of loam, seeds, and soil, topped by a live plant such as mulberry or the tea scenting agents, bergamot and jasmine. Fortune accompanied the cases to Hong Kong to ensure that they were safely dispatched on four different vessels. When they were received in Calcutta, Hugh Falconer was delighted to find that the seeds had germinated, reporting that *"the young tea-plants were sprouting around the mulberries as thick as they could come up."* Fortune wrote, *"This method will apply to all short-lived seeds, as well as to those of the tea plant. It is important it should be generally known"* and he recorded later with satisfaction, *"Owing to the excellent arrangements made [at Calcutta] by Dr. Falconer and at Allahabad by Dr. Jameson, they reached their destination in the Himalayas in good order...the Himalayan tea plantations could now boast of having a number of plants from the best tea-districts of China..."* That was an under-statement. Within a few years, the Himalayan tea plantations were abundant with Fortune's plants and their offspring, tended by many expert Chinese cultivators and producers of black tea, recruited by Fortune and lured to India by attractive three-year contracts with the Honourable Company.

The close involvement of Scots in the remarkable history of tea does not end there. While the climate of the western Himalayas in Uttar Pradesh is well-suited to the cultivation of tea, a still better climate is to be found in the eastern Himalayan foothills, specifically around the town of Darjeeling. Its superintendent, a surgeon-major in the Company's Bengal Medical Service, was Archibald Campbell, from the island of Islay. Campbell was a knowledgeable doctor, naturalist and geographer, and friendly with Sir Joseph Dalton Hooker, alumnus of Glasgow University, Director of Kew Gardens, and closest associate of Charles Darwin. During Hooker's three years of exploration in the Himalayas, Campbell negotiated his entry to Sikkim, bordering Tibet, from where Hooker collected plants and wrote to Darwin describing the natural history of northeast India. When Campbell received a consignment of Fortune's seedlings from Saharanpur, he carefully cultivated the plants and established the first tea plantation in Darjeeling, now considered to be the source of the 'champagne' of teas.

Robert Fortune made more collecting trips to Asia, including to Taiwan and Japan. When the Second Opium War and the so-called 'Indian Mutiny' displaced the East India Company, he visited China again in 1858 on behalf of the United States Government, commissioned to send tea seeds to America, which he did. Some 30,000 plants were cultivated by the US Patent Office and distributed to the southern states, but the combination of the Civil War and high costs made American tea production uncompetitive. Fortune's fees were never paid by the US Government, but he retired a very rich man, made wealthy by his foreign employments and acquisitions, and auctions of his exotic plants. Within his lifetime, India surpassed China as the world's major producer of tea. He died in London in 1880, aged 68, leaving £40,000 – indeed a fortune – to his much-neglected children and wife Jane, and a rich legacy of plant species bearing his name.

3   The telephone and the Big Bang: Alexander Graham Bell

There is no obvious connection between the origin of our universe and the invention of the telephone. The link is Alexander Graham Bell, born in Edinburgh in 1847, the second of three sons, to his mother Eliza Grace Symonds, an amateur artist, and his father, Alexander Melville Bell, known as 'Sandy' or more formally 'Melville', who was at that time a lecturer in phonetics and speech elocution at the city's University. Bell senior's own father, the first Alexander, born in St Andrews in 1790, was also a teacher and an expert on speech disorders, who lived and

*Illustration 5;
Alexander Graham
Bell c.1880*

worked in London since his divorce from his wife, Elizabeth Baird, after she had fallen pregnant in a scandalous affair with the Rector of Dundee Academy, one William Murray. Melville Bell became famous internationally as the creator of 'Visible Speech' – a system of symbols and diagrams to aid the formation of sounds in the profoundly deaf, illustrating the position and movement of the lips, tongue and throat. Ironically, his wife Eliza suffered progressive hearing loss and became almost completely deaf herself.

The combination of his mother's hearing impairment and his father's professional interests would heavily influence Graham Bell's development. Young Alex, pronounced in the family as 'Alec', was a sensitive, inquisitive and inventive boy, and encouraged by his mother, showed talent in art and music too. Famously, and possibly apocryphally, he taught the family's Skye terrier to growl continuously while he manipulated her lips and vocal cords to say 'Ow-ah-oo-ga-ma-ma' in a passable imitation of 'How are you grandmama?'. His time at Edinburgh's Royal High School was unexceptional, and he left aged 15 to live for a year in London with his grandfather Alexander. That year of study and discussion under his grandfather's tutelage was the catalyst for Alec's deeper interest in acoustics and speech. He returned to Scotland as a 'pupil-teacher' at Weston House Academy in Morayshire, reimbursed in fees and lodgings in return for instructing classes in elocution and music.

Now was deemed the time for some higher education, and Alec enrolled at the University of Edinburgh joining his elder brother Melville, who had inherited their father's teaching duties. Bell senior added to his many publications with his tour-de-force, *A New Elucidation of the Principles of Speech and Elocution*, published in 1863. Two years later, he moved to a family house in London after grandfather Bell passed away in April 1865. Tragedy lurked nearby. The dread disease tuberculosis, usually fatal, was rampant in 19th century Europe, responsible for a quarter of all deaths, and spread by means unknown. It is typified by suppurating abscesses in the lungs, spine and other organs, which were named 'tubercles' by the Scottish doctor Matthew Baillie, the pioneer of pathology, and a nephew of John and William Hunter. Extreme anaemia and the pallor of people infected by TB led to the label 'white plague'. The associated loss of weight from the 'consumption' could be rapid and severe, and its lethality, particularly in younger victims, made it the 'robber of youth'. Its main route of transmission was by air, spread by cough droplets, and in crowded cities the disease was endemic. Soon after the family's move, their youngest son Edward became pale and thin, and was diagnosed with tuberculosis. He weakened progressively and died in May, 1867 with his brother Alec at his bedside. The young Graham Bell wrote in his diary, "*Edward died this morning at ten minutes to four o'clock. He was only eighteen years, eight months old."*

The next year, Alec completed matriculation exams and enrolled at University College London, to attend lectures in anatomy and physiology, while experimenting with methods to produce vowel and consonant sounds from artificial windpipes and tuning-forks, and tutoring 'deaf-mute' patients in a private school for the deaf in South Kensington. He returned hastily to Edinburgh on the news that his elder brother Melville was sick. Known in the family as 'Melly', now married and an expectant father, he was coughing blood, losing weight, lacking energy and unable to continue to deliver his classes. Alec took over his elocution and speech tuition duties while Melly rallied enough to welcome his newly arrived son, named Edward, before suffering the heart-breaking loss of the baby, who died soon after birth. Melville took his wife to London to join his parents there, and Alec was never to see him again, as the white plague of tuberculosis took Melly's life, in May 1870, at the age of twenty-five.

When Alec re-joined the family in London, his distraught parents were immediately alarmed by his condition – thin, pale, feverish, and according to his doctors, dangerously ill with the consumption. His father took remarkable and decisive action. Remembering that in his own youth, he had recovered from illness by convalescing in the clean air of Newfoundland, he wound up the family's teaching commitments in London and Edinburgh, and prepared them for emigration to Canada. In July, just two months after Melville's death, 'Professor' Bell, his wife Eliza, Alec and Melly's widow Caroline sailed for the New World on the *SS Nestorian*. Alexander Graham Bell was 23 years old, and two years previously, the first transatlantic telegraph cable had been laid on the seabed, between London and New York, by the *SS Great Eastern*.

Guided by a friend of the family, the Reverend Thomas Henderson, the Bells settled into a home near Brantford, Ontario, and Graham Bell's health improved. Their house was near the Six Nations Indian

Reservation, and he transcribed the previously unwritten Iroquoian language into Visible Speech symbols. As his health recovered further, he delivered a series of lessons on Visible Speech to Sarah Fuller's staff at the 'School for Deaf-Mutes' in Boston, after initial sessions had been taught by his father. These were so successful that in September, 1872, Graham Bell rented a suite of two rooms in the fashionable South End of Boston, and established a teaching practice there and in nearby towns, delivering direct instruction to deaf children and demonstrating his methods to other teachers. His choice of location was lucky. A couple of months later, the Great Boston Fire destroyed the whole downtown business district, despite its world-leading system of telegraphic fire alarms. Bell's residence was untouched.

In October, at the Clarke School for the deaf in Northampton, Massachusetts, he met a man who would turn out to be one of the most influential in his life. Gardiner Hubbard, the school's president, was a lawyer, entrepreneur, political lobbyist, and the father of Mabel, struck deaf ten years earlier by scarlet fever, when she was just five years old. On the education of deaf children, Hubbard and Bell thought alike. A few years later, they would realise that they had another common interest - in the communication marvel of the age, telegraphy. Another chance meeting would also mould Bell's future. Thomas Sanders was a wealthy leather merchant, based in Salem, and father to George, his first son, who had been born deaf. 'Georgie' was too young for Sarah Fuller's day school, but she referred Sanders to Bell, who was soon entrusted with Georgie's entire education. Georgie came, with his nurse, to live next to Bell's house, and started to make good progress.

In 1873, despite his lack of formal qualifications, Bell was appointed professor of vocal physiology and elocution at Boston University's new School of Oratory, and he migrated his classes to there. Years later, one of his most famous pupils was Helen Keller, deaf and blind through childhood illness, who became a political activist, author and lecturer. She was to write, *"Hearing is the deepest, most humanizing, philosophical sense man possesses, and lonely ones all over the world, because of Dr Bell's efforts, have been brought into the pleasant ways of mankind."*

Bell had already been experimenting with ways to transmit vibrations and sounds, initially with the thought of helping deaf lip-readers to distinguish between 'B' and 'P'. His inventive mind was blossoming, and he became intrigued by the possibility to send sound over telegraph wires. He accepted the offer of Georgie's parents of room and board in Salem, to continue Georgie's tuition, and was provided with a workshop. During the winter of 1873-4, remembering the work of Heinrich Helmholtz and his 'electric tuning-fork', he experimented in evenings and weekends with his idea of a 'harmonic telegraph', a system to transmit multiple tones simultaneously over a single wire by using tuning-forks or tuned reeds, electro-magnets and circuit-breakers to produce pulses at different frequencies, which could be similarly separated out at the receiver – an early form of frequency division multiplexing. He saw a demonstration of Scott de Martinville's 'phonautograph', the earliest sound recording device, which used a funnel-shaped horn, diaphragm and stylus to mimic the human ear and write the pattern of sound waves on a moving surface. Bell dispensed with the artificial ear and used a real dissected human middle-ear, ossicle bones and eardrum for his experimentation, to produce an 'ear phonautograph'. Unusual certainly, but it was formative in Bell's thinking about the transduction of sound to movement. He wrote, *"I was struck with the remarkable disproportion in weight between the membrane and the bones that were vibrated by it. It occurred to me that if a membrane as thin as tissue paper could control the vibration of bones that were, compared to it, of immense size and weight, why should not a larger and thicker membrane be able to vibrate a piece of iron in front of an electro-magnet?"*

In the middle of 1874, back in Ontario for work and a holiday, Bell made a breakthrough realisation. If the vibrations of magnetised reeds or diaphragms could be used to induce a fluctuating, or undulating current in an electromagnetic coil, rather than just making and breaking the circuit, then the amplitudes as well as the frequencies of sound waves could be transmitted. This was an essential requirement of any system that could faithfully reproduce the nuances of human speech. He made a sketch of an apparatus he called the 'harp telegraph', with a transmitter consisting of a row of magnetised steel reeds, tuned to different acoustic frequencies, and vibrating within a long electro-magnet. A similar electro-magnet at the receiver would detect the undulating current, and set an equivalent set of reeds into oscillation, hopefully sufficient to reproduce the sound created by voicing into the transmitter's reeds. It was only a sketch. Bell lacked the equipment and skill to make the system there and then, and he doubted that it would generate enough current to work over useful distances. He mentioned it to nobody, but on his return to Massachusetts he showed the sketch to Moses Farmer, the electrical engineer and inventor, to test the validity of the concept. Farmer said, wisely and presciently, *"Please keep this paper, as a record of the conception of the idea, in case anyone else should at a future time discover that the vibrations of a permanent magnet will induce a vibrating current of electricity in the coils of an electro-magnet."* Bell wrote home to Ontario from Boston on November 23rd, describing the idea and writing, *"I have scarce dared to breathe [it] to anybody for fear of being thought insane...I was uncertain of the fundamental principle."*

Bell did, however, mention his harmonic telegraph idea, in an autumnal visit to the grand Cambridge home of his pupil, Mabel Hubbard, and her parents. Gardiner Hubbard was instantly attentive. His interest in telegraphy was long-standing, and he had publicly accused the Western Union Telegraph Company of using its near-monopoly to hold back on using multiple channels, to the detriment of the American economy. He had lobbied Congress to charter a private corporation, the 'United States Postal Telegraph Company', to deliver telegrams at half the prevailing costs. 'The Hubbard Bill' came close to passage in 1874, but in a Senate committee hearing, William Orton, president of Western Union, made a decisive defence. His company, Orton said, had already acquired the patent for duplex transmission from its inventor, Joseph Stearns, and moreover had recently bought the patent for quadruplex transmission (two channels in each direction) from Thomas Edison. This, said Orton pompously, *"may be called the solution of all difficulties in the future of telegraphic science."* Hubbard's bill fell, but now he saw the potential of Bell's idea to out-perform the Edison system five or six times over.

Financial backing for Bell's ideas was clearly needed. Bell had offered his harmonic telegraph proposal to the British Post Office's Superintendent of Telegraphs, only to be told, dismissively, to submit his invention for consideration, and that *"in the event of your method of telegraphy appearing to be both original and useful, all questions of remuneration shall rest entirely with the postmaster-general."* Bell took American citizenship, and Thomas Sanders and Gardiner Hubbard each invested funds in return for an equal share in Bell's inventions, asking him to focus his efforts on developing the harmonic telegraph. Realising that he needed technical help to implement his ideas, Bell approached the electrical shop of Charles Williams Jr in Boston, which Farmer and Edison had also used, and enlisted a young engineer, Thomas A. Watson. In early March 1875, Bell filed a patent application for an *'Improvement in Transmitters and Receivers for Electric Telegraphs'*, which described a harmonic method of generating multiple signal channels, plus a method for the facsimile transmission of handwriting, a so-called 'autograph telegraph'. In the following July, the American engineer Elisha Gray was granted a US Patent for an *'Electric Telegraph for Transmitting Musical Tones'*, which also used multiple channels. Gray was 38 years old, the co-owner of Western Electric, a major supplier of equipment to Western Union, and he was to prove the ablest of Bell's competitors, though his focus was initially on the transmission of musical tones or chords - not on using frequency multiplexing for messaging.

As required by the Patent Office, Bell and Watson had constructed a working six-channel prototype of the harmonic telegraph, comprising spring-steel reeds driven by electro-magnets and tuned to make-and-break the circuit at specified frequencies, with equivalently tuned reeds in the receiver. Bell and Sanders took it to Hubbard's house in

Washington DC for a crucial demonstration. Hubbard told them that William Orton would also attend to take a look. Orton was impressed, and asked Bell to give another demonstration in New York, using the Western Union's real long lines. The demonstration, on a mid-March morning, went extremely well, with multiple channels of morse signals clearly received over a two-hundred mile stretch of actual telegraph line wire. Orton was even more impressed, but was unhappy about Hubbard's participation in Bell's project. Western Union had been damaged by his activities, and they would not invest in further development if Hubbard was involved. But, they would be interested if Bell returned with a finished product. Hubbard subsequently offered to withdraw since his presence was detrimental. Bell would not hear of it, and, urged on by his two investors in the 'Bell Patent Association', continued to develop the harmonic telegraph, while maintaining his 'day job' at Boston University and some of his private teaching.

Bell wanted to remain in Gardiner Hubbard's good books for another reason too. He had fallen in love with his pupil, Hubbard's daughter Mabel, now 17 years old. Bell was almost 11 years her senior, and in the summer of 1875, he wrote to Mabel's parents to reveal his predicament. They were shocked, and decided that Mabel was too young even to be told of Bell's feelings. Bell's mother was similarly hostile when she learned of her son's intentions. Surprisingly, given her own deafness, she worried that Mabel was 'congenitally deaf and dumb', (which clearly she was not), and that any children would be congenitally deaf too. Mrs Hubbard asked Bell to hide his feelings for a year. Mabel, unaware, continued to regard Bell as her respected tutor, and nothing more.

With Thomas Watson, Bell continued his spare-time work on the harmonic telegraph, but with diminished enthusiasm. On June 2nd, 1875, while running tests between rooms in the attic of the Williams workshop, they had a problem. One of the steel reeds in the receiver was not responding, and suspecting that it was stuck to the electro-magnet, Bell disconnected the transmitter battery and asked Watson, next door, to free the reed. To Bell's astonishment, when Watson twanged the receiver reed, the corresponding reed in Bell's room vibrated, audibly. This was the unlooked-for proof that the 'harp telegraph' idea was not only valid in principle, but also in practice – and that enough undulatory transmission current could be generated to be useful, even in the absence of a battery. Within a month, Bell and Watson had reconfigured the system to use diaphragms rather than steel reeds, and when Bell sang into the transmitter, Watson heard him on the receiver. In a postscript to a note to Sarah Fuller regarding Georgie Sanders, Bell wrote, *"Transmitted vocal sounds for the first time…with some further modification I hope we may be enabled to distinguish… the timbre of the sound. Should this be so, conversation viva voce by telegraph will be a fait accompli."*

Gardiner Hubbard, however, was unimpressed, and wanted progress on the harmonic/autograph telegraph system. The next months proved stressful for Bell, with conflicting claims on his time from Boston University, Hubbard, promoting Visible Speech, tutoring Georgie Sanders, and his evolving love affair with Mabel, which had complicated his relationship with his own parents. He was financially stressed too, and had needed an advance from Lewis Baxter Monroe, Dean of the School of Oratory, to meet his living costs. Nevertheless, by October, Bell had drafted a patent application covering his new voice transmission methods. On Thanksgiving Day, Mabel's eighteenth birthday, they were engaged. On the morning of Valentine's Day 1876, his documents were filed in the Patent Office in Washington. The application, called *'Improvement in Telegraphy',* described ways to impress an undulating current on a telegraph wire, using vibrating membranes and electro-magnets, or 'liquid transmitter' variable resistance devices, and mentioned voice transmission as one possible application. But the patent was not filed by Bell. Gardiner Hubbard, based in Washington, had heard that Elisha Gray was in town and frequenting the Patent Office where Bell's preliminary documents had already been submitted, and admiringly discussed. Fearing that the details had been leaked, Hubbard took decisive action and filed the patent without Bell's explicit authorisation. The same day, just hours later, Gray filed a patent 'caveat', announcing his intention to file a claim for the invention of a speaking telephone, based on the liquid transmitter variable resistance principle, within the next three months. It said, *"I claim as my invention the art of transmitting vocal sounds or conversations telegraphically, through an electric circuit."*

Whether Gray conceived his solution independently, or had his mind primed by leaked news of Bell's progress, is still a matter for conjecture. As an accomplished and inventive electrical engineer, it is plausible that Gray invented alone, though the document filings on the very same day strongly suggest information leakage. In any case, the immediate result was an anxious wait for Bell and his partners, while the Patent Office checked the timings of the submissions, and the possible 'interferences' between Bell's application and Gray's caveat. At the end of February, Bell wrote to his father, *"If I succeed in securing that Patent without interference from the others, the whole thing is mine – and I am sure of fame, fortune and success if I can only persevere in perfecting my apparatus."* Bell's patent was granted a week later. In the longer term, litigation on the priority of the details of the invention would continue for many years. But Bell's patent, *'Improvement in telegraphy'*, United States No. 174465, would withstand legal challenges and turn out to be one of the most valuable patents ever granted. By the time the patent was awarded on March 7th, four days after Bell's twenty-ninth birthday, he had pulled together his various innovations to make a fully working telephone. Three days later, in his Boston rooms, the first intelligible telephone call was made from room to room, using a liquid variable resistance transmitter and a tuned reed receiver. The message was *"Mr. Watson, come here – I want to see you"*.

The words could be heard, but only just. In the following months Bell abandoned the liquid transmitter in favour of electro-magnets and diaphragms, ready for demonstration at the Philadelphia International Exhibition in May, to celebrate the centennial of American independence. There he met one of the exhibit judges, Sir William Thomson, the world-renowned Professor of Natural Philosophy at Glasgow University, aged almost 52, and later ennobled as Lord Kelvin.

Recounting the meeting, Bell wrote, *"what was my delight, when he addressed me, to hear a good broad Scotch accent tinging his utterance!"* On hearing the demonstration of voice transmissions over the telephones, Thomson was astounded, and shouted *"Where is Mr Bell? I must see Mr Bell!"* He later pronounced Bell's telephone to be the most wonderful thing he had seen in America. Two months later, travelling through Boston, Thomson helped Bell experiment with voice transmission over a real long distance telegraph line, and he took duplicates of the receiver and transmitter back home to Scotland. In August, in his opening address to the annual meeting of the British Association for the Advancement of Science, Thomson described Bell's invention as *"the greatest by far of all the marvels of the electric telegraph."* That endorsement and the ensuing publicity in the journals *Nature* and *Scientific American* cemented Bell's reputation as the brilliant inventor of the telephone. At the end of Bell's breakthrough year of 1876, he received the Centennial Exhibition's Gold Medal Award for Electrical Equipment, accompanied by a glowing accolade signed by Sir William, in which Thomson described the Bell telephone as being of transcendent scientific interest, and predicted the extension of the range of the telephone to hundreds of miles.

Bell forecast to Mabel that, *"When people can order everything they want from the stores without leaving home, and chat comfortably with each other by telegraph over some bit of gossip, every person will desire to put money in our pockets by having telephones."* A further patent amplified the rather cursory treatment of the telephone in *'Improvements in Telegraphy'* and Bell, Hubbard and Sanders agreed that Thomas Watson should have a ten percent share in the 'Bell Patent Association'. The patents were offered to Western Union for $100,000, but Orton balked at the price, saying the telephone was nothing but a toy. The Bell Telephone Company was formed on 9th July 1877, with Sanders as Treasurer and Hubbard as a trustee. Mabel and Alec were married two days later, and Bell transferred all but ten of his 1,497 shares in the Company to Mabel as a wedding gift. They would have two sons and two daughters, with only the girls, Elsie and Marian, surviving beyond early infancy.

The rest, as they say, is history – though not an entirely straightforward one. Initially, the Bell Telephone Company was steered by Sanders and Gardiner Hubbard, who took the dual role of President and Chairman after assuming power of attorney over his

When In Quarantine

PEOPLE who are in quarantine are not isolated if they have a Bell Telephone.

The Bell Service brings cheer and encouragement to the sick, and is of value in countless other ways.

Friends, whether close at hand or far away, can be easily reached, because Bell Service is universal service.

THE CENTRAL UNION TELEPHONE CO.

Telephone Building, E. High St.

R. B. HOOVER, Manager – Springfield, Ohio

Illustration 6: Bell System advertisement c.1918 during the Spanish Flu pandemic

daughter's shares. Their early decision to lease, rather than sell telephones was critical in the Company's success. Hubbard's astute business brain led to European expansion, with the incorporation of the International Bell Telephone Company in Belgium in 1879, and two years later the American Bell Telephone Company was acquired by its own subsidiary, the American Telephone & Telegraph Company (AT&T), for financial and tax purposes. Western Electric was subsumed by American Bell, and as it grew, the 'Bell System' became synonymous with the national telephone network in the USA, and a by-word for corporate power and wealth.

Thomas Sanders sold his shares for nearly a million dollars before losing most of his money in a disastrous investment in a Colorado gold mine. The welfare of his adult son, Georgie, was guaranteed by Bell. Thomas Watson's ten percent share of the Company made him a millionaire, and after resigning in 1881 he became a shipyard owner and Shakespearean actor. As other investors came on board, Gardiner

Hubbard, already wealthy, stepped back to pursue wider interests including the creation of the National Geographic Society. Mabel and Alexander Graham Bell became increasingly affluent, and when Bell received the Volta Prize from the French government, worth 50,000 francs, he began to create endowment funds and institutions around the country, including, with Hubbard, the journal *Science*. In later life his inventiveness was undimmed. His long list of inventions and developments included the metal detector; the photophone for voice transmission on beams of light; hydrofoils; and early aircraft controls.

The Bell Telephone Company inherited the founder's regard for the value of innovation. Its research and development arm, the Bell Telephone Laboratories, descended from its Electrical and Patent Department, and the Volta Laboratory set up by Bell in Washington DC after his prize award. In the 20th century, Bell Labs became a world-leading centre for advances not only in telecommunications, but in all the physical sciences. At its peak it employed more than 25,000 research engineers and scientists from around the globe, based in several sites in New Jersey. Its many achievements, which have gained nine Nobel Prizes, include the invention of the transistor; the demonstration of the wave nature of matter through electron diffraction; the definition of the fundamental limits to the transmission and detection of information, derived by Nyquist and Shannon; and the early development of the laser and fibre-optics. But perhaps the most fundamental Bell Labs discovery was serendipitous.

In 1964, two Bell Labs scientists at the Holmdel NJ site, Arno Penzias and Robert Wilson, were using radiometers for use in satellite communication experiments. They detected faint microwave-frequency noise at 4080 MHz that they could not explain and could not eradicate. It came from all directions equally, and they investigated and eliminated various possible causes, from some kind of terrestrial interference to the degrading effect on the antennae of built-up pigeon droppings. Then suspecting an extra-terrestrial origin, they contacted the astrophysicist Robert Dicke of Princeton University, who confirmed that they had actually detected the background radiation predicted by theorists as the remnant of the Big Bang origin of the universe. For the discovery that confirmed the theoretical basis of the Big Bang, Penzias and Wilson shared the 1978 Nobel Prize in physics. Even Graham Bell could hardly have imagined that his legacy would include the shedding of light on the mystery of the origin of our universe.

Alexander Graham Bell died, much accomplished, honoured and revered, in 1922, aged 75, at his private estate, Beinn Bhreagh, the beautiful mountain, in Nova Scotia. Mabel died less than a year later. They are interred together, near the top of the mountain.

4 Adventurous doctress: Mary Grant Seacole

In the opening paragraph of her autobiography, first published in 1857, Mary Seacole wrote, *"I was born in the town of Kingston, in the island of Jamaica, some time in the present century. As a female, and a widow, I may be well excused giving the precise date… But I do not mind confessing that the century and myself were both young together… I am a Creole, and have good Scotch blood coursing in my veins. My father was a soldier, of an old Scotch family; and to him I often trace my affection for a camp-life, and my sympathy with what I have heard my friends call 'the pomp, pride, and circumstance of glorious war.' Many people have also traced to my Scotch blood that energy and activity which are not always found in the Creole race, and which have carried me to so many varied scenes; and perhaps they are right… but I am sure I do not know what it is to be indolent."*

Mary Jane Grant was born around 1805, and her Scottish father seems to have played little role in her life, or that of her brother, or sister Louisa. Even their father's identity is uncertain, but most probably he was Captain, then Major, James Grant, born in 1770 and an officer in the British Army's 60th (Royal American) Regiment of Foot. The regiment was a kind of foreign legion, manned by religiously Protestant officers drawn from across Europe, and raised originally to defend the American colonies against Native American and French attacks. James Grant was stationed in Jamaica from 1802 until 1815, when his whereabouts become unknown.

Aside from the large military presence, there was a sizeable population of Scottish expatriates in Jamaica. Arrivals began after the failed attempts to colonise Darien on the Panamanian isthmus in the 1690s, and around 17,000 young Scots emigrated to the West Indies between 1750 and 1800, attracted by the business opportunities afforded by the cultivation of tobacco and sugar. Jamaica was their primary destination, where many worked in the merchant firms based in Kingston. A professional class of Scots emerged, mainly practicing law and medicine. Ownership of sugar plantations (and their enslaved workers) was seen as a certain, rapid path to wealth, and many Scottish plantation owners made fortunes by exporting sugar to Europe, and especially to Great Britain, mainly shipped to Glasgow.

Mary Grant's mother was a free Creole, that is, a native-born resident of Jamaica, of mixed ancestry and heritage, and the daughter of a white father and black mother. She ran a boarding-house called Blundell Hall, in Kingston, and most importantly, she was a 'doctress', a healer skilled in the practice of traditional Caribbean herbal medicine. Blundell Hall therefore doubled as a convalescent home for sickly Europeans recovering from tropical diseases or the wounds of battle. Young Mary copied her mother's practices, and wrote, *"It was very natural that I should inherit her tastes; and so, I had from early youth a yearning for medical knowledge and practice which never deserted me…. And I was very young when I began to make use of the little knowledge I had acquired from watching my mother, upon great sufferer – my doll… and whatever disease was most prevalent in Kingston, be sure my poor doll soon contracted it."* From the age of about 12, she would assist her mother in attending invalid military officers or their wives, and her contacts with foreign patients led to a yearning for travel – especially to England. As a young woman, she made several trips to London, to visit a merchant family, the Henriques, with a female relative. Each trip lasted a year or two, interspersed with time at home in Jamaica. During a Jamaican sojourn in 1836, she accepted a proposal of marriage from Edwin Horatio Hamilton Seacole, a merchant, who in his family's legend was an illegitimate son of Horatio Nelson and Emma Hamilton. Nelson, who was stationed in the West Indies for nine years from 1771, had nearly died from malaria and was nursed back to health by another Jamaican doctress, Cubah Cornwallis. The family legend has doubtful plausibility, though Edwin may indeed have been Nelson's godson.

Mary and Edwin Seacole together established a provisions store in the port of Black River, in southwestern Jamaica, but Edwin's health, never robust, declined suddenly and the business was abandoned. They returned to Blundell Hall, which had been destroyed and rebuilt after much of Kingston was ravaged by a great fire. Edwin's condition worsened, despite Mary's nursing, and he died in October 1844. When her mother died soon afterwards, Mary immersed herself in the infirmary and the practice of doctressing. Her reputation grew as a skilful healer and nurse. An epidemic of cholera killed some 32,000 Jamaicans in 1850, and she treated many patients with her standard regimen of good nutrition, fastidious hygiene, and a caring empathy. The rich paid, and the poor were treated for free.

By now a widow and in her mid-forties, Seacole's thirst for adventure was unquenched. With her servant Mac and a young maid, she travelled dangerously up the River Chagres, named by Columbus the 'River of Crocodiles', to the town of Cruces, Republic of New Granada, in the Panamanian isthmus. Her mission was to help her brother manage his ramshackle hotel and provisions store, built to cater for the crowds of gold-diggers rushing to and from California. Later she vividly described the muddy, squalid, lawless, and disease-ridden state of the town. An outbreak of cholera meant that her medical skills were soon required. On one occasion, she performed an autopsy on an infant victim in order to improve her knowledge of the effects of the disease. She wrote, *"But the knowledge I had obtained thus strangely was very valuable to me, and was soon put into practice... I have no doubt that at first I made some lamentable blunders, and, may be, lost patients which a little later I could have saved... The simplest remedies were perhaps the best. Mustard plasters, and emetics, and calomel; the mercury applied externally, where the veins were nearest the surface, were my usual resources. Opium I rather dreaded, as its effect is to incapacitate the system from making any exertion, and it lulls the patient into a sleep which is often the sleep of death. When my patients felt thirsty, I would give them water in which cinnamon had been boiled... Above all, I never neglected to apply mustard poultices to the stomach, spine, and neck, and particularly to keep my patient warm about the region of the heart. Nor did I relax my care when the disease had passed by, for danger did not cease when the great foe was beaten off. The patient was left prostrate;*

strengthening medicines had to be given cautiously, for fever, often of the brain, would follow. But, after all, one great conclusion, which my practice in cholera cases enabled me to come to, was the old one, that few constitutions permitted the use of exactly similar remedies, and that the course of treatment which saved one man, would, if persisted in, have very likely killed his brother."

Almost inevitably, Mary contracted cholera herself, but she recovered in a few days. She opened her own boarding house, on the model of her brother's, and became adept in the treatment of wounds inflicted by the knives and guns which were ubiquitous in the chaotic town. Her education, mixed-race heritage and light-brown complexion, which gave her elevated status in Jamaica, made her the target of casual and hurtful racism in New Granada, imposed especially by travellers from the slave-owning states of America. After failing to persuade her brother to quit Panama, she returned to Kingston on the British steamer *Eagle,* having been shamefully ejected from an American ship because of her colour. Back in Jamaica, she was confronted by a raging outbreak of yellow fever – spread by mosquito bites, causing severe illness of short duration and frequently, death. A cure was not known then, and is still unknown now, though a modern vaccine is safe and effective. The Jamaican medical authorities asked Mary to become the nursing superintendent at the military camp at Up-Park, a mile from Kingston. She went there and did her best, but could do little to mitigate the severity of the epidemic.

Another bout of restlessness, together with the need to wind up the affairs of her hotel business, took Seacole back to New Granada. In Colón, now the entrance to the Panama Canal, she opened another provisions store, and stayed for three months. At the invitation of the mayor, who had owned the local gold-mine, she moved 70 miles west to Escribanos, at the mouth of the River Belen. Thomas Day, a relative of her late husband, managed the gold mine, and invited Seacole to join the enterprise. She noted, *"Of course, my medical skill did not rust for want of practice at Escribanos. The place was not healthy, and strangers to the climate suffered severely. A surgeon himself, sent there by the West Granada Gold-mining*

Company, was glad to throw his physic to the dogs, and be cured in my way by mine;
while I was fortunately able to nurse Mr. Day through a sharp attack of illness."

In 1853, war had broken out between Russia and an alliance of the United Kingdom, France, and the Ottoman Empire. News reached Seacole of the escalating conflict on the Crimean peninsula, and she knew that the regiments of many of her former patients were involved in the fighting. In the autumn of 1854, she set sail for England, equipped with references that she hoped would persuade the British Army to send her to Crimea. The testimonials included one from the medical officer of the Gold-mining Company. *"I became acquainted with Mrs. Seacole...at Colon, on the Isthmus of Panama, and have had many opportunities of witnessing her professional zeal and ability in the treatment of aggravated forms of tropical diseases. I am myself personally much indebted for her indefatigable kindness and skill at a time when I am apt to believe the advice of a practitioner qualified in the North would have little availed. Her peculiar fitness, in a constitutional point of view, for the duties of a medical attendant, needs no comment."*

Despite her evident experience, her personal lobbying of the British Secretary of War, and interviews with associates of Florence Nightingale, Seacole's offers of assistance to the war effort were rebuffed. Typically, she decided to make her own way to Crimea, to establish a 'British Hotel' for invalids, in her own way and at her own cost. She printed and distributed business cards announcing that 'Mrs Mary Seacole...has taken her passage in the screw-steamer *Hollander,* to start from London on the 25th of January, intending on her arrival at Balaclava to establish a mess table and comfortable quarters for sick and convalescent officers.' Sailing first to Constantinople, she arranged to meet Thomas Day, who was already in Balaclava, to resurrect their business partnership and establish the 'Hotel' and a provisions store near the British forces camp at Sevastopol. In Constantinople, (present-day Istanbul) Florence Nightingale was working in the Barrack Hospital at Scutari, and Mrs Seacole went there to present her references and explain her plan. Nightingale offered her support, and found for Mary the only overnight bed available in the hospital, in the washerwomen's quarters.

In February 1855, Mary Seacole, in her 50th year, arrived in the port of Balaclava, accompanied by a Greek servant hired in Turkey, and the stores and provisions advised as essential by Thomas Day. Immediately she began tending the sick and wounded on the wharf-side of Balaclava, and spent weeks in that work, sleeping overnight aboard an ammunition ship, and striving to protect her precious stores from persistent and often successful theft. By April she had built and had

Illustration 7: The only known photograph of Mary Seacole (c.1873)

established the 'British Hotel' near Kadikoi village, halfway between Balaclava and the Sevastopol military camp. Largely constructed from packing cases, driftwood and iron sheets, it enclosed a stable-yard and was stocked with provisions from Constantinople and London. By June, Mrs Seacole's matronly figure, in her brightly coloured dresses, and accompanied by her mules, was a familiar sight at the battlefront. She took medicine, bandages, lint, needles and thread to stitch wounds, as well as food, wine and spirits. Behind the lines, the British Hotel provided medical treatment, an officer's club, and a good, clean canteen for troops. She hired local cooks, servants and guards, and took to wearing conspicuously a double-barrelled pistol - unloaded - to protect her staff and minimise the loss of her property to thieves of all nationalities: Crimean, Greek, Turk, Zouaves from Algeria, as well as miscreant soldiers from the allied armies of the West.

'Mother Seacole' as she became known, remained in Crimea throughout the War, and supplied medical aid in the attack on Redan, where a quarter of the British force was wounded or killed. In the Russian offensive against French, Sardinian and Ottoman troops at the Battle of the Chernaya, she dispensed her care, under fire, to the maimed and dying of all sides. The London *Times* reported in September 1855, that Seacole was a *"warm and successful physician, who doctors and cures all manner of men with extraordinary success. She is always in attendance near the battlefield to aid the wounded and has earned many a poor fellow's blessing."* Mary supplied practical support too, and a British medical officer recorded *"the acquaintance of a celebrated person, Mrs. Seacole, a coloured women who out of the goodness of her heart and at her own expense, supplied hot tea to the poor sufferers [wounded men] while they are waiting to be lifted into the boats... She did not spare herself if she could do any good to the suffering soldiers. In rain and snow, in storm and tempest, day after day she was at her self-chosen post with her stove and kettle, in any shelter she could find, brewing tea for all who wanted it, and they were many. Sometimes more than 200 sick would be embarked in one day, but Mrs. Seacole was always equal, to the occasion."*

The Crimean War reached its climax when the Siege of Sevastopol ended with allied troops entering the city on September 9th, 1855. Mary Seacole had obtained a special pass to advance with her mule-train, and she was the first woman to enter the burning town, providing her potent mix of nursing and nutrition to the exhausted armies. Peace was at last achieved with the signing of the Treaty of Paris in the spring of 1856, and the armies began to evacuate. By then the financial position of the Seacole and Day enterprise was dire, with a surplus of unsaleable provisions and animals, large debts, and a growing number of creditors demanding recompense. Mary's adventurous spirit endured, and before leaving Crimea she *"made various excursions into the interior, visiting Simpheropol and Baktchiserai. I travelled to Simpheropol with a pretty large party, and had a very amusing journey. My companions were young and full of fun, and tried hard to persuade the Russians that I was Queen Victoria, by paying me the most absurd reverence. When this failed they fell back a little, and declared that I was the Queen's first cousin. Anyhow, they attracted crowds about me, and I became quite a lioness in the streets of Simpheropol, until the arrival of some Highlanders in their uniform cut me out."*

Mrs Seacole returned to England by meandering routes, probably enforced by her lack of money. She arrived in London fairly impoverished, and, again with Thomas Day, opened a canteen in Aldershot, which lacked funds for investment and failed to prosper. She was declared bankrupt on November 7th 1856. Her cause was taken up by the war correspondents of the British press, and both *The Times* and *Punch* magazine supported fund-raising efforts to alleviate her plight. Money was raised from the general public and many prominent people, including the Duke of Wellington and Admiral Prince Victor, Count Gleichen, Queen Victoria's half-nephew, who credited Mary for saving his life when he was struck by cholera in Crimea, and had been a frequent visitor to the British Hotel. In early 1857, Seacole and Day were discharged from bankruptcy, but not to universal approval. A few months later, receiving a letter from Mrs Seacole, *Punch* published an ironic response, suggesting she was a mere 'Vivandière' or 'Sutler' – a follower of army camps working for profit from the sale of provisions – concluding, *"Hands England has plenty to help her if there are any hearts to move them, and put them into pockets…Who would give a guinea to see a mimic sutler-woman, and a foreigner, frisk and amble about the stage, when he might bestow the money on a genuine English one, reduced to a two-pair back, [a second-floor room at the back of a house] and in imminent danger of being obliged to climb into an attic?"* Florence Nightingale had likewise become ambivalent, and based presumably only on hearsay, later insinuated that Seacole had kept 'a bad house' in Crimea.

Mary wrote, or possibly dictated, an autobiography describing her travels, in the *Wonderful Adventures of Mrs Seacole in Many Lands,* published in July 1857 and which sold well at one shilling and sixpence a copy. She returned to Jamaica and lived there for several years before coming back to London, again in some financial difficulty. Funds to help her were raised again, and Count Gleichen carved a marble bust of Seacole for the Royal Academy Exhibition of 1872, which is now displayed in Kingston's Institute of Jamaica. She died in May, 1881, aged around 76. Her estate was valued at more than £2500, and her sister Louisa was the main beneficiary of her will. Count Gleichen received a diamond ring, said to have been a gift to Mary's late husband, from Lord Nelson. Her

Illustration 8: Statue of Mary Seacole by Martin Jennings at St Thomas' Hospital, London

grave is in St Mary's Roman Catholic Cemetery in Kensal Green, London.

Recent years have seen a strong revival of interest in Mary Seacole's adventurous achievements, and in 2004 she was named in first place in an online poll of *100 Great Black Britons.* A two-dimensional sculpture was erected in Paddington in 2013, and, amidst some controversy regarding its siting, her statue was unveiled at St Thomas' Hospital in 2016. Perhaps most fittingly, the Mary Seacole Awards, instituted by the Royal Colleges of Nursing and Midwives, recognise leadership and development in nursing, healthcare and midwifery, and have been awarded annually since 1996.

5

The Real Deal:
Elijah McCoy

There are several contending theories as to the origin of the phrase 'the Real McCoy'. Who – or what – was the real McCoy? One of the first examples of the usage dates from 1856, in the Scottish National Dictionary, which refers to a line in an old poem *Deil's Halloween*, *"A drappie o' the real McKay"*, possibly derived from the product and advertising of G. Mackay & Co, whisky distillers in Edinburgh. In turn, that phrase may derive from the home of one chief of the clan Mackay, in Reay, on the north coast of Caithness – hence the Reay Mackay. By the end of the 19th century, the phrase was in common use in America, and the controversial champion boxer, Norman Selby, was known as Kid 'The Real' McCoy. Anecdotally, his nickname arose because there were so many imitators in boxing booths around the country. A doubtful drunk met the slightly-built Selby in a bar and challenged him to prove that he was the genuine article. Having been put on the floor knocked out, the drunk recovered and confirmed that 'he's the real McCoy!'.

However, there is no doubt that Elijah McCoy, as an inventor, was the real deal. He was born in Colchester, Ontario in 1843 or 1844, to Mildred and George McCoy, fugitive slaves who had escaped to Canada from Kentucky on the 'Underground Railroad', and had presumably inherited their surname from a Scottish plantation owner. They had twelve children in all, ten of them born as free Canadian citizens between 1839 and 1859. George McCoy had joined the All-Black Militia of the Canadian Army, and had fought for the British government against the Upper Canada Rebellion of 1837-8. He was rewarded by the grant of 160 acres of farmland near Colchester, on the northern shores of Lake Erie, and Elijah and his siblings attended schools for black children in the township.

From a young age, Elijah had a clear aptitude with tools and for things mechanical, and his parents encouraged him to consider a career in engineering. In 1859, when he was around 16 years old, they sent him to Edinburgh to study the subject, and at about the same time the family moved across the Canadian border to the town of Ypsilanti, Michigan, as free citizens, where George established a tobacco business. Whether Elijah set out for Edinburgh from Michigan or Ontario is unclear. Either way, he spent several years in Scotland learning his trade as an engineering apprentice, and probably by taking classes at Edinburgh University, though his attendances are not recorded. He returned to the United States after the end of the American Civil War, as a 'Master Mechanic and Engineer', and re-joined his family in Ypsilanti. He was married, in 1868, to Ann Elizabeth Stewart who died only four years later, just 25 years old.

As a black man in the newly reunited States, McCoy struggled to find highly-skilled work, and he became a fireman and 'oiler' for the Michigan Central Railroad. This required frequently oiling the engine bearings, and sometimes walking the length of the stationary train to lubricate, with oil from an oil-can, the axles and bearings of each coach-wheel. Automatic oiling devices had already been developed to lubricate the valves and cylinders of a steam engine. These used the engine's steam to displace oil from appropriately-positioned reservoirs onto the moving parts. McCoy may have been aware of these, and anyway decided to develop his own automatic lubrication device. After a couple of years of experimentation, he had developed his 'lubricating oil cup', and patented it in July 1872, as an *Improvement in Lubricators for Steam-Engines*. It also used steam pressure, and included a system of valves and a sprung piston to displace oil, rather than the direct displacement of oil using condensed water in some other designs. McCoy's lubricators went into manufacture and wide usage on the Michigan railroad, and proved their efficiency and quality. According to legend, inferior

Illustration 9: Elijah McCoy c.1900s

imitations were also produced, but engineers knew the difference, and wanted the 'real McCoy' device.

In 1873, McCoy remarried, to Mary Eleanora Delaney, also the child of runaway slaves. He continued to improve his invention, and took out Canadian patents over the next few years, having been given a promotion at work to instruct his colleagues on the operation of the lubricators. He left the Michigan Central Railroad in 1882 to concentrate on his further developments, and acted as a consultant both to railroad companies and the Detroit Lubricating Company, settling in that city. Mary and Elijah had no children, and as McCoy's expertise gained him widespread respect, Mary became active in community affairs, involving herself in a number of organisations and the women's suffrage movement. She was the only black member of Detroit's exclusive Twentieth Century women's club, founded to promote 'peace, charity, equity and a higher civilisation'. When she complained about the burden of ironing, McCoy invented a folding, portable ironing table, and patented it. He went on to hold more than 50 patents for inventions made during his lifetime, including a lawn water sprinkler, a collapsible support for the tops of horse-drawn (or motorised) buggies, treads for rubber tyres, and heels for shoes. McCoy improved his most successful invention in 1916, when he added solid graphite as additional lubrication in his device, in an invention simply entitled '*Lubricator*', assigning 52% of the US patent to a Francis H. Warren of Detroit. Many of McCoy's patents were assigned to the 'Ypsilanti Lubricator Company', and in 1920 he established his own manufacturing company.

In 1922, the McCoys were injured in a motor vehicle accident, and Mary later died. Elijah suffered permanent injuries, and his physical and mental health declined. He died in Detroit's Eloise Hospital in 1929, and is remembered as an entrepreneur and one of the first, and most prolific, African-American inventors of the industrial age.

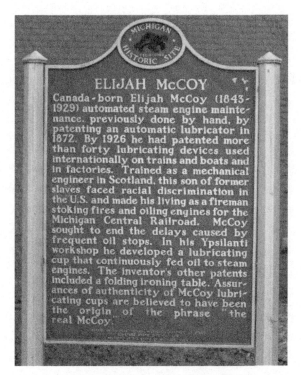

Illustration 10: Commemorative historical marker in Ypsilanti, Michigan

6

Pneumatic tyres:
John Boyd Dunlop

Dunlop's name will be forever associated with the pneumatic tyre, and justifiably so. But the story, as usual with inventions, is complicated. John Boyd Dunlop was a veterinary surgeon, born into an Ayrshire farming family in 1840, and qualifying aged 19 from the veterinary school founded by William Dick, now part of Edinburgh University. He worked as a vet, based in the city, for eight years before migrating to Belfast in 1867, and established a practice which eventually grew to become one of the largest in Ireland. Four years after moving, Dunlop married Margaret Stevenson, also of farming stock, and they had a son and a daughter.

In 1887, their son Johnnie, then nine years old, complained of his tricycle's uncomfortable and jarring ride as he cycled on the un-macadamised stretches of Belfast's streets. The wheels of the tricycle were equipped with solid rubber tyres, first invented nearly 50 years earlier by the American Charles Goodyear, who had developed the toughening process of vulcanisation (and was subsequently involved in a patent dispute with Thomas Hancock of the Charles Macintosh company). Young Johnnie's dissatisfaction with his tricycle was taken seriously, and his father began to experiment with a practical solution. Dunlop constructed an air-filled tube from rubber sheet and tacked it down with a covering of linen, around the periphery of a wooden disc. When he tested the performance of this crude wheel against one of the tricycle wheels, by rolling them both across the cobbles of their courtyard, the superiority of the air-tyred wheel was obvious. He solved his son's immediate discomfort by fastening air tubes and covers to two

Illustration 11: John Boyd Dunlop

rims of wood which he fitted over the existing tyres of the tricycle's rear wheels. By February, 1888, this was proving highly successful and a whole new tricycle frame was ordered and fitted with air-tube tyres.

Dunlop demonstrated the innovation to an impressed group of Belfast businessmen, and a patent application was made in July, which used the word 'pneumatic' for the first time. It was granted in December, 1888, as British patent number 10,607, *'An improvement in tyres of wheels for bicycles, tricycles, or other road cars'*. Arrangements were made to have pneumatic tyres manufactured in Edinburgh, and Dunlop used Edlin & Co. of Belfast to build and sell cycles equipped with the tyres. When the captain of a local cycling club used an Edlin cycle with Dunlop tyres to win a racing competition, against superior riders mounted on solid-tyred cycles, someone took notice. Harvey Du Cros was an Irish boxing and fencing champion, president of the Irish Cyclists' Association, and six of his sons formed *'The Invicibles'* team of racing cyclists. Two of them had just been defeated in the race. Du Cros soon identified the inventor of the marvellous new tyres, and introduced himself to Dunlop. Within a few months, Du Cros set up a company with Dunlop based on an existing Dublin cycle shop, to form the Pneumatic Tyre and Booth's Cycle Agency Ltd., an arrangement that immediately provided some cash flow. Dunlop assigned his patent to the new company in return for £500 and 3,000 of the total 25,000 shares. 15,010 shares were offered publicly at £1 each in 1889, of which around two-thirds were taken up.

Another British patent, no. 4,116, *'Improvements in Wheel-Tires for Cycles and other Vehicles'*, was granted to Dunlop in March 1889, and a similar American patent, *'Wheel tire for cycles'* was filed in March 1890, describing *"an external covering [A] composed of a layer or fold of india-rubber, which is thickened at that portion which comes in contact with the ground. An inner expansible tube [B], also of india-rubber, contains the air or gas under pressure...I provide a non-return valve, which is inserted through an aperture formed for the purpose on the metallic rim."* But, there was an obstacle. To his surprise, Dunlop learned that he was not actually the inventor of the air-filled tyre. That accolade belonged to another Scot, Robert William Thomson, who had made the invention and patented it 44 years

Illustration 12: Robert William Thomson, inventor of the pressurised, air-filled tyre

earlier. Thomson, born in Stonehaven in 1822, was a creative innovator whose adolescence had been spent in various apprenticeships in Aberdeen, Dundee, and Charleston, South Carolina. As a young man he spent time with Michael Faraday in London, as a civil engineer in Glasgow, and worked for Robert Stephenson, the English railway engineer, before forming his own railway consultancy business. He was 23 years old when he patented his pressurised air-filled tyre, first in Great Britain and then in France, in 1846, and the USA in 1847. The tyre of his 'aerial wheel' consisted of a hollow belt of canvas coated on both sides with vulcanised rubber, and enclosed in an outer casing of leather which was bolted to the wheel. At the time, rubber was an expensive commodity, there were no motor cars, and cycles were in their infancy. The first pedal-driven bicycle had been constructed reputedly by the Dumfriesshire blacksmith, Kirkpatrick Macmillan, only a few years before, in 1839. Macmillan achieved the distinction of being allegedly the first cyclist to be fined for inflicting injury, after colliding with a young girl in Glasgow, in 1842, after an impressive ride of 40 miles. Thomson's arial wheel was used in a few horse-drawn carriages, but he took his invention no further. He did go on to patent a self-filling fountain pen, and introduced numerous innovations including mobile steam cranes, solid rubber tyres for steam tractors, and during his time working in Java, new machinery for sugar production.

The discovery of Thomson's arial wheel patent caused a problem. Dunlop's pneumatic tyre patent was declared invalid and was revoked, barely a year after the flotation of the new company. Harvey Du Cros responded quickly by acquiring the 1890 patent for a detachable pneumatic tyre, invented by Charles Kingston Welch of London. Dunlop and Du Cros travelled to England to inspect the invention, which used an embedded wire bead to secure the tyre on the wheel rim. They bought the rights to Welch's patent for £5,000 and employed the inventor. Around a month later, another important and consequential patent for a detachable pneumatic tyre was lodged by William Erskine Bartlett, the American-born managing director of the North British Rubber Company in Edinburgh. In this case the tyre was secured or 'clinched' to the rim by a beaded edge and kept in place by air pressure.

Tyre manufacture continued in Dublin until 1892, when the city Corporation raised a court case objecting to the smell of naptha and rubber from the factory. Though the company won the case, the Corporation appealed and Du Cros promptly moved the business to Coventry, the centre of the nascent cycle industry. Around the same time, Du Cros learned that Edlin & Co. were also manufacturing pneumatic tyres in Coventry, infringing Dunlop's second patent, of March 1899, called *Improvements in wheel tyres of cycles and other vehicles, and in means for securing the same to the wheel rims'*, and possibly infringing the Welch patent too. Du Cros wrote repeatedly to offer licences to Edlin, who responded with an attempt to secure a court injunction to restrain Du Cros from *"threatening, or continue to threaten, the Plaintiffs… with any legal proceedings or liability…"* The court ordered an inspection of the Edlin tyres to determine infringement, which was confirmed, and the motion for an injunction was thrown out.

Dunlop continued to live quietly in Dublin, allowing Du Cros to lead the development of the company as managing director. Nevertheless, Dunlop took out a total of 17 patents for improvements in cycle and tyre design, including a sprung-frame bicycle. Du Cros recruited his team of six sons into the business, and sent them around the world to establish the company. Arthur Du Cros became general manager and another son, Harvey, became a major investor in the Austin motor company. In 1896, Du Cros and Arthur agreed to buy the Bartlett patent for £200,000 pounds, thus removing the North British Rubber Company as direct competitors. The same year, Du Cros secured his

Illustration 13: John Boyd Dunlop c.1915

fortune when he sold the company for £3 million to a speculative financier, Ernest Hooley, who did some minimal reorganisation and quickly re-sold the company as the Dunlop Pneumatic Tyre Company in a £5 million public flotation. Du Cros remained as head of the company until his death in 1918, having been the Member of Parliament for Hastings for two years from 1906, succeeded as its MP by his son Arthur.

John Boyd Dunlop had resigned from the Pneumatic Tyre Company and Booth's Cycle Agency in 1895, a year before its sale, citing concern for the state of his health, but seemingly also in a deteriorating relationship with Du Cros and his sons. By the end of that year he had sold four-fifths of his shares, for around £100,000, a fraction of their value a few years later. He brought a case against F.F. MacCabe, the editor of the Irish Field, to the Dublin High Court in 1897, charging that he had been fraudulently induced to sell 2,000 of his company shares at a discount. The money to finance the purchase was allegedly traced to Du Cros. Dunlop won the case and was awarded £1,000 in compensation. He continued though to live comfortably, travelling to America to address the Society of Automobile Engineers, becoming a director in Dublin businesses and investing in the Australian wool trade.

When he died in 1921, still in Dublin aged 81, his estate was valued at only £9,867 but the company which bore his name had become a global business, diversified into motor and aircraft tyres, rubber hoses, and sports equipment. In 1926 the company acquired the Charles Macintosh Group and it expanded further into clothing and footwear.

The original inventor of the air-filled tyre, Robert William Thomson, retired from business in Java in 1862, and settled in Edinburgh. He continued to invent, and took out patents for control mechanisms for steam engines, improvements to traction engines, and produced an early design for a continuous 'caterpillar' tracked vehicle. He died in 1873 and is buried in the city's Dean Cemetery.

7 Star-spangled skies: Williamina Fleming

On March 1st 1900, the Curator of astronomical photographs at the Harvard College Observatory wrote in her journal, *"In the Astrophotographic building of the Observatory, 12 women, including myself, are engaged in the care of the photographs; identification, examination and measurement of them; reduction of these measurements, and preparation of results for the printer. The measurements made with the meridian photometers are also reduced and prepared for publication... From day to day my duties at the Observatory are so nearly alike that these will be but little to describe... My home life is necessarily different from that of other officers of the University since all housekeeping cares rest on me, in addition to those of providing the means to meet their expenses. My son Edward, now a Junior in the Mass. Inst. of Technology, knows little or nothing of the value of money..."*

More than two decades earlier, Williamina Paton Fleming had arrived in Boston from Scotland, aged 21 and married just the year before, with her husband James Orr Fleming, an accountant 15 years her senior, and a widower after the death of his first wife. A year later, in 1879, when Williamina was in her first pregnancy, her husband left her and her unborn child.

Williamina, known as 'Mina' for most of her life, was born in Dundee in 1857, and raised and educated there, where her father, Robert Stevens, was a carver and gilder. He died when she was seven years old. Bright at school, and no doubt needing to supplement the family income, she is said to have begun as a pupil-teacher at the age of 14, and is described as a 'teacher' on her marriage certificate. As an immigrant to America, after the desertion of her husband and the birth of her son, she worked as a maid. She was hired by Edward Charles Pickering, professor of astronomy at the Massachusetts Institute of

Technology and director of the Harvard College Observatory. Impressed by her diligence and intelligence, he also paid her to do some part-time administrative work at the Observatory.

Pickering was a pioneer of the use of photography in astronomy, and invented the meridian photometer, an instrument which used mirrors and prisms to bring together a stellar image with that of a star of known brightness, so that their magnitudes could be compared. Photographs of star fields showed more reliable and more detailed images than the naked eye, but the large quantity of photographic plates being generated in the Observatory was causing an analysis backlog. Irritated by the poor work being done by his (male) employees, Pickering reputedly shouted *"my Scotch maid could do better!"*. He taught Mina how to analyse the spectra of stellar images with a magnifying glass, and she became the first of the 'Harvard Computers', a group of women who worked on the glass plates to measure and categorise the stars.

The first-ever photograph of the lines in a stellar spectrum had been taken of the star Vega, by Henry Draper, a doctor and amateur astronomer, in 1872 at his private observatory in New York State. His studies also of the solar spectrum established the presence of oxygen in the sun. More than thirty years before that, his father, John William Draper, had been the first to photograph the moon through a telescope. After Henry's death at the age of 45 in 1882, his wealthy widow, Mary Anna Palmer, created the Henry Draper Memorial fund at the Harvard Observatory, to carry on his investigations. The endowment enabled Pickering to expand his workforce, and photographic plates were commissioned also from the Observatory's southern station in Arequipa, Peru. Many more 'Harvard computers' were hired, including Anna Winlock, a daughter of Pickering's predecessor as director of the Observatory, and Antonia Maury, Henry Draper's niece and a graduate in physics and astronomy. They were placed under Williamina Fleming's supervision, and most were paid 25 cents an hour, for a seven hour day, six days a week, with one month paid vacation per year. The Observatory paid men the same for computing work, but few applied.

Soon, a sizeable group of women were engaged full-time on the 'Draper Catalogue' project, aiming to list the positions, magnitudes and spectral types of stars in all parts of the sky.

In addition to her supervisory duties, Fleming's own everyday work continued, examining and classifying the spectra of stars, and occasionally her alertness led to the discovery of new objects. Most famously, in 1888, when studying a

Illustration 14: The Horsehead Nebula (Barnard 33) in the constellation Orion

plate containing images of the constellation in Orion, she noticed a faint smudge under the easternmost star in Orion's Belt. She recorded *"A large nebulosity extending nearly south from Zeta Orionis for about 60 minutes [of arc]. More intense and well-marked on the following side, with a semi-circular indentation 5 minutes in diameter 30 minutes from Zeta."* This was the magnificent 'Horsehead Nebula' in Orion, now known to be a cloud of gas and dust, where new stars are forming, around 1,600 light-years distant from Earth.

The Harvard Computers team expanded further, and some deprecators called it 'Pickering's Harem'. Florence Cushman worked at the Observatory from 1888 until 1937, three years before her death at the age of 80. Henrietta Swan Leavitt, a graduate woman of independent means, joined in 1893, and demonstrated the logarithmic relationship between the luminosity and periodicity of variable stars, enabling the first 'standard candle' in astronomy and the measurement of distance to far-flung objects. Annie Jump Cannon, an outstanding physics graduate from Wellesley College, joined later, in 1896. Almost completely deaf after an attack of scarlet fever, she shared that disability with Leavett, who also suffered from acute deafness, possibly from the same cause.

A system to categorise the mountain of measurements was clearly needed. The usual system at the time had been developed by an Italian priest, Angelo Secchi, based on visual observations which divided spectra into four classes, depending on which lines were the brightest. As photographs were more sensitive, Fleming found she could distinguish 17 classes, based on the strength of the hydrogen absorption lines in the spectra. With Pickering, she labelled them A to O, in order of decreasing intensity, with the letter P used for

Illustration 15: Williamina Fleming c.1890s. Courtesy of Harvard College Observatory

nebulae and the letter Q used for unclassifiable stars. The Pickering-Fleming system was used in the Draper Catalogue of 1890 to classify its 10,449 celestial objects. Fleming published two papers in the *Astrophysical Journal*, on the peculiar spectra of newly discovered variable stars, but most of her observations were published by Pickering, with full credit given to her measurements.

Antonia Maury, who had an unfortunate habit of irritating Pickering, annoyed him again by departing from his and Fleming's system when she was assigned to study the more dispersed spectra formed by using two or three prisms in front of the telescopes. Maury additionally considered the width and sharpness of the spectral lines, because it seemed to give a more natural classification. But her nomenclature was complex, and classification required the examination of more than one plate for each star. Pickering refused to allocate the extra resources and Maury left the team in 1892. Nevertheless her system had merit, and with Pickering's consent it was picked up by Annie Jump Cannon four years after Maury's departure from Harvard. Cannon dropped the criterion of spectral sharpness and rearranged Fleming's classes to exclude spurious categories resulting from observational anomalies. The resulting classes O, B, A, F, G, K, and M described the hottest to the coolest stars, and forms the basis of the modern Harvard system of stellar categories. Generations of astronomy students remember the order of classes by the mnemonic 'Oh, Be A Fine Girl/Guy – Kiss Me!'.

In 1893, Fleming addressed the Congress of Astronomy and Astrophysics at the World's Fair in Chicago. In her speech, '*A Field for Woman's Work in Astronomy*', she reminded her audience of the pioneering female astronomers – Caroline Herschel, Maria Mitchell and Mary Somerville – and pointed to the benefits that could be achieved by recruiting more women to the profession. She described the work of the Draper Catalogue project and gave full credit to Maury, Cushman and others of the *"corps of about forty assistants, seventeen of whom are women, and twelve…engaged, more or less, on the photographic work"*, concluding, *"While we cannot maintain that in everything woman is man's equal, yet in many things her patience, perseverance and method make her his superior. Therefore, let us hope that in astronomy, which now affords a large field for woman's work and skill, she may, as has been the case in several other sciences, at least prove herself his equal."*

During her career, Fleming examined nearly 200,000 photographic plates, and classified the spectra of the 10,341 stars published in the first Draper Catalogue of Stellar Spectra. She discovered ten novae, around 59 nebulae, and more than 300 variable stars, while showing that the 'variables' had certain spectral characteristics. In 1910 she discovered the first white dwarf star, 40 Eridani. Her work was recognised by the awards of honorary memberships of the American Astronomical Society, the Royal Astronomical Society, and their French and Mexican equivalents.

Williamina Fleming died of pneumonia in 1911, aged 54, having completed 30 years of service in the Harvard Observatory. She left behind her son, Edward, who graduated from MIT and became a mining engineer in Chile. Fleming was succeeded as the curator of photographs by Annie Jump Cannon, who wrote an obituary of Mina in the journal *Science*, in which she described Fleming's many achievements, and her personality, saying, *"of a large-hearted, sympathetic nature, and keenly interested in all that pertains to life, she won friends easily, while her love of her home and unusual skill in needlework, prove that a life spent in the routine of science need not destroy the attractive human element of a woman's nature."* Work continued under Cannon's supervision, and by 1924, the Draper Catalogue had expanded to include the spectral observations of more than 200,000 stars. The beautiful nebula discovered by Williamina around a pair of white dwarf stars, in the southern constellation of Centaurus, is named Fleming 1.

Illustration 16: The planetary nebula Fleming 1 seen with the European Southern Observatory's Very Large Telescope

8 The fact of fingerprints: Henry Faulds

The uniqueness of an individual's fingerprints is not obvious, and is in many ways surprising. First to record the fact, and promote its potential for criminal detection, was a doctor, Henry Faulds, born in Ayrshire, and at the time working as a medical missionary in Japan. He was trained and qualified in medicine after an unpromising start to his academic career. After his father's business had to be wound up, he left school at the age of 12 or 13, and worked in an uncle's grocery shop, and as a clerk for a Paisley shawl manufacturer. In later life he would say that *"this seemed to me an utter waste of time"* but that classifying the various intricate patterns in the shawls assisted in his fingerprint research. At the age of 21, he enrolled at the University of Glasgow to study logic, mathematics, and classics, before going on to study medicine and gaining his physician's licence at the Andersonian medical school. He joined the Church of Scotland, and in 1871, aged 28, he was sent to Darjeeling in India where he worked in a hospital for the poor. Perhaps the conservatism of the mainstream church was not to his liking. Faulds returned to Scotland after two years, and joined the more liberal United Presbyterian Church. In September 1873, he married Isabella Wilson, the daughter of an innkeeper, after his new church asked him to found a mission in Japan. This he did, with his new wife, the next year – the first English-speaking mission in the country.

The mission was based at Tsukiji Hospital in a foreign concession near Tokyo, and Faulds established a teaching programme for Japanese medical students, soon lecturing fluently in their native language. He introduced the antiseptic methods he had learned under Joseph Lister in Glasgow, and dealt with outbreaks of rabies and cholera. After opening a school for the blind, he produced Bibles with raised lettering for the use of the students. His account of his time in Japan, *Nine Years in Nipon*, vividly describes the language, customs, geography and botany of the country.

In 1880, the journal *Nature* published a letter sent by Faulds from Japan, in which he reported both an interesting observation and a practical suggestion. In his communication, *'On the Skin-furrows of the Hand'* he wrote, *"In looking over some specimens of 'prehistoric' pottery found in Japan I was led, about a year ago, to give some attention to the character of certain finger-marks which had been made on them while the clay was still soft. Unfortunately all of those which happened to come into my possession were too vague and ill-defined to be of much use, but a comparison of such finger-tip impressions made in recent pottery led me to observe the characters of the skin-furrows in human fingers generally."* Faulds described how he had recorded the curves and whorls in the fingerprints of many European and Japanese people, and some monkeys, using printer's ink on slightly dampened paper, and he suggested, *"When bloody finger-marks or impressions on clay, glass etc. exist, they may lead to the scientific identification of criminals."* He also mentioned anecdotal reports that Chinese criminals had in the past been made to give impressions of their fingers, and supplemented his letter with examples of the fingerprints he had obtained. To satisfy himself that fingerprint patterns were persistent and unalterable, he experimented on himself and his students by shaving fingertips with abrasives and razors.

Around the time Faulds submitted his paper to *Nature*, he also wrote to Charles Darwin to highlight his discoveries and seek the great man's support. Darwin was unwell, and forwarded the letter to his half-cousin, the eminent polymath Francis Galton. Perhaps aware of Galton's elitism, he wrote, *"The enclosed …may perhaps interest you, as it relates to a queer subject. You may perhaps say: hang his impudence…"*

Galton wrote back, *"I will take Faulds' letter to the Anthro. [the Anthropological Society] and see what can be done; indeed, I myself got several thumb impressions a couple of years ago, having heard of the Chinese plan with criminals, but failed… to make out any large number of differences… Anyhow I will do what*

I can to help Mr Faulds in getting these sort of facts and in having an extract of his letter printed."

Nothing further seems to have happened, but Faulds' letter in *Nature* prompted an interested response the next month from Sir William Herschel, the eldest son of Sir John Herschel, the famous astronomer. Sir William had been an Imperial Civil Service Officer in India, and there, he wrote, he had been in the habit of using fingerprints as signatures, to identify government contractors, people applying for money in pension offices, and prisoners in jails, to avoid impersonation. He confirmed that in his experience, fingerprints of individuals were unaltered after 20 years.

Faulds quit the life of a missionary doctor, and returned to Britain with his wife and two daughters, Agnes and Isabella, in 1886. He went into medical practice, initially in London, and repeatedly badgered Scotland Yard to use fingerprinting to solve crimes, even offering to set up a fingerprint bureau for them, at his own expense. The police were unpersuaded of its practicality. Not so the American author Mark Twain, who somehow picked up on the idea for his 1894 novel *Pudd'nhead Wilson*, whose lawyer hero brings a murderer to justice through his collection of local fingerprints. Possibly Twain had read the Faulds correspondence in *Nature*. Or, he had heard of a talk by a microscopist, mentioned briefly in *The American Journal of Microscopy* in 1877, which reported, *"Hand Marks Under the Microscope — In a recent lecture, Mr Thomas Taylor, microscopist to the Department of Agriculture in Washington DC, exhibited on a screen a view of the markings on the hand and the tips of the fingers, and called attention to the possibility of identifying criminals, especially murderers, by comparing the marks of the hands left upon any object with impressions in wax taken from the hands of suspected persons. In the case of murderers, the marks of bloody hands would present a very favorable opportunity. This is a new system of palmistry."*

As another possibility, Twain may have heard of the work of Francis Galton, whose interest in fingerprinting had at last been aroused, and he was applying his considerable intellect to the subject with scientific rigour. On May 25th 1888, he gave a lecture at the Royal Institution that was reproduced in *Nature* the following month as a notice called '*Personal Identification and Description*'. It surveyed the physiological options for uniquely identifying human individuals, and Galton wrote , "*I cannot hear of any elaborate system of finger-marks having ever been employed in China for the identification of prisoners. It was, however, largely used in India, by Sir William Herschel, twenty-eight years ago… He described his method fully in 'Nature', vol. xxiii, p76)… also a paper by Mr Faulds in the next volume…*" Apart from being unduly generous to Herschel's sparse report of his practices in India, Galton mistakenly reversed the real precedence of the Faulds and Herschel papers in *Nature*, and he seemed to have completely forgotten the letter from Faulds that he had been given by Darwin, eight years before. Galton compounded his crime in 1892, when he published a comprehensive study, *Fingerprints*, in which he credited Herschel for bringing "*the method of fingerprints into regular official employment*". When he did once refer to Faulds, who he said, "*seems to have taken much pains*", he managed to mis-spell his name. This began many years of irritated correspondence, mainly from the highly frustrated and exasperated Dr Faulds, some of it directed at Herschel, who was relatively innocent.

Galton's scientific eminence meant that his publications caught the attention of the government of Herbert Asquith, which was concerned that police forces were failing to detect persistent offenders. A committee of inquiry was set up in 1893 to propose better methods of identification. In a committee-like fudge, they recommended a system of anthropomorphic measurements called 'Bertillonage' where the length and breadth of the head, left forearm, left foot and left middle finger would be recorded, with the back-up of a fingerprint system, "*first suggested, and to some extent applied practically, by Sir William Herschel.*" The committee's report infuriated Faulds, who had not been asked to provide evidence, and whose 1880 'careful study of the subject' was mentioned, but in his view, inadequately. He wrote another letter to *Nature*, in 1894, concerning the committee's report. "*My 'careful study' of*

Illustration 17: Dr Henry Faulds c.1890s

the subject is mentioned there, and an article of mine…is referred to.. although Mr Galton spells and indexes my name incorrectly. That article, I believe, is absolutely the first notice of the subject contained in English literature." After pointing out the lack of any publications by Herschel prior to his own, he concluded, *"I have not the slightest wish to diminish the credit that may be due to Sir W. Herschel. What I wish to point to is that his claim ought to be brought out a little more clearly than has yet been done, either by himself or Mr Galton. What precisely did he do, and when?"*

The Bertillonage measurement system, named after the French anthropologist Alphonse Bertillon, was applied in many countries in the late 19th century. It fell into disrepute after the events of 1903, when a black man named Will West was sentenced to a US Penitentiary in Kansas. It was discovered that there was another man already imprisoned, called William West, whose Bertillon measurements were almost identical. According to Bertillonage, they were the same person. Crucially, their fingerprints were sufficiently different that they were distinguishable. It was later surmised that the men were identical twins, separated at a young age. The fact that even identical twins have non-identical fingerprints has been known for many years since, and is due to the partially random development of fetal fingerprints after about seven months in the womb. Genes determine the general characteristics of the patterns, but the flow of amniotic fluids around the fetuses, and their position in the uterus, creates a micro-environment that is slightly different from hand to hand and finger to finger.

The main interest of fingerprints for Sir Francis Galton, as he later became, was in the determination of race and heredity, and he devised a classification scoring system based on loops, arches and whorls. Sir Edward Henry, who was Inspector General of Police in Bengal, had introduced a thumbprint system to identify criminals in 1892, and he extended and improved Galton's system in his 1901 book, *Classification and Uses of Finger Prints*. Henry became Commissioner of the Metropolitan Police in 1903, and his book made no reference at all to Faulds, or his system of 'syllabic' fingerprint classification.

Two years later, Faulds published his own short book, *Guide to fingerprint identification*, which was harshly reviewed in *Nature* by Galton, who wrote, at least this time recording Faulds' name correctly, *"though his letter of 1880 was… apparently the first printed communication on the subject, it appeared years after the first public and official use of fingerprints had been made by Sir William Herschel, to whom the credit of originality that Dr Faulds desires to monopolise is far more justly due…Dr Faulds in his present volume recapitulates his old grievance with no less bitterness than formerly. He overstates the value of his own work, belittles that of others, and carps at evidence recently given in criminal cases. His book is not only biased and imperfect, but unfortunately contains nothing new that is of value."*

Another reviewer was not so critical, though maybe not quite so well-informed. In the *Law Times*, reviewer T.H., purportedly the Anglo-Irish writer Tighe Hopkins, wrote, either through error or mis-print, that Faulds was the only expert to give evidence to the government committee. In fact many witnesses were called, and apart from Galton, they were mainly police officers or prison warders. Faulds was not called as a witness and Herschel was not interviewed either. T.H. wrote that Faulds' claims to honourable mention in fingerprint identification had been strangely overlooked, and described his book, which cautioned the need for great scientific care in fingerprint analysis, as *"altogether a very sane little treatise"*.

Fingerprint bureaux were established around the world, in Argentina, India, New Zealand, the USA, and, by Edward Henry, in the Metropolitan Police. The first man to be convicted by fingerprint evidence in the United Kingdom was Harry Jackson, who in the course of his burglary of a house in London, left a number of fingerprints on a freshly painted windowsill. The first British murder trial that used fingerprint evidence was that of the Stratton brothers, Alfred and Albert. The case was known as the 'Mask murders', due to the ladies stocking-tops left at the crime scene, in a paint shop in Deptford, south London. On the morning of 27th March, 1905, the shop manager, Thomas Farrow, was found beaten to death, and his wife was discovered, barely still alive, in the upstairs bedroom. She died a few days later. A single usable 'latent' thumbprint was found on an empty cashbox in the shop, which was identified by the Met Police Finger Print Department as having been made by Alfred Stratton's right thumb. At the trial, the brothers pleaded not guilty and Henry Faulds, who believed the fingerprint match to be unreliable, sat with the defence team, though he was not called as an expert witness. Other evidence, including witness statements, and the brothers' possession of money and the possible murder weapons, was sufficient to convict them, and they were hanged. Faulds continued to argue that the fingerprint identification was flawed, contending that the print was too smudged, and that different magnifications were used in the photographs presented to the jury. In his *Guide to fingerprint identification* he repeated that view, writing, *"I have already given reasons for maintaining that such a low class, hazy smudge as that in question cannot in any case whatever be relied on to yield good evidence for identification. Those elements that are at all visible are not clearly enough printed to prevent different 'readings' of the text."* He continued in his writings to argue that the highest standards should be applied in presenting fingerprint evidence, and that prints from several fingers were needed to prove identification. As expertise in fingerprint analysis and pattern recognition improved, that opinion was widely rejected.

Faulds continued to work as a medical doctor, in the Midlands, and published *Dactylography: the study of fingerprints* in 1912 and *A manual of practical Dactylography* in 1923. Even in later life, his old grievances and

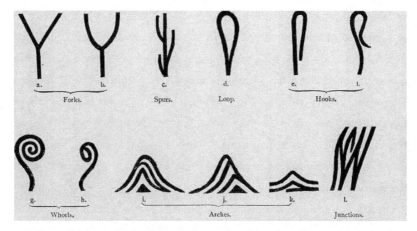

Illustration 18: Distinguishing features as illustrated in 'Guide to fingerprint identification' (Faulds, 1905)

combative spirit remained. He fired more shots, including those in a 1917 letter to *Nature*, entitled *The Permanence of Finger-Print Patterns,* in which he re-stated the dubious reliability of just a single fingerprint, compared to those taken from all ten fingers, and in referring to *The Origin of Finger-Printing,* Herschel's book of the previous year, concluded, *"Sir William, in his review of the history of this discovery, has not made any reference to my little contributions on the subject. He, however, did my priority of publication in your columns of November 22, 1894, and for that 'gift granted' I must feel grateful."*

Herschel had never been particularly assertive in claiming credit for the 'discovery' of fingerprints, and in the last year of his life, he said of Faulds, *"he had come to the conclusion, by original and patient experiment, that fingerprints were sufficiently personal in pattern to supply a long-wanted method of scientific investigation, which should enable us to fix his crime upon any offender who left finger-marks behind him, and equally well to disprove the suspected identity of an innocent man (for all of which I gave him, and still do so, the credit due for a conception so different from mine.)"*

Henry Faulds continued to write, and contend, on the history of fingerprinting, while practicing medicine in England. He died, aged 86, in Stoke-on-Trent in 1930, still battling for the recognition he believed he had been denied. His cause was adopted by several supporters, most notably the Scottish advocate George W Wilton, who petitioned the government at least five times until 1961, unsuccessfully, for a Civil List pension for Faulds' two daughters, and published several pamphlets and a book, *Fingerprints: History Law and Romance,* to promote Faulds' legacy.

In his award-winning 1986 album, *Graceland,* the musician Paul Simon sang *"it was the myth of fingerprints…"* But the uniqueness of human fingerprints is an indisputable truth, and one that is now of immense utility in forensic science. As with many discoveries, rather than a breakthrough by a single individual, realisation dawned through an accumulative appreciation, by many people. Henry Faulds was one of the foremost of them, and probably history's most vigorous proponent of the fact of fingerprints.

9 Moving mountains: Maria Ogilvie Gordon

The foundations of the science of geology were laid largely by two Scots, James Hutton and Sir Charles Lyell. Beginning with his observations of rocks at Glen Tilt in Perthshire, and Salisbury Crags in Edinburgh, Hutton recognised that the interior of the Earth is hot, and that it is this heat which drives the creation of new rock formations. In turn, he hypothesised, erosion of rocks by weather creates sediments which are deposited on the seabed, then consolidated by heat and pressure, and eventually uplifted to form new land masses and mountains ranges. These remarkably acute insights were presented to the Royal Society of Edinburgh in 1785, in a two-part paper, the *Theory of the Earth*. In the next century, Charles Lyell further developed this gradualistic view of rock formation over immense periods of time, and by studying extant geological processes, asserted that *"no causes whatever have… ever acted, but those now acting"*. Lyell's masterwork, *Principles of Geology*, subtitled '*An attempt to explain the former changes of the Earth's surface by references to causes now in operation*' not only detailed the relevant field-study evidence, but presented a 'grand new theory of climate' which recognised long-term climate changes and related them to the changing physical geography of the planet. By the time Maria Ogilvie was born, in Aberdeenshire in 1864, Lyell was in his late sixties, and *Principles of Geology* was in its ninth edition. She would become one of the foremost geologists of her time. Her field research was conducted exclusively in the Dolomite region of the South Tyrol, and led to new understanding of how mountain ranges are formed.

Maria Matilda Ogilvie was born the eldest daughter among the eight children of Maria Matilda Nicoll and the Reverend Alexander Ogilvie, a teacher and later headmaster of what became Robert Gordon's College in Aberdeen. They were a scholastic and high-achieving family. On her father's side, her uncles included the headmaster of George Watson's College, Edinburgh, the Rector of the Established Church Training College in Aberdeen, and the Chief Inspector of Schools in Scotland. Her siblings would become scientists, engineers, doctors, or church ministers. One of her brothers, James, became Moderator of the General Assembly of the Church of Scotland, while another brother, Francis, was a scientist who served as Principal at Heriot-Watt College and was knighted for services to education. Aged nine, Maria was sent to boarding school in Edinburgh where she excelled. She spent summer holidays at home, hiking and climbing with her brother Francis in the hills surrounding Royal Deeside. After leaving school, her interest was in becoming a pianist, and she spent nearly a year in England at the Royal Academy of Music. Then deciding to pursue a scientific career, she started her studies at what is now Heriot-Watt University in Edinburgh before completing her degree at University College London, where she specialised in geology, botany and zoology.

Maria graduated with the gold medal in zoology and comparative anatomy, and in 1891 she moved to Germany to continue her studies at the University of Berlin, where a friend of her family was the professor of geology. Even with the help of that influential friend, Baron Ferdinand Freiherr von Richthofen, she was not allowed to enrol. It would be several years before women were permitted to enter German state universities. Professor von Richthofen was one of the most prominent members of the aristocratic family that would include the two aircraft fighter aces, the brothers Manfred, known as the Red Baron, who was killed in action during World War I, and Lothar, who died in an air crash in 1922. The Professor and his wife, Baroness Irmgard von Richthofen, resolved to assist Maria in finding a way to begin her research. They accompanied her to the University of Munich, where it was agreed that she could work in the institute of palaeontologist, Karl von Zittel, and the zoologist Richard Hertwig, though she was still not formally admitted to the University.

That summer, the von Richthofens took Ogilvie to the mountainous South Tyrol on a month-long holiday and field-work excursion. The Professor had carried out a geological mapping of the region, and he suggested that she should investigate the geology of three regions in particular: Schluderbach, St. Cassian, and Cortina d'Ampezzo. The party hiked from Corvara to the high meadows which for years had yielded a wealth of fossils that shed light of the geological evolution of the mountains. Maria was enthralled by the beauty of the area, and wrote, *"Precipitous rocks, generally of a creamy or rose-tinted crystalline dolomite, rise to great heights above the green-swelling passes and grazing land… The barrenness of the Dolomite mountains is such that even chamois rarely frequent their clefts and tablelands; snow caps them during nine months out of twelve, and is perpetual on the highest summits."* She was introduced to local guides and innkeepers, and it required little persuasion to convince her to conduct her field studies in the Dolomites. Although von Richthofen had to return to Berlin, and she was largely unsupervised, she received encouragement and support from British geologists, including her fellow Scot, Sir Archibald Geikie, who arranged for her a research grant of £100 from the Royal Society, and Charles Lapworth, latterly a teacher of English at Madras College in St Andrews, who helped her with the presentation of her first publication. The long paper, published in the *Quarterly Journal of the Geological Society of London* in 1893, described Ogilvie's study of the detailed stratigraphy of the mountains, and formed the basis of her successful DSc submission to the University of London – the first woman to achieve that distinction. In her paper, she unravelled the complex ordering of the folded and faulted strata of the Dolomites. By identifying microscopic differences in the fossil corals, crustaceans and sponges found in the wider area, she disproved the theory that the fossiliferous beds across the entire Dolomite range had been formed by the uplift of a single, ancient coral reef. In the appreciative words of J.W. Gregory (later, and for 25 years, the professor of geology at Glasgow), *"The Authoress's work had destroyed faith in the most famous fossil atoll…Careful zonal collecting in these beds was greatly needed…"*

In 1895, Maria married an Aberdeen physician, Dr John Gordon, and they would have four children together. As Dr Ogilvie Gordon, Maria continued to spend her summers on field work in the South Tyrol, sometimes accompanied by her husband, and published more papers and monographs on the fossilised corals in the Dolomites. She had shown that the 'coral-reef' theory was the wrong explanation for the fossil corals, not least because they occurred only as clumped, thin layers within limestone where the predominant fossil remains were of plant algae. Another explanation was required, and also for two other features peculiar to the Dolomites: the circular and elliptical mountains with precipitous limestone walls; and the C-shaped depressions in the heart of the massif, that contained twisted rocks from the Jurassic and Cretaceous periods, between 200 million and 66 million years ago.

In his presidential address to the geology section of the British Association, in 1892, Charles Lapworth described rock strata as being to the geologist what species are to the biologist, or heavenly bodies to the astronomer. He gave a brilliant exposition of contemporaneous geological knowledge, in which he explained how the continuous evolution and folding of the earth's crust produces both the high coastal mountain ranges and deep oceanic depressions which characterise our planet. Summarising his view of the 'tectonic', or dynamic, processes involved, he concluded, *"The account of the simple rock-fold which I have already given you is of the most elementary kind…But … The simple fold becomes a folded fold, and the compound septum twists not only vertically but laterally. On the surface of our globe this double set of longitudinal and transverse waves is everywhere apparent. They account for the detailed disposition of our lands and our waters, for our present coastal forms, for the direction, length, and disposition of our mountain-ranges, our seas, our plains, and lakes… The whole surface of our globe is thus broken up into fairly continuous and paired masses, divided from each other by moving areas and lines of mountain making and crust movement…"* He pointed to the interaction of two crustal waves, at right-angles, as the origin of whole planes of contrary motion, known as 'thrust-planes' or 'overfaults'.

Illustration 19: Maria Ogilvie Gordon c.1900

Ogilvie Gordon applied these concepts in understanding the structures of the Dolomites, but she thought that they were not quite the whole story. After more field studies, in 1899 she published another long paper in the *Quarterly Journal* in which she explained the peculiarities of the southern Tyrolian mountains in terms of 'crust-torsion' – a twisting caused by the inter-crossing of an east-west thrust movement with an earlier north-south pressure. Her paper included detailed diagrams of sections through the Sella Massif and the Gröden Pass to illustrate the concept, and she concluded that the features she recorded were indeed of 'secondary and tectonic origin', created after the initial formation of the range. This research resulted in the award, in 1900, of a PhD from the University of Munich, from where she and Agnes Kelly, the Australian-born Anglo-Scottish zoologist, were the first women to obtain doctorates.

By then, Ogilvie Gordon had given birth in quick succession to her first children, a daughter, Coral, and a son, John, who would later write fondly of family summers spent in the Tyrol, as Maria continued in her multiple roles of wife, mother, and paleo-geologist into the twentieth century. In 1904, she suffered the death of her infant daughter, Mary Monica, at just nine months old. Maria eventually resumed field studies in the Dolomites, but they were interrupted by the outbreak of the First World War, which also resulted in the loss of her hand-coloured geological maps of the region, which went missing in Munich just as they were ready to be printed. All geology trips halted, she helped to distribute food and clothing to the needy in Aberdeenshire, and did voluntary work in local hospitals. She had become increasingly politicised, as a promoter of women's rights, and as early as 1907 she was active in women's associations. In the introduction to her 1909 monograph on the western Dolomites, she wrote, *"But from August 1908 to August 1909 my duties as Honorary Corresponding Secretary to the International Council of Women were exceptionally heavy; two large international meetings in Switzerland and Canada fell within that period, and it is only now, when I have retired from the Secretaryship, that I have been able to write an account of my geological researches of 1907 and 1908."* She presided over a meeting of the National Union of Women Workers in 1914, and a chaired a 1917 meeting of the Women's Citizen Association.

Soon after the end of the War, Maria's husband John died, aged 68, and he was buried beside their infant daughter, in Allenvale Cemetery by the banks of the River Dee. Ogilvie Gordon, now aged 55, moved the family home to London, where her brothers Francis and William had already settled. She joined the Liberal Party and volunteered as a court magistrate – a ' Justice of the Peace' – and chaired the Marylebone Court of Justice. Chosen as the Liberal prospective parliamentary candidate for Hastings in the General Election of 1923, she lost to the Unionist, but she managed to push the Labour Party hopeful into third place. She served as president of the National Council of Women of Great Britain and Ireland from 1916 to 1920, was a vice-president of the International Council of Women, and worked in the post-War negotiations in the League of Nations, forming the Council for the Representation of Women. Amazingly, she somehow found the time to resume her geological field-work in the Dolomites, now a part of Italy in the aftermath of the Great War.

In her career in geology, Ogilvie Gordon published more than 30 papers and monographs. She translated into English the major work of her old mentor, Karl von Zittel, *Geschichte der Geologie und Palaeontologie* (History of Geology and Palaeontology). In 1927, she published her voluminous major work, *The Gröden, Fassa and Enneberg areas in the South Tyrolean Dolomites,* and the following year, in two volumes for amateurs, a geological tour guide to the western Dolomites, *Geologisches Wanderbuch der westlichen Dolomiten.* Recognition from geological associations was overdue, but in 1931, she was made the first honorary member of the

Geological Survey of Austria, and the next year she was the first woman to be awarded the Lyell Medal of the Geological Society of London, one of its highest honours. Her dedication to the advancement of women's rights brought her the award of a DBE from the government of Ramsay MacDonald in 1935, and the same year she became Dame Maria, she was made an honorary Doctor of Laws by the University of Edinburgh

Undoubtedly established as Scotland's first outstanding female geologist, Ogilvie Gordon died in London in 1939, aged 75, and her ashes were interred in the grave of her husband and their daughter, in Aberdeen. She is memorialised in the University of Munich's library by the *Maria Ogilvie Gordon Raum*, which hosts the map collection of the department of geology. In her beloved Dolomite mountains, a new genus of fern was discovered in the fossil record, and in the year 2000, Maria's contributions to palaeontology were remembered when it was named *Gordonopteris Iorigae.*

10 Surgery and suffrage: the Scottish Women's Hospitals for Foreign Service

The town of Nainital lies among the cool hills and cold lakes of the outer Himalayas in northern India. Now the capital of the modern state of Uttarakhand, it was a hill-station and the seat of provincial government at the height of British Empire rule. In 1864, India's so-called 'Lake District' was also the birthplace of Elsie Maud Inglis, third youngest of the nine children of Harriet Thompson and John Forbes David Inglis, who was Chief Commissioner of the region in the Civil Service of the East India Company. Elsie's parents, liberal and enlightened by the standards of the time, had her and her only sister schooled in India, and educated just as well as their sons. Their life was comfortable, until Imperial intentions harshened under a new Viceroy, the 1st Earl Lytton, Robert Bulwer-Lytton, who launched an invasion of Afghanistan, which ignited the 'Second Anglo-Afghan War'. John Inglis fundamentally disagreed with Lytton's policy. In 1876, he resigned from the Civil Service, aged 56. His wife and younger children returned with him to Edinburgh, spending two years en route in Tasmania, where three of his sons had settled.

In Edinburgh, Elsie attended the Institution for the Education of Young Ladies in Charlotte Square. After a year in finishing school in Paris, she resolved to study medicine, which was still difficult for British women, despite the best efforts of Elizabeth Garrett Anderson and the Edinburgh Seven. Elsie's medical studies were delayed when her mother contracted scarlet fever, and required her daughter's nursing care. When

Harriet Inglis died from the disease in 1885, Elsie decided to remain in Edinburgh with her father. He was fully supportive of her ambition, and when Sophia Jex-Blake opened the Edinburgh School of Medicine for Women in 1886, Elsie began her medical training there.

Jex-Blake's oversight of the new medical school soon became a problem for many of the students. As both the Director and Dean of the School, she was accused of being bullying and over-controlling. When she expelled two sisters from Bo'ness, Grace and Ina Cadell, for remaining at their clinical studies in Leith Hospital after 5pm, in contravention of School rules, they sued. They won their case two years later, and each received £50 in damages.

Elsie Inglis withdrew from the Edinburgh School at the end of the summer term of 1889, having become hostile to Jex-Blake and her treatment of the Cadells. With her father, she established the Scottish Association for the Medical Education of Women, and they soon gathered a group of influential backers. One of them was Sir William Muir, Principal of the University of Edinburgh, who had been Lieutenant-Governor of the North-West Provinces in India, and was a friend of John Inglis. Another was Sir Alexander Christison, who became the first president of the Association, and was trying to undo the anti-female legacy of his father, Professor Robert Christison, who had been the most vehement opponent of the Edinburgh Seven. Funds were raised and the Edinburgh College of Medicine for Women was established in direct competition with Jex-Blake's institution.

Fifteen students including Inglis and the Cadell sisters were enrolled for the winter term of 1889-90, and eighteen lecturers agreed to provide their services. Clinical study access was arranged with the Glasgow Royal Infirmary, helped by William Macewen, the Regius Professor of Surgery at Glasgow, who was a strong supporter of medical education for women, and who would soon be knighted for his services to neurosurgery - a field of medicine he pioneered. Jex-Blake's students transferred or moved away to Glasgow, Dublin or London, and her School was closed down.

First Grace Cadell and then Elsie Inglis obtained the 'Triple Qualification', a licence to practice medicine awarded jointly by the Royal College of Physicians of Edinburgh, the Royal College of Surgeons of Edinburgh, and the Faculty of Physicians and Surgeons of Glasgow. Both doctors were deeply dissatisfied by the standard of medical care available to women, and both also became politically active. Scottish universities began to admit women students in 1892, with single-sex medical classes.

Illustration 20: Dr Grace Ross Cadell (1891)

Inglis took her first post as a resident medical officer at Elizabeth Garrett Anderson's New Hospital for Women in London, followed by a spell in Dublin at the Rotunda Hospital, which was a world-leading centre in obstetrics. She returned again to Edinburgh in 1894 to nurse her father through his final illness. The same year she started a general practice with Jessie Macgregor, who was a fellow student from their days at Jex-Blake's medical school. Perhaps inspired by her experiences in London and Dublin, Inglis created the Medical Women's Club, with the aim of starting a hospital for women. Grace Cadell, who specialised in obstetrics and gynaecology, was a leading member, and in 1899 they established a seven-bed hospital for women in pregnancy and post-natal confinement, called the George Square Nursing Home. It was later moved and re-named The Hospice, with Cadell as medical director.

As she grew ever more political, Elsie Inglis was appointed secretary of the Edinburgh National Society for Women's Suffrage, and worked closely with Millicent Fawcett, the leader in England of the National Union of Women's Suffrage Societies. Grace Cadell became a more directly active suffragette, and president of the Leith branch of the

Women's Social and Political Union (WSPU), founded in 1903 by Emmeline Pankhurst, with the slogan *'Deeds, not words'*. Four years later, Cadell joined the militant, pacifist Woman's Freedom League. When she refused to pay taxes in protest of the denial of her right to vote, her furniture was seized and publicly sold at Edinburgh's Mercat Cross. She supported the Scottish Suffrage Campaign, which launched arson attacks on specific properties including Ayr Racecourse and Leuchars Railway Station. When imprisoned suffragettes went on hunger strike, and were subjected to horrible and cruel force-feeding, through tubes painfully inserted down the throat through the mouth or nose, she gave them medical advice, and care after their release.

Hunger-striking as a radical political protest was not introduced by the WSPU leaders, but spontaneously, by Marion Wallace Dunlop, an artist and author from Inverness who claimed descent from the mother of William Wallace. In July 1909, she was sent to Holloway Prison in London for stencilling a passage from the Bill of Rights on the wall of St Stephen's Hall in the Houses of Parliament. When she was refused the treatment due to a political prisoner rather than a common criminal, she began her fast, which lasted 91 hours before she was released, on the grounds of ill health. Her action was endorsed by the WSPU and hunger-striking became a standard method of protest for imprisoned suffragettes.

The following September, the Liberal government of Prime Minister Asquith and Home Secretary Herbert Gladstone responded by sanctioning the forcible feeding of inmates. Among the prisoners was Lady Constance Lytton, daughter of Lord Lytton, the Viceroy of India whose policies had prompted the resignation of John Inglis. Arrested and jailed in Newcastle in the autumn of 1909, Lady Lytton was not force-fed but was released after two days, ostensibly because of a weak heart. She believed that her identity and status had protected her, and she assumed the guise of a working-class woman. As 'Jane Warton' she was arrested for protesting outside Walton jail in Liverpool, and force-fed eight times, by a medical doctor. She wrote, *"The pain of it was intense… my jaws were fastened wide apart, far more than they could go naturally. Then he put down my throat a tube which seemed to me much too wide and was something like four feet in length… I choked the moment it touched my throat until it had got down. Then the food was poured in quickly; it made me sick a few seconds after it was down and the action of the sickness made my body and legs double up, but the wardresses instantly pressed back my head and the doctor leant on my knees. The horror of it was more than I can describe."* Once her true identity became known, she was hastily released.

Most in the medical profession were anti-suffrage and were complicit or silent in the face of the physical abuse, though 116 doctors sent a memorandum of protest to Asquith. In 1912, three doctors reviewed

Illustration 21: Agnes Forbes Blackadder (1894)

the damaging effects of force-feeding. One of them was Agnes Forbes Blackadder, born near Dundee, and the first woman to graduate from the University of St Andrews, in 1895. A few years after graduation, she married another doctor, Thomas Savill, and as a dermatologist at St John's Hospital, London, she was the first female to be appointed as a consultant in a British hospital that did not cater exclusively for women. In their comprehensive *Preliminary Report on the Forcible Feeding of Suffrage Prisoners,* published in the *British Medical Journal,* Blackadder Savill and her colleagues began, *"It has been stated by the Home Secretary that the practice of forcible feeding is unattended by danger or pain"* and went on to demonstrate that nothing could be further from the truth. Drawing on personal examinations of suffragette prisoners, and ninety written statements from those subjected to forced feeding, they delivered a wholly damning assessment of the physical and psychological effects of the practice. Referring to the attitude of the latest Home Secretary, Reginald

McKenna, they concluded, *"We cannot believe that any of our colleagues will agree that this form of prison torture is justly described in Mr McKenna's words as 'necessary medical treatment' or 'ordinary medical practice'."* The Government's response was the 1913 *Prisoners (Temporary Discharge for Ill-Health) Act*, commonly referred to as the 'Cat and Mouse Act' which allowed the release of women at risk of death from hunger-strike, only for them to be recalled to prison when returned to health, for the cycle to begin again.

Suddenly, the stand-off between the Government and the suffrage movement was broken, in August of 1914, when Britain declared war on Germany after the outbreak of war in Europe. At that time, Elsie Inglis was practicing obstetric medicine in Edinburgh at the Bruntsfield Hospital, which she had merged with The Hospice. She was nearly fifty years old, but she offered her medical services to the War Office, proposing a 100-bed hospital to be staffed by women, and deployed anywhere on the Western or Eastern fronts. Reputedly she was rebuffed with the patronising words of an official, *"My good lady, go home and sit still."* Sir George Beatson, who had established the ground-breaking Glasgow Cancer Hospital, was just as unhelpful, having *"nothing to say to a hospital staffed by women."*

Inglis took the idea to the Scottish Federation of Women's Suffrage Societies, of which she was the honorary secretary, proposing that the Federation should give organised help to Red Cross work. The minutes of their meeting of October 3rd noted that *"Dr Inglis reported in her estimate that a thousand pounds would be sufficient to equip and pay salaries of one Unit of 100 beds for six months. Each Unit to consist of four doctors (two seniors and two juniors), ten trained nurses, six dressers, two cooks, an administrator, and a clerk. Suggested that one Unit might go to Serbia where the need is very great."* A letter had been received from Millicent Fawcett offering the promotional support of the National Union and its newspaper, the *Common Cause*. The Federation's committee was persuaded. Inglis travelled to London at the end of the month, and gave a rousing fund-raising speech at the Kingsway Hall, which was received enthusiastically. After she returned to Edinburgh, she received a letter from Fawcett saying that her stirring appeal had already raised three thousand pounds. A new organisation was formed: the Scottish Women's Hospitals for Foreign Service, soon known as just the SWH. Its uniform was to be 'hodden grey', with facings of Clan Gordon tartan.

Illustration 22: Dr Elsie Inglis, founder of the SWH, in uniform

Appeals raised funds from far beyond the suffrage movement, and by November, £5,400 had been subscribed. The Cambridge University women's colleges of Girton and Newnham offered to raise another £1,500 to equip another Unit. By early December, funds in hand exceeded £6,500, affording the possibility to establish several hospitals. SWH emissaries were already abroad, seeking out optimal locations.

From France, Dr Alice Hutchison, born in Dalhousie, India and the daughter of a medical missionary, reported to Inglis that, *"there is not a single barn left at Calais for wounded pouring in. I must dash up to Edinburgh if possible on my return, as I came… with a fortnight's luggage. If it's impossible, I'll manage somehow – I am delighted to do this trip for you."* It was impossible - an outbreak of typhoid in the Belgian Army had Hutchison spending three months in Calais, put in charge of another doctor and ten nurses, battling the disease. From Serbia, Robert Seton-Watson, the historian and polemicist who wrote as *'Scotus Viatus'*, and who was honorary secretary of the Serbian Relief Fund, telegraphed Inglis: *"Serbian Government gratefully accepts expedition. Writing details."*

In establishing a larger presence near the Western Front, the SWH was helped by the Vicomtesse de La Panouse, the wife of the French ambassador in London. She identified the Abbey of Royaumont in the Île de France, about 25 miles from Paris, as a suitable location. By

Illustration 23: Dr Frances Ivens, chief medical officer at Royaumont

January 1915, a hospital unit of 96 beds in four wards was ready to accept patients into the charge of Dr Frances Ivens and her team. Royaumont Hospital became especially renowned for its care of patients during the Battle of the Somme, in which more than three million men fought on all sides and more than a million were wounded or killed. The hospital was expanded to 600 beds and treated mainly French and north African wounded, with the doctors and surgeons working with little sleep in teams of four, on up to 150 admissions per day. Research was also undertaken at Royaumont. It focused on the treatment of gas gangrene, and the hospital had a car with X-ray equipment that was donated by the National Union of Women's Suffrage Societies. The X-ray car was used to great effect, particularly to make early diagnoses of gangrene, by Agnes Blackadder Savill, who spent many months as the radiographer at Royaumont, returning to her position in London when there was a lull in the fighting.

The French War Office asked the SWH to open another hospital, which was established at Troyes under Chief Surgeon Louise McIlroy, who was the first woman to obtain an MD from Glasgow University. The Troyes hospital was named the Girton and Newnham Unit, and was housed in tents to provide mobility. As well as in France, the Unit was deployed in Serbia and Salonika, Greece.

Other SWH units were established in Serbia, Corsica, Greece and Romania. As Elsie Inglis had already noted, the need in Serbia was very great, with only 300 army doctors struggling to support half a million troops. An SWH unit was sent out in early 1915, first to the hospital in Salonika, then to northern Serbia, where they discovered the hospital at

Kraguievatz to be overwhelmed by wounded - Serbian soldiers and Austrian prisoners - as well as an epidemic of typhus. No-one in the SWH organisation had expected Elsie Inglis to go to the battlefronts herself, but when the head of the Serbian unit fell sick and appealed for help, Inglis went out with more staff, and established three more hospitals in Serbia. Belgrade had already fallen to Austrian forces, and in the winter of 1915, with the German and Bulgarian armies, they forced a hazardous Serbian retreat over the mountains into Albania. Some SWH

Illustration 24: Dr Louise McIlroy, chief medical officer of the Girton and Newnham Unit

Illustration 25: Dr Alice Hutchison in Russian cap and coat during internment, 1915-16

medical staff went too, while others, including Inglis and Alice Hutchison, stayed behind with their patients. They were captured and interned, for three months. Inglis was ordered to manage a Serbian prisoner-of-war hospital, until the SWH staff were repatriated to Britain via Vienna and Zürich in early 1916.

Back home, Inglis continued to push passionately for more medical aid to be sent to the Serbians, and in the spring she was the first woman to receive the Order of the White Eagle, the highest honour Serbia could bestow. Within a few weeks, the Serbian ambassador in London asked Inglis if the SWH could equip and manage up to four field hospitals in Russia, to support the many Serbs, Croats and Slovenes serving in the Russian Army. In August, Inglis sailed from Liverpool for Archangel with 75 staff aboard, including three doctors. From

Archangel, they travelled some 2,700 km south to Odessa, and then on to Medgidia in eastern Romania where they established two field hospitals. By December, the Russian armies were in retreat and the field hospitals were repeatedly moved over the winter, complicated by military unrest and indiscipline due to the Russian Revolution of March 1917. The unit remained stationed in Romania and modern Moldova until late summer.

Elsie Inglis had known before leaving Britain for Russia that she had cancer. In September 1917, she collapsed and was unable to continue to work as a surgeon, though she continued to direct her unit for a while. She returned to Archangel in November, and then sailed with the SWH unit and the whole redeployed Serb division, to Newcastle, where she died the day after arriving. Her body lay in state at St Giles' Cathedral in Edinburgh before she was buried at the city's Dean Cemetery. The newly-renamed Elsie Inglis Unit of the SWH was inspected by King George V and Queen Mary, and returned to Salonika to join the Girton and Newnham Unit before moving on to complete their service in Serbia.

Over the course of World War I, hundreds of thousands of patients were treated by the SWH and more than 1000 women served in the Units, many receiving no pay or recognition. Frances Ivens and 22 of her staff in the Royaumont Hospital were awarded the Croix de Guerre by the French authorities. After the War, Ivens returned to medical practice in Liverpool where she was instrumental in the establishment of two new hospitals. She was married at the age of sixty, to a man she had known since student days.

Alice Hutchison was awarded Serbia's Order of St Sava, and the Belgian Order of the Palm Leaf, for her management of many hospital units during the conflict. She settled in London and specialised in the care of children, holding several appointments at the Tavistock Clinic, the South London Hospital for Women, and the Great Ormond Street Hospital for Sick Children. Her interest was also in child psychology, and she wrote *Motives of Conduct in Children* and *The Child and His Problems*.

Louise McIlroy established a nurses training school for Serbian girls and finished her war service as a surgeon at the Royal Army Medical Corps hospital in Constantinople. She was a consultant at the Royal Free Hospital and became the Professor of Obstetrics and Gynaecology at the London School of Medicine for Women - the first woman to be appointed to a medical professorship in the United Kingdom. She was awarded an OBE and in 1929 she was made a Dame Commander of the Order of the British Empire. She never married, and retired to live with her sister in Ayrshire.

Agnes Blackadder also practiced medicine in London and based on her Royaumont experience, where she had installed a piano, she became convinced of the therapeutic benefit of music. In 1923 she published *Music, Health and Character,* and she edited her husband's encyclopaedic textbook, *Savill's System of Clinical Medicine.*

Grace Cadell never served with the SWH and during the Great War she adopted four children. She died aged 62 in the village of Rumbling Bridge, Clackmannanshire, and left considerable wealth to her family and to two charities: a hospital for destitute women and children, and another which funded medical education for women. Just a few days before her death, the suffrage movement had its first success. On February 6th, 1918, Royal Assent was given to the *Representation of the People Act*, which allowed women over the age of 21 to vote in local government elections, and gave women over the age 30, and who met minimum property requirements, the right to vote for United Kingdom parliamentary candidates. Ten years later, the electoral franchise was extended to women on equal terms with men.

11

Pandemic ! Fighting the Spanish Flu: James Niven

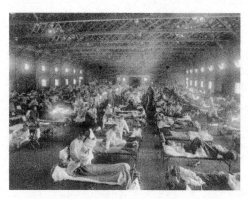

Illustration 26: Emergency hospital at Camp Funston, Kansas, on the outbreak of the epidemic

Pandemics, that is, epidemics that spread beyond national borders, worldwide, are of course not new. Most people these days are at least vaguely aware of the so-called Spanish Flu epidemic, but are unsure of when, where and what it was. Two facts are worth stressing. First, it had little to do with Spain, and second, the 1918 influenza pandemic was the most severe and deadly in recent history. There is no consensus on where the disease originated, but it was identified in a U.S. Army soldier, Private Albert Gitchell, on March 4th 1918, at Camp Funston in Fort Riley, Kansas. He complained of a sore throat, cough, headache and fever, and by the end of the day around 100 soldiers had reported similar symptoms. It seems likely that the infection was passed to humans from chicken farms in the state – we know now that the responsible agent, an H1N1 virus, has avian origins. Within the week, Fort Riley had as many as 500 hospitalised soldiers, and the disease infected other training camps. Over the summer, the infections seemed to subside, while huge numbers of American soldiers were sent to Europe to engage in what would prove to be the final months of the First World War. Driven by the troop movements, the disease spread with alarming speed.

As the Great War drew to its violent conclusion, a fatal wave of the influenza pandemic swept across the world. By October, cases had been reported in 24 countries, and resulted in many deaths from pneumonia. Unusually, this flu seemed highly dangerous to young adults – 20 to 40 years old – as well as children and the elderly. Wartime censorship of the press played down the impacts, except in Spain, which was a neutral country in the conflict. There, newspapers freely published the names of the dead, and spread the misconception of a 'Spanish' flu.

One of the highest rates of influenza morbidity was among the U.S. Army in Europe. Overall, 26% of U.S Army soldiers were infected, more than one million men, resulting in nearly 16,000 deaths in the American Expeditionary Forces, and 30,000 deaths in training camps even before soldiers could embark for France. The flu fatalities actually exceeded the American death-toll of 26,000 in 'America's deadliest battle' – the Meuse-Argonne offensive of September and November 1918, which involved 1.2 million U.S. troops. The pandemic struck all the combatants. The German Army recorded over 700,000 cases, and acknowledged 14,000 deaths, while the British Expeditionary Forces admitted to 313,000 infections in France. The future Nobel Prize winner and discoverer of antibiotics, Alexander Fleming, was stationed in Boulogne-sur-Mer as an officer in the Royal Army Medical Corps, and had to carry the corpses of flu victims to makeshift cemeteries after orderlies had gone sick. At the end of the War, on Armistice Day, November 11th, the scene was described by Sister Catherine Macfie at casualty clearing station number 11. *"We moved up to St André after the army went into Lille, and almost immediately we started taking in wounded and many…who had Spanish influenza as well… The boys were coming in with colds and a headache and they were dead within two or three days. Great big handsome fellows, healthy men, just came in and died. There was no rejoicing in Lille the night of the Armistice."* In 1918, knowledge of the infective agent causing the disease was very limited. Many scientists mistakenly attributed influenza infections to 'Pfeiffer's bacillus', a bacterium often found in patients' bodies, and which indeed is implicated in producing highly lethal pneumonias. In some scientific circles there was dawning recognition of the existence of other infective agents that were not bacteria – viruses. The distinction was academic. Given the absence of either antibiotics or antiviral medicines, treatment of the influenza focused on palliative care.

The end of World War I was followed by the return and demobilisation of around 65 million soldiers worldwide. The influenza followed them home, as it had previously followed soldiers on home leave. In Great Britain, the Spanish Flu had been officially declared an epidemic on June 23rd, 1918, and the civilian death rate in that year was 3,129 per million of population, surpassing even the mortality rate in the cholera epidemic of 1849. People wanted the answers to three basic questions. How can I avoid the infection? How do I find a doctor if I have symptoms? What are the effective treatments for the illness? The response of Britain's doctors was varied. Public health measures were the responsibility of the Local Government Board, but the second wave of infection in autumn 1918 took most civilians by surprise. The Local Government Board issued warnings that were often belated, recommending self-isolation if suffering symptoms, the use of handkerchiefs to avoid spreading infection, and a wash of potassium permanganate in the nose and mouth. The initial need to maintain wartime production led to jam-packed buses and trains. People were warned, but urged to carry on. In the British parliament, the pandemic was not even mentioned until the end of October. The cautious attitude of the Chief Medical Officer of the Local Government Board might explain the lack of alacrity. Sir Arthur Newsholme remarked, *"I know of no public health measure which can resist the progress of pandemic influenza"* and he resisted all forms of quarantine, later noting *"the difficulty of preventive measures in wartime"*. For patients struck down, getting hold of a doctor was not easy, even for those who could afford the services of a physician. More than half of the medical profession had been assigned to the military, and they were slow to be demobbed. A letter to the Manchester Guardian in 1919 illustrated the widespread concerns: *"On March 1 you published a letter written by an eminent physician in which he very strongly recommended the use of permanganate of potash for influenza. On February 28, at the Medical Conference on Hygiene, sitting in London, the use of such a solution was [characterised as] a 'horrible remedy.' Which of the two is to be believed? The other day I was talking to a district nurse in a suburb only*

Illustration 27: Dr James Niven

a short distance from Manchester, and was told that she was attending patients prescribed by four medical men, yet each doctor had a different method of dealing with this plague."

Responsibility for public health in Manchester lay with a ferociously intelligent Scottish doctor, James Niven, who had already distinguished himself in the clinical fight against tuberculosis and in his campaign to have TB classed as a notifiable disease. Born in Peterhead, and an Arts graduate of the University of Aberdeen, he went on to Queens College Cambridge and was 8th Wrangler in the Mathematical Tripos exams of 1874, maintaining a family tradition – three of his four brothers were also Cambridge mathematics wranglers. Switching to study medicine, he trained and qualified at St Thomas' Hospital in London. Niven's approach to public wellbeing and the control of infectious disease was notably proactive. As medical officer for health in Oldham from 1886, he drove improvements in the standards of housing, the supply of water, disposal of refuse and sewage, and the reduction of smoke pollution. He was sent to Berlin to work with Robert Koch, who had recently isolated the TB bacillus, and took Koch's methods back to the Oldham General Hospital when he returned. On his appointment as medical health officer for Manchester in 1894, Niven was just as focused, and he accelerated the clearance of 23,000 slum houses along with the conversion of 85,000 houses from pail toilets to water closets.

He pioneered the practice of health visiting, and as lecturer in public health at Manchester University, he worked with its laboratory to sanitise the city's milk supply. Somehow he found the time to be an examiner in sanitary science at Cambridge, and serve as president of both the Manchester Statistical Society and the epidemiological section of the Royal Society of Medicine.

The Spanish Flu epidemic burst upon the city of Manchester towards the end of June 1918, and Niven wrote that it *"flared up with extraordinary rapidity, and sank away at the beginning of August ... Unhappily there are no data available here for the first outbreak to show the latent period of the disease, and, therefore, its speed of travel. It is certain, however, that it swept over schools and works with very great rapidity."* In contrast to the relaxed approach of the central government, Niven produced 30,000 advisory leaflets, distributed to newspapers, factories and to private houses by health visitors, and he had 500 large warning posters positioned conspicuously throughout the city. He began visiting schools and workplaces to promote hand hygiene, good ventilation and the need for light and space. Where disinfection was needed, he recommended a 2% formalin spray. Cinemas and elementary schools were closed, and infected patients were asked to self-isolate for ten days. Niven organised the mass provision of free food, especially baby milk, and said *"So far as one can judge at present, in checking further outbreaks, it will be necessary to rely chiefly on general preventative measures ... to include the maintenance of a reasonable distance between the sick and the healthy, care of the hands, avoidance of common towels and common soap, careful washing out of common basins, avoidance of the handling in common of food to be afterwards cooked, and other like precautions; above all, the immediate segregation of persons attacked."* The total number of Mancunians infected during spring and summer was estimated at 100,000. The number of influenza deaths was tiny - just 332.

The respite was short. A second wave of infection in the autumn was far more virulent, and modern retrospective analysis indicates a possible new strain of virus with increased lethality, as Niven himself suspected. Another 150,000 handbills were printed and distributed throughout the city, warning of the highly infectious and 'very fatal' nature of the disease, and giving detailed instructions on hygiene and isolation measures. Crowded rooms were to be avoided, and the sick were to be immediately isolated, in well-ventilated but heated single rooms in the household if possible, as well as in factories and workshops. In cases of illness at work and inability to walk home, the telephone number 'City 8680 Medical' was given to call for an ambulance.

Between October 1918 and the following January, Niven recorded 1,715 flu deaths in Manchester, 59% of these in females, with the rate of fatalities peaking in November in the weeks after the Armistice Day celebrations. Delays in burials, caused by shortages of coffins and coffin-makers, prompted an exasperated Niven to bemoan the desire for fancy funerals, with relatives of the dead *"insisting on strict observance of custom, with its paraphernalia of hearse, coaches and elaborate oak coffin."* The British Prime Minister, David Lloyd George, visited Manchester on a ceremonial visit at the beginning of the second outbreak, and contracted the infection. He spent ten days confined to bed with fever in an improvised sickroom within Manchester Town Hall, and needed to be respirated. Hordes of people had lined the streets and crowded into Albert Square to see him receive the keys to the city – no doubt contributing to the second flare-up of the contagion. Lloyd George required several months of recuperation but eventually made a full recovery.

On November 14th, Manchester's Monsall Fever Hospital received a phial of prototype 'influenza vaccine', sent by Sir Arthur Newsholme, for trial. The value of smallpox vaccine was well recognised, and there was great hope that an effective flu vaccine could be developed. The basis for the experimental vaccines was the assumption that the causal agent of influenza was Pfeiffer's bacillus, and as well as killed bacillus, dead pneumococci and streptococci bacteria were usually added to the vaccine cocktail. The medical superintendent at the Monsall offered inoculations to staff, and five nurses volunteered. One of them suffered an attack of Spanish Flu 15 days later. Despite various claims of success for vaccines against the influenza, all the cocktails were ineffective, since all were based on the erroneous assumption. It would be another 20 years before influenza viruses were correctly identified and effective vaccines were approved. Without a cure for the flu, many doctors prescribed medicines they thought might alleviate the worst symptoms, particularly aspirin, which in 1917 had come free of Bayer's patent. In America, some physicians recommended up to 30 grams per day, a dose now known to be toxic. Many deaths in autumn 1918 are now suspected to have been caused or hastened by aspirin poisoning.

On November 20th, Niven advised the closure of Sunday schools, achieving only partial success, and schools were closed again in December. There was resistance to Niven's unpopular advice and writing later he said, "It is difficult to understand the perversity of those who neglected, or withstood the request to close." His public health team regulated admission to places of entertainment, with a view to ensuring good ventilation and the exclusion of children aged under 14 years. Niven's scrutiny of all possible pathways of transmission was intense. He noted, regarding licensed public houses, "During this outbreak my attention was drawn to the general custom of handing practically uncleansed glasses, containing beer, to customer after customer. The time available did not appear to the bar-keeper to admit of more complete cleansing. I communicated with the Clerk to the Licensing Justices, who did all that was possible to remedy the practice complained of; but matters concerning food and drink are probably not so important as those which bring infected matters in contact with the nose, as occurs from infected towels and hands. Hence, the care of the hands is all important."

The Local Government Board, chaired by Sir Auckland Geddes and advised by their Chief Medical Officer, was trying to keep up with events and achieve a tricky balance between public health and economic stability. On 22nd January 1919, Niven advised the Chief Constable of Manchester that the requirements of the Board's and his own regulations should be relaxed. That was unfortunate. A third wave of Spanish Flu was approaching, and took hold of the city in early February. By the middle of the month, the restrictions were back in place. The outbreak peaked in March, subsided again and had faded away by mid-May. According to Niven's revised statistics, the third wave claimed another 1,349 lives, and his detailed analysis of the data showed that no discernible immunity had been conferred on people who had suffered attacks in the previous outbreaks. Niven's finalised data showed a total of 3,814 deaths in Manchester – population around 731,000 – a mortality rate of 0.5%. Niven was rightly lauded and lionised for his heroic efforts to contain the epidemic. But for all his proactivity and enlightened measures, the rate of mortality in Manchester was no better than that experienced in the other major cities of England. In Great Britain as a whole, the final toll of excess deaths from Spanish Flu and its complications was close to 230,000. The official Registrar General data showed approximately 198,000 deaths in England and Wales. The Scottish Registrar General also calculated the excess death numbers and recent research suggests a likely death toll of 33,000 in Scotland. Globally, the Spanish Flu had a much more serious impact. Around 500 million people were infected, more than a quarter of the world's population. Most estimates of the number of worldwide deaths vary between 30 and 100 million. Fatalities in India alone amounted to 12-17 million, around 1 in 20 of the population, and very high mortality rates were seen in Alaska, South America, Indonesia and some Pacific Islands.

By the summer of 1919, the pandemic faded away as the most vulnerable had perished and presumably many others developed some immunity. The severity and infectivity of the Spanish Flu has puzzled modern researchers, prompting a group of American experts to track down the virus, sequence its genome, and recreate it in the bio-secure laboratories of the Centers for Disease Control (CDC) in Atlanta, Georgia. In 1997, Jeffrey Taubenberger of the Armed Forced Institute of Pathology in Washington D.C. extracted the RNA of the virus from a post-mortem lung tissue sample collected and preserved 79 years earlier. This was supplemented, remarkably, by a virus sample retrieved from a grave frozen in the Alaskan permafrost of a small settlement called Brevig Mission, that had been decimated by the flu pandemic. The genetic analyses showed that the 1918 virus was related to modern strains of swine and avian flu viruses, and was one of the family of influenza 'A' H1N1 viruses, named for the variants of the haemagglutinin and neuraminidase protein-producing genes they contain. The reconstructed 1918 virus was used to infect laboratory mice and chicken embryos. The results confirmed the exceptional virulence of the Spanish Flu, and its ability to invade lungs very quickly and cause severe lung damage, often followed by bacterial infections. In the lungs of mice four days after infection, the amount of 1918 virus found was 39,000 times higher than that produced by one of the comparison modern flu viruses. The studies concluded that no single component of the 1918 virus made it so pathogenic, but rather it was the unique combination of all its eight genes that made it so deadly.

Since 1918, the world has seen three more influenza pandemics, in 1957 (H2N2, 'Asian flu'), 1968 (H3N2 'Hong Kong flu') and 2009 (H1N1, 'swine flu'). All of these were caused by descendants of the Spanish Flu virus, but none were as damaging as first feared. The 2009 swine flu virus, designated A/H1N1pdm09, is now one of the seasonal flu viruses that circulate every winter. Completely distinct from influenza viruses, a class of pathogens called coronaviruses have caused widespread respiratory infections in a succession of pandemics in 2002-3 (SARS-CoV), from 2012 (MERS-CoV), and in 2020-21 (Covid 19, SARS-CoV2). Although distinct, the diseases they cause have similarities to the effects of the Spanish Flu, though as yet with a much lower rate of deaths. The control measures used against Covid 19, and the desperate attempts to develop a vaccine, would be very familiar to James Niven.

Niven retired in 1922 and the following year published his *Observations on the History of Public Health Effort in Manchester*. Over the course of his 28 years in charge of Manchester's public health, the annual death rate in the city declined from 24.2 to 13.8 per thousand of population, thanks to his relentless pressure for improvements in sanitation and housing conditions, as well as his battles against tuberculosis and the Spanish Flu. But he found his retirement depressing. His wife Margaret had died 10 years before, his two daughters had left home, and he moved into lodgings. He visited the Isle of Man in 1925, and on 25th September he paid his hotel bill, left a note with his bag, and disappeared. The next morning, his body was found in a local harbour near Douglas. An inquest found that he had taken poison before drowning. His note requested that he should be buried at sea.

12

The disputed discovery of insulin: John J.R. Macleod and Frederick Grant Banting

Even thousands of years ago, healers were aware of a particular strange and rare disease which caused weight loss, extreme thirst, and excessive urination. Around the 3rd century BCE, Greek physicians termed the condition 'diabetes' meaning 'to go through'. Diagnosis was often done by assessing the sweetness of the urine – by tasting, or testing its attractiveness to flies or ants. Galen speculated that the condition was an affliction of the kidneys, but the cause of the disease was a mystery, and a definitive diagnosis was likely to be a death sentence. In 1678, the Oxford physician Thomas Willis, one of the first Fellows of the Royal Society, added another term to the description – 'mellitus', meaning sweet or honeyed. More recently, diabetes was recognised as a fatal scourge, particularly of the young. In 1890, the reported death rate in the USA from diabetes, for children under 15 years of age, was 1.3 per 100,000, rising to 3.1 in the year 1920. A similar trend was observed in European countries. By then, several important facts had been established.

The first insight that diabetes was a complex condition was gleaned by Matthew Dobson, a physician and natural philosopher born in Yorkshire in 1732. He enrolled in the University of Glasgow when he was 18 years old, and studied under the famous chemist and doctor, William Cullen, before moving on to qualify in medicine at the Edinburgh Medical School. While working in Liverpool, Dobson demonstrated conclusively that the urine of diabetic patients contained sugar, and that their blood serum was also sweet. He observed that in some patients the disease led to death within a few weeks, while others lived much longer, and suspected that there were two types of the disease. Astutely, he concluded that diabetes was some kind of imperfect digestion that affected the whole body, and not a disease of the liver or kidneys.

Dobson's findings prompted the Scottish military surgeon, John Rollo, to investigate dietary treatments for diabetes. While working in London in 1797, as Surgeon-General of the Royal Artillery, Rollo published *An Account of Two Cases of the Diabetes Mellitus*, describing the symptoms of a diabetic officer, Captain Meredith, who was drinking around 16 pints of water per day and voiding about 24 pints of urine in a 24 hour period. Rollo used Dobson's test for glycosuria - sugar in the urine - to monitor the condition and prescribed a special diet consisting principally of *"animal food; for breakfast, a pint and a half of milk mixed with half a pint of lime water, bread and butter; at noon, plain pudding made of blood and suet only; at dinner, game, and old meats which have been long kept, and as far as the stomach may bear, fat and rancid old meats, as pork, taking care always to eat in moderation; for supper, the same as breakfast."*

The dietary regimen was the least of the patient's discomforts. His drinking water was dosed with alkaline salts; his skin was rubbed with hog's lard every morning; two 'ulcerations' were inflicted and maintained on his skin immediately opposite each kidney; and his bowels were kept regularly open by a pill of aloes and soap. He must have craved his bedtime draught, *"of twenty-five drops of tartarified antimonial wine and twenty-five of tincture of opium."* Remarkably, Captain Meredith's symptoms improved in only two days, and after two months, despite a brief and understandable delinquency into drinking tea and beer, his urine was normal, and his weight recovered enough to resume his duties. A second patient, a 57-year-old general officer, was prescribed the same treatment to good effect. When he went home, he deviated from the menu, and the 'pissing disease' returned. Rollo's dietary treatment worked, and from that he drew some general inferences, most of them wrong. He concluded that diabetes mellitus was a disease of the stomach, causing an increased secretion of gastric fluid. Nevertheless, he had demonstrated that the elimination of carbohydrates and sugar from the diet had a positive effect. In 1889, the role of the pancreas in diabetes was clearly implicated when German physicians, Oskar Minkowski and Joseph von Mering, showed that removing the organ from dogs resulted in diabetic symptoms, and death.

Twenty years before that, during his doctoral research, their compatriot Paul Langerhans had identified *"islands of clear cells"* scattered throughout the pancreas, which became known as the Islets of Langerhans. Their function was not known, but their role in diabetes was increasingly suspected. At the University of Aberdeen, two doctors, John Rennie and Thomas Fraser, noted that dosing diabetic patients by mouth with 'ordinary pancreas' had not improved the condition., and that various writers had pointed out how the Islets of Langerhans benefited from a rich blood supply and appeared to be unique. Rennie and Fraser observed that in the pancreas of most fish, the Islets were independent of the rest of the pancreatic gland. Courtesy of the Aberdeen Fish Market, they proceeded to test the effect of administering extracts of piscine Islets, in various forms, to five severely diabetic patients in the local Royal Infirmary. Although very far from being a controlled trial, the effects of the treatment seemed clear in each case: a reduction in urine volume and sugar content, in one case dramatically so. Unfortunately, the dosages were small, the patients were severely ill at the start of the treatment, and two of them died in hospital.

The growing evidence was that the Islets of Langerhans held some powerful secrets and secretions. Another German physiologist, George Ludwig Zülzer, added to that belief when he had some success treating diabetic dogs using an extract from calf pancreases he called 'Acomatrol'. When he tried it on a dying human patient, who was in a diabetic coma, he observed some improvement. The patient died when the supply of extract was exhausted. In 1909, around three years after the experiments of Zülzer and of Rennie and Fraser, the Belgian Jean de Mayer suggested that the mysterious and as yet unidentified substance should be called *insuline* after the Latin for 'island'. His suggestion went largely unnoticed until seven years later when, apparently independently, the term 'insuline' was used and brought into common use by the Professor of Physiology at the University of Edinburgh, Edward Albert Shäfer, one of the founders of endocrinology - the study of hormone-producing glands and their disorders.

Shäfer was an influential and interesting character. His father was born in Hamburg, and became a naturalised British citizen. Edward was born in England, and as a young man, he owed his scholarship, and mentoring at University College London, to the Scottish anatomist and physiologist, William Sharpey. Later in life, after the death of his son, John Sharpey Shafer, in World War I, he preserved Sharpey's name by adding it to his own, in an unusual act of gratitude, remembrance, and hyphenation. Professor Sharpey-Shafer, as he would become, was appointed to the chair of physiology in the University of Edinburgh in 1899. He was the co-discoverer of adrenaline, and introduced the term 'endocrine' for the secretions of the eponymous system of bodily glands. It was in 1916 within his seminal textbook, *The Endocrine Organs*, that he described how the Islets of Langerhans must secrete a substance which,

"passes into the blood and affects carbohydrate metabolism and carbohydrate storage in such a manner that there is no undue accumulation of glucose in the blood. Provisionally, it will be convenient to refer to this hypothetical autacoid as 'insuline'. It must, however, be stated that it has yet to be determined whether the active substance is present as such in the pancreas or whether it exists as 'pro-insuline' which becomes elsewhere converted..."

Many others would become curious about that, too. One of them was John James Rickard Macleod, a Scottish physiologist and biochemist. He was born in Clunie, Perthshire in 1876 and educated in Aberdeen after his clergyman father moved there. After taking his medical degree with great distinction from Aberdeen University, he studied biochemistry for a year in Leipzig, and then lectured in physiological chemistry at the London Hospital Medical School. He was offered the chair in physiology at the Western Reserve University in

Cleveland, Ohio, at the age of just 27, and he emigrated to the USA in 1903, with his new wife, Mary McWalter, a talented artist. It was in Cleveland that Macleod developed a strong interest in the metabolism of carbohydrates. From 1907, he published a series of papers entitled *Studies in Experimental Glycosuria I-XII*, summarised in a monograph, *Diabetes: its Pathological Physiology*, in which he explored the action of the nervous system, primarily

Illustration 28: John J.R. Macleod

on glycogen disfunctions of the liver. In 1914, he reviewed some of the failed attempts to isolate the secretive pancreatic hormone, and noted the extreme technical difficulties in determining the behaviour of sugars in the bloodstream, due to limitations in the available measuring techniques. As a naturally cautious researcher, always guided by the evidence, he favoured the view that excess sugar in the blood - hyperglycaemia - was due to the over-production of sugar in the liver. However, there was mounting evidence that the real cause of diabetes mellitus might be a general inability of cells to 'burn' sugar, and that led Macleod into elaborate studies of respiration as a way to estimate the levels of sugar oxidation in the body. His accumulated knowledge was published in his famous textbook, *Physiology and Biochemistry in Modern Medicine*.

With the outbreak of the Great War, Macleod reportedly became frustrated by the initial neutrality of the USA, and after 15 years in Ohio, he accepted the multiple roles of Professor of Physiology, Director of the Physiological Laboratory, and Associate Dean of the Medical Faculty at the University of Toronto. His career was hugely impacted at the end of 1920, when he was approached by a 29-year-old Canadian doctor, Frederick Grant Banting, with a request.

Banting, the youngest of five children of parents of Irish and Scottish descent, had served as a military doctor in France and was wounded in

1918 at the Battle of Cambrai. For his bravery in treating other wounded men, for 16 hours in the midst of the battle, he was awarded the Military Cross. After the War, he returned to Canada to complete his medical training in surgery and orthopaedics. When he approached Macleod asking for help with his idea, he was in general practice in London, Ontario, having been unable to gain a hospital position. Banting's interest in diabetes had been prompted by reading the literature on the pancreas, and in particular a paper by Moses Barron, a researcher at the University of Minnesota. In *The Relation of the Islets of Langerhans to Diabetes*, Barron comprehensively reviewed the results of various experiments on live rabbits, cats and dogs which revealed something very significant. When the main pancreatic duct was closed off by ligatures, the ordinary cells of the pancreas were atrophied by its bottled-up digestive secretion, trypsin. Most of the pancreas dissolved away over a period of a few weeks, and was replaced by connective tissue. However, the Islets were left normal and intact, and the animals showed no rise is either urine- or blood-sugar levels, and in fact showed no ill effects whatsoever.

Despite his lack of expertise in either diabetes or endocrinology, Banting was enthused. Here was a method, he thought, to reduce a pancreas to its essential Islets, and possibly to isolate the hidden hormone at last. Macleod knew that this had been tried before, but he agreed to provide Banting with advice, laboratory facilities, and ten dogs, to experiment on. This was initially to transplant an atrophied, but Islet-rich pancreas into a dog which had its pancreas removed, to demonstrate the restoration of normal metabolism. Macleod also provided the help of one of his medical summer students to assist Banting in performing dog pancreatectomies, and he suggested a research plan which moved from transplants to the injection of extracts of atrophied pancreas, explaining to Banting how to prepare an extract. Two potential summer assistants, Charles Best and Clark Noble, tossed a coin to see which of them would work with Banting. The toss was won by Best, a 22-year-old student, originally from Maine. After starting Banting and Best on the work over the first few weeks, Macleod left Toronto in the middle of June for a holiday in Scotland for the rest of the summer of 1921.

The casualty rate of the experimental dogs was high, but at the end of July, Banting and Best began injecting de-pancreatised

Illustration 29: Frederick G. Banting (right) and Charles H. Best c.1924

dogs with saline extracts of chilled, atrophied pancreas, and observed reductions in blood sugar. When Macleod returned in September, he asked them to repeat and extend their experiments, but to abandon the surgical transplant approach. The result was a heated clash between Macleod, a methodical, careful scientist, and Banting, who was impatient, new to research, and of the opinion that he had already done enough to show the efficacy of the extract of atrophied pancreas.

Macleod decided to add another member to the team in the shape of James Collip, a young but knowledgeable biochemist from the University of Alberta who was on a six-month fellowship at Toronto. By that time in December, Banting and Best had found that they could in fact dispense with the involved procedure of pancreas duct ligation and atrophy, and instead use fetal calf or fresh cow pancreas. Banting presented the results at a New Haven meeting of the American Physiological Society showing that intravenous injections of the extract reduced blood sugar levels by around a half. However, his nervous, inexperienced presentation was not well received. The audience was highly critical - Banting was apparently unaware that Zülzer and others had obtained similar results years before. And, although just like theirs, Banting's extract was likely to be impure, he had collected no data on toxic side-effects. Macleod, as chairman of the session, stepped in to try to rescue him from the criticism, but Banting saw this as an attempt to

Illustration 30: James B. Collip at McGill University

steal credit, and their relationship continued to sour. Nevertheless, and despite the unknown purity of Banting and Best's extract of beef pancreas, Macleod persuaded Professor Duncan Archibald Graham, chief physician at Toronto General Hospital, to allow the injection a severely diabetic 14-year-old boy, Leonard Thompson, with 15ml of the substance, on January 11th, 1922. It produced only slight reductions in glycosuria and hyperglycaemia, and resulted in the formation of an abscess. The treatment was immediately stopped.

The addition of James Collip to Macleod's team quickly yielded improved results, though the new presence was resented by Banting, who pitted himself and Best against Collip in a race to purify the extract. Collip succeeded by using fairly standard biochemical methods of filtration, precipitation by alcohol, and low-temperature distillation *in vacuo* to isolate and remove harmful proteins in the extract, producing pure serum for the first time. When he went to Banting's laboratory to give him the news, he told him that he would share the purification method with Macleod alone. Reputedly it was only the intervention of Best to restrain Banting that prevented a physical attack on Collip.

At the Toronto Hospital, on January 23rd, young Thompson was started on another series of injections with the purified extract. His blood sugar level dropped to normal, and his glycosuria disappeared, without harmful effects. This demonstrated for the first time the complete efficacy of the internal extract of the pancreas, a result that had been sought for more than 30 years. Glory for the team came almost immediately. Macleod presented a summary of all the research in early May to a meeting of the Association of American Physicians, and was rewarded by a standing ovation. Not for the first time, Macleod proposed that the active substance should derive its name from the Islets of Langerhans, and the term *insulin* became accepted. In the discussion, together with other warm compliments, the physician and dietician F.M. Allen said, *"Undoubtedly we are all agreed in congratulating Dr Macleod and his collaborators upon their almost miraculous achievement. Others have reduced glycosuria and hyper-glycemia with pancreatic elements. I have done so myself; but the obvious reason why these experiments have proved nothing is found in the great toxicity of such extracts...If as seems to be the case, the Toronto workers have the internal secretion of the pancreas fairly free from the toxic material, they hold unquestionable priority for one of the greatest achievements in modern medicine, and no one has the right to divide the credit with them."*

Banting, Best and Collip filed Canadian and US patent applications on the method of extraction in early 1923. Just months later, in one of its speediest recognitions of any scientific discovery in its history, the Nobel committee awarded the Nobel Prize in Physiology or Medicine to Macleod and Banting, 'for the discovery of insulin'. Since a maximum of three people can share a Nobel Prize, the glory was not equally spread, though the prize money was. Banting announced that he would give half of his to Best, and Macleod did the same for Collip. Sadly, the bitter arguments continued. Banting believed that Macleod was undeserving of a share of the Prize, and that Collip had received an undeserved share of the kudos. He insisted on an alphabetical ordering of the author names in the team's publications (which of course, ensured that his name came first).

The facilities at Macleod's laboratory were not suited to producing large quantities of insulin, and soon after the purification process was demonstrated, it was decided to grant a production licence to the American drug company, Eli Lilly. In the middle in 1922, Lilly produced batches of porcine insulin which were shipped to Toronto for testing. By the autumn, they had produced much purer insulin using isoelectric precipitation instead of alcohol to remove proteins, and by early 1923 they claimed enough capacity *"to supply the entire needs of the civilised world."* In fact, Eli Lilly had been granted only a one-year exclusive licence to produce insulin for the USA and Latin America. The Toronto team assigned their patents to the University, which licenced other manufacturers including its own non-commercial Connaught Laboratories.

After the award of the Nobel Prize, Macleod resumed his research interests, which included the study of the unusual pancreatic physiology of *teleost* fish, which had been advantageous to Rennie and Fraser in their experiments many years before, and he showed conclusively that insulin is derived from the Islets and not the ordinary tissue of the pancreas. In 1928, Macleod returned to Scotland to become the Regius Professor of Physiology at his *alma mater*, the University of Aberdeen, and refrained from engaging in the argument over the discovery of insulin. He later became Dean of the Medical Faculty and a member of the UK's Medical Research Council, and he proved his long-standing view that the central nervous system has a role in carbohydrate metabolism. He died in Aberdeen in 1935, aged 59, actively researching as well as painting, motorcycling and golfing, despite suffering from chronic arthritis. He and Mary had no children. During his career, he published more than 200 papers and 11 books or monographs, as well as seven editions of *Physiology and Biochemistry in Modern Medicine*.

Banting remained at the University of Toronto where he was elected to the specially-created Banting and Best Chair of Medical Research, where he focused on cancer, silicosis and the mechanisms of drowning. Further controversy ensued when he accused the Hudson's Bay Company of exploiting and harming the indigenous population of northern Canada. He and Best continued to promote their version of the discovery of insulin, and he and Macleod never spoke again. In 1934, he was made a Knight Commander of the British Empire, and the following year he became a Fellow of the Royal Society. Banting was twice married, and in later life he became one of Canada's best-known amateur painters. He died in 1941, of injuries and exposure after initially surviving the crash of the plane in which he was travelling from Newfoundland. He is memorialised in the names of many educational institutions, and by the annual Banting Lectures on diabetes. The

Banting Research Foundation supports health and biomedical research in Canada.

Charles Best succeeded John Macleod as Professor of Physiology at Toronto, in 1929. He received many awards including the Order of the Companion of Honour, and Fellowships of the Royal Society of London and of Canada.

James Collip left Toronto to return to Edmonton where he became head of the University of Alberta's new department of biochemistry, before moving on to hold the equivalent position at McGill University between 1928 and 1941, where he continued his research in endocrinology, particularly on the parathyroid hormone. In 1938, he was awarded the prestigious Cameron Prize for Therapeutics by the University of Edinburgh, as were, in separate years before him, Macleod, Banting, and Sharpey-Shafer.

Bovine and porcine insulins were progressively improved as a treatment for what is now known as Type I diabetes, by the addition of substances, including zinc and protamine, to prolong their effect. The amino acid structure of insulin was determined in 1951 by Frederick Sanger, resulting in another Nobel prize. That enabled the synthesis of insulin, almost simultaneously by several researchers, in the mid-1960s, which prompted the development of fully synthetic insulin in 1975. Today, most sufferers in developed countries can control their Type I diabetes with injections or the continuous infusion of synthetic insulin by pump, and various developments continue to develop an orally administered insulin, or an equivalent. A convenient finger-prick test to monitor blood sugar content was developed by Ian Shanks in the 1980s – and that is another story.

13 First men on the Moon: Neil Armstrong and Alan Bean

It may be stretching the concept a little, but perhaps the most far-flung representatives of the Scottish diaspora are to be found among the twelve Apollo astronauts who were the first men to walk on the Moon. The very first, Neil Armstrong, and the fourth, Alan Bean, were of course, Americans. However, they were both proud of their Scots ancestors. Three years after his truly epic achievement, Commander Armstrong visited Langholm, the traditional seat of the Clan Armstrong, in Dumfries and Galloway, to receive the freedom of the town. Possibly it was his customary politeness, but Armstrong said *"The most difficult place to be recognised is in one's home town. And I consider this now my home town."* When Alan Bean clambered back aboard *Intrepid*, the Apollo 12 lunar module he had guided to the surface of the Ocean of Storms, he was said to have left a piece of fabric of the Clan McBean tartan on the Moon. He later clarified, *"I took Clan McBean tartan to the Moon and returned it to Earth... I did, in fact, give a piece of the tartan to the Clan McBean and also to the St Bean Chapel in Scotland. And I've still got some of it in my possession. I did not, however leave any of it on the Moon."*

Neil Alden Armstrong was born in Ohio, on August 5th 1930, the first child of Viola Louise Engel and Stephen Koenig Armstrong. Stephen's antecedents came mainly from Scotland, Germany, and north England. Nine generations earlier in his paternal line, George Armstrong was born in the Scottish borderlands in 1565. At the time, the border between Scotland and England was indistinct and fluid. Many of the Armstrongs were notorious reivers – rustlers of cattle and sheep – in the disputed lands of Galloway, Dumfriesshire and

Cumberland. In the year 1530, a force led by King James V of Scotland had captured Johnnie Armstrong, the leader of the raiders, and he was hanged, with 36 of his men, at Carlanrig, near the source of the River Teviot. Luckily for all concerned, George and his offspring seemed to be on the right side of the law. His son, the first Adam Abraham Armstrong, survived to the age of 60 and died in 1672. He said to be buried in Castleton Cemetery, near Langholm. Adam's grandson, Adam Abraham Armstrong III, died in 1749 and is buried not far away, in Canonbie. It was his son, the fourth Adam Abraham, who emigrated to America, with his second wife Margaret, in around 1735. The adventurous Armstrongs became some of the earliest settlers of Cumberland County in Pennsylvania, and their son John was born in Chambersburg in 1736. His descendants moved into Virginia and Ohio after the end of the American War of Independence in 1783.

From a young age, Neil Armstrong was in love with aircraft and flying. When he turned sixteen and was still at high school, he took his first flying lessons, in Aeronica 'Champ' high-wing light planes, at the airfield near the family home in Wapakoneta. The next year he enrolled at Purdue University to study aeronautical engineering, under the Holloway Plan – a kind of sandwich-degree scholarship supported by the US Navy, designed to produce well-qualified pilots. He was called up to the Fleet Aircraft Service in 1949, after two years of study. Training completed, he saw action in the Korean War, and had a narrow escape when his Grumman F9F Panther fighter-bomber struck defensive cables strung across the hills. He ejected safely and was picked up by friendly forces. When he was released from active duty in 1952, he returned to Purdue to complete his engineering studies, and graduated three years later. At a Purdue party, he met Janet Shearon, and they were married in 1956. They would have three children together - Eric, Karen and Mark. Sadly, their daughter Karen died in January 1962, aged two, from complications related to a brain tumour. By then, Armstrong was a test pilot for the National Aeronautics and Space Administration (NASA) at the High-Speed Flight Station in Edwards

Air Force Base in California, flying many experimental aircraft including the Bell X-1B and North American X-15 supersonic rocket planes. In the same year, Armstrong was selected as one of NASA's "Next Nine" – 'Astronaut Group 2', which included another civilian test-pilot, Elliot See, as well as Frank Borman, Jim Lovell, and others.

Alan Bean was born in 1932 in Texas, to Arnold Bean and his wife Frances Caroline Murphy, not long before they moved to Minden, Louisiana. Arnold was a soil analyst and expert in flood control, employed by the US Government. His father's ancestry, through their paternal line, points to the suitably intrepid John MacBean or MacBayne, born about 1634 at Strathdearn, near Inverness, and who was the first of the clan to settle in America. During the Wars of the Three Kingdoms, in Scotland, Ireland and England, MacBean fought in David Leslie's defeated Royalist army at the Battle of Worcester in 1651. Around 10,000 Royalists and Covenanters, mainly Scots, were taken prisoner and most of them were deported to the West Indian and American colonies. John MacBean, mis-recorded as John Beme, arrived in Boston, with 270 other deportees, on the freight-ship *John and Sara* in February, 1652. MacBean (by now just Bean) was sold into indentured servitude to Nicholas Lissen, an owner of sawmills at Exeter in New Hampshire. A few years later, John married Lissen's daughter Hannah, and was given 20 acres of land as a dowry. Hannah died in the birth of their third child. John eventually married her sister, Margaret, and they had another nine children. John Bean of Exeter, as he became known, died as an old man in 1718, and is buried in the Congregational churchyard of that New England town.

Alan Bean's early life had some similarities to that of Neil Armstrong. After high school, Alan enlisted in the US Naval Reserve and then, while studying aeronautical engineering at the University of Texas in Austin, he joined the Naval Reserve Officers Training Corps, and was commissioned after graduating in 1955. After flight training and a four-year tour of duty, in 1960 he enrolled in the US Naval Test Pilot School in Maryland, where one of his instructors was Pete Conrad, two years Bean's senior. Conrad had been an early astronaut candidate for NASA's original Project Mercury, racing against the Soviet Union to make the first human spaceflight, and was successfully selected for 'Astronaut Group 2', along with Armstrong. No doubt encouraged by Conrad's enthusiasm and success, Bean swiftly applied to NASA and was recruited in 1963, as one of 'Astronaut Group 3', alongside Buzz Aldrin, David Scott, and Mike Collins, among others.

Project Gemini, the successor to NASA's Mercury project, was based on twin-crewed spacecraft and had two main objectives. First, to close the gap in the 'space-race' where the Soviet Union was in pole position with its record-breaking Vostok orbital flights of first Yuri Gagarin and then Valentina Tereshkova. Second, to respond to the challenge of President John F. Kennedy's ringing speech of May, 1961, to a joint session of Congress, in which he said: *"With the advice of the Vice President, who is Chairman of the National Space Council, we have examined where we are strong and where we are not, where we may succeed and where we may not. Now it is time to take longer strides - time for a great new American enterprise - time for this nation to take a clearly leading role in space achievement, which in many ways may hold the key to our future on Earth. I believe we possess all the resources and talents necessary... I therefore ask the Congress... to provide the funds which are needed to meet the following national goals.*

"First, I believe that this nation should commit itself to achieving the goal, before this decade is out, of landing a man on the moon and returning him safely to the Earth. No single space project in this period will be more impressive to mankind, or more important for the long-range exploration of space; and none will be so difficult or expensive to accomplish. We propose to accelerate the development of the appropriate lunar spacecraft. We propose additional funds for...unmanned explorations — explorations which are particularly important for one purpose which this nation will never overlook: the survival of the man who first makes this daring flight. But in a very real sense, it will not be one man going to the moon--if we make this judgment affirmatively, it will be an entire nation. For all of us must work to put him there."

Neil Armstrong made his first spaceflight in March of 1966, as Command Pilot of Gemini 8, with David Scott of the US Air Force, also on his first journey into space. The mission was to conduct the rendezvous and first docking of two spacecraft in orbit – an operation that would be required in lunar voyages – and would indicate that NASA had overtaken Soviet space technology. Scott was prepared and scheduled to spend two and a half hours outside the Gemini craft, 'spacewalking' between it and the unmanned Agena target rocket craft, practising the use of a backpack unit for astronaut manoeuvring, and bolting and unbolting a metal plate, with a specially designed contra-rotating power tool. On March 16th, both the Agena and Gemini launches were successful, and about six hours later Armstrong made the rendezvous and first-ever space-dock, reporting to Mission Control, *"Flight, we are docked…really a smoothie. No noticeable oscillations at all."* That situation did not last long, as the two coupled craft went into an unstoppable roll. Suspecting a failure of the Agena's attitude control system, Armstrong undocked, only for the Gemini to go into an end-to-end tumble at about one revolution per second. Unknown to the astronauts, or to Mission Control who were now beyond telemetry range, an attitude control thruster had jammed on. Scott had the presence of mind to reactivate the Agena's ground control systems before they undocked, and that craft was used again in a subsequent mission. Armstrong was forced to start the Gemini's re-entry thrusters to regain control, and they made a successful emergency return to Earth.

Alan Bean was selected as back-up Command Pilot for Gemini 10, but had to wait for his first spaceflight until the second phase of the Apollo programme. That project started disastrously. In January, 1967, the first planned mission, Apollo 1, ended in tragedy when a fire in the Command Module killed all three astronauts while on the launchpad in a pre-flight test. Gus Grissom, Roger Chaffee and Ed White died after an electrical fault started an uncontrollable fire in the capsule's combustible nylon materials, and pressurised oxygen atmosphere. After an investigation, all manned Apollo flights were suspended while systems were rapidly re-designed, and a nitrogen-oxygen mixed atmosphere was substituted for future launches. Grissom had been reported as saying, about the risks of spaceflight, *"If we die we want people to accept it… we hope it will not delay the programme. The conquest of space is worth the risk of life."*

Crewed Apollo flights resumed with the successful launch of Apollo 7 in October, 1968. The flight proved the design of the Command and

Illustration 31: 'Earthrise' photographed by Bill Anders from lunar orbit in Apollo 8

Service Module which would fly three-man crews to lunar orbit, though Apollo 7 carried no lunar module. With astonishingly fast progress, NASA launched Apollo 8 just two months later, the first crewed launch on the huge Saturn V rocket, and the first manned spacecraft to leave Earth orbit, carrying Frank Borman, Jim Lovell and William Anders on a three-day Christmas journey towards the Moon. They completed ten lunar orbits in around twenty hours, and were the first humans to see the far side of the Moon, and to witness 'Earthrise' – the appearance of our beautiful blue and white planet above the lunar horizon. After a flawless mission, the Apollo 8 astronauts splashed down in the northern Pacific Ocean on December 27th, 1968.

Two more test missions were needed. The first was to qualify the flying and docking capabilities of the lunar module, which was completed by the Apollo 9 crew of McDivitt, Scott and Schweickart while orbiting the Earth. The second was a full dress rehearsal for landing on the Moon, testing all the systems and procedures that would be required. In May, 1969, Apollo 10 flew to the Moon, to survey the planned future landing area in the Sea of Tranquillity. Thomas Stafford and Gene Cernan took the lunar module *Snoopy* down to within 16 kilometres of the Moon's surface while John Young orbited above in command module *Charlie Brown*. The intent to meet President

Kennedy's deadline was serious though, and Neil Armstrong had been told months before that he would command Apollo 11 and be the first to step on the Moon, with Buzz Aldrin as his lunar module co-pilot.

Launch day, July 16th, was covered by the global press and TV networks. The visionary science fiction and space writer, Arthur C. Clarke, said to BBC journalists, *"This is the last day of the old world… at lift-off I cried for the first time in twenty years, and prayed for the first time in forty."* Safely launched, Apollo 11's journey to lunar orbit took three days of relatively uneventful spaceflight. The descent to the Moon's surface in the lunar module *Eagle* was more exciting. Almost exactly 100 hours after launch from Cape Kennedy, Mike Collins, the pilot of the Command Module *Columbia*, pressed the button to detach the lunar module containing Armstrong and Aldrin, and confirmed that its landing legs were completely extended and undamaged. Unknown to the astronauts, but fully recognised by Mission Control in Houston, the Soviet unmanned craft *Luna 15* was also in orbit around the Moon, being readied to land in an attempt to return some lunar soil to Earth before the Americans. The 12-minute powered descent of *Eagle* was due to be made with the help of its onboard Apollo Guidance Computer, designed at MIT - and said to have a performance similar to the Apple II, Commodore 64 and ZX Spectrum computers of the late 1970s, but with erasable (RAM) memory of just 2,048 16-bit words and only 36k words of fixed (ROM) memory. Five minutes into the descent, as the *Eagle*'s landing radar acquired the surface, the guidance computer calculating height and rate of descent started to flag a repeated '12-02' alarm at intervals of about half a minute, complaining of memory overflow, and re-booting each time. Aldrin called down, asking, *"Houston, you're looking at our Delta-H program alarm?"* With seconds to decide whether or not to abort the landing, the assessment at Mission Control was that they could provide the missing descent altitude data from the ground, and their instruction was *"we're GO on that alarm"*. At 3,000 feet, about nine minutes into the descent, the computer flagged a different memory alarm and again the decision was 'Go'. Armstrong took manual control of the throttles to find a suitably flat landing site, clear of boulders. This took longer than expected, and at altitude 30 feet, Mission Control warned *"30 seconds [of descent motor propellant remaining]"*. After a few more seconds, Armstrong reported *"Houston, Tranquillity Base here. The 'Eagle' has landed"*. The search for a safe spot to settle down had required them to fly 4 miles beyond the planned landing site.

Illustration 32: Neil Armstrong in the Apollo 11 lunar module after walking on the Moon

After several hours of system checks and a meal mainly sucked out of plastic pouches, the astronauts began to de-pressurise the cabin, having donned cumbersome spacesuits that gave them 2 hours 45 minutes of oxygen to explore the surface. Armstrong opened the hatch and climbed down the ladder to stand on the foot of the lunar module. He said, *"The LM footpads are only depressed in the surface about one or two inches. Although the surface appears to be very fine grained, as you get close to it, it's almost like a powder. Now and then it's very fine. I'm going to step off the LM now."* Then, after a pause, *"That's one small step for [a] man, one giant leap for mankind."* When he was joined by Aldrin, the pair spent two hours collecting soil and rock samples, and taking photographs, before clambering back inside the module to rest, and then to prepare for lunar take-off. Around the same time, the robotic Soviet craft *Luna 15* was crashing ruinously into the Mare Crisium, the Sea of Crises, about 500 miles away. Armstrong and Aldrin left on the Moon their spacesuit boots and backpacks, a US flag, an Apollo 1 mission patch honouring Grissom, Chaffee and White, and two medals commemorating the dead cosmonauts Yuri Gagarin and Vladimir Komarov. The whole of *Eagle*'s

Illustration 33: Alan Bean of Apollo 12 beside a mock-up of the lunar module

descent stage and landing gear was left behind, with a cylindrical steel plaque attached to one of the legs, which read,

"HERE MEN FROM THE PLANET EARTH FIRST SET FOOT UPON THE MOON JULY 1969 A.D. WE CAME IN PEACE FOR ALL MANKIND."

...

The drama of the next Apollo mission took place at the beginning of the journey. With an all-Navy crew of Pete Conrad, Alan Bean and Richard Gordon, the flight of Apollo 12 in mid-November was briefly jeopardised 36 seconds into the launch, when two lightning strikes caused the main power system to trip out. Conrad later recalled, *"I heard the master alarm and glanced over to the caution-and-warning panel, and it was a sight to behold."* Backup power switched in, and Bean restored telemetry. Fortunately, the guidance computer's memory had retained the course trajectory data that would be urgently needed. The mission objectives were to land the lunar module *Intrepid* very precisely in the Ocean of Storms, within moonwalking distance of *Surveyor 3*, an automated probe which had landed in April 1967, and to set up several science experiments on Moon's surface. This time the landing site for the lunar module was found to be ideal, and Conrad and Bean settled *Intrepid* down about 200 yards from the *Surveyor* craft, with 58 seconds of fuel to spare. Around three hours later, Conrad descended the ladder, filmed by a remotely-deployed colour TV camera. When he was joined by Bean, they worked on setting up the scientific instruments. The energy required by the instruments in the surface experiments package was supplied by a plutonium-238 radioisotopic thermal generator and an arrangement of thermocouples providing 74W of electrical power at

30V DC. During the first four-hour period of 'extra-vehicular activity' on the Moon, Bean had difficulty removing the plutonium fuel core from its protective housing, which was designed to remain intact during re-entry to Earth's atmosphere, in the event of an accident. Hitting the fuel cell casing with a hammer did the trick, and all the instruments were successfully set up: a laser reflector, dust detector, a seismometer; and a magnetometer. A solar wind spectrometer and a suprathermal ion detector were together intended to measure the flux and energies of electrons and positive ions reaching the lunar surface from space, or generated by ultraviolet ionisation of the thin lunar atmosphere. A central transmitter station was set up to relay the gathered data back to Earth. Unfortunately, the tube of the colour TV camera, the instrument probably of most interest to the watching public, was destroyed when Bean inadvertently pointed the camera at the Sun while moving its position.

Altogether Bean and Conrad spent more than 31 hours in extra-vehicular work, including the collection of more rocks and soil, and a moonwalk to *Surveyor 3* to retrieve samples of its structure and equipment. The lift-off and ascent to rendezvous with Dick Gordon in the Command Module *Yankee Clipper* went flawlessly and the return to Earth, for 21 days of quarantine, was nearly perfect.

Alan Bean and Pete Conrad would each make one more spaceflight. In the fourth space mission of his career, Conrad commanded *Skylab 2* in 1973, the first manned mission to the space station, and with his two crewmates repaired damaged external components while establishing a record of 28 days for human spaceflight duration. The same year, Bean commanded the *Skylab 3* mission. On approach to the space station in the Apollo Service Module, a propellant leak developed in a thruster. Docking was successful, but six days later, another thruster started to leak. The crew continued their research on the effects of space on human physiology, and worked on a range of biological experiments. Launching a rescue Apollo craft was considered, but the crew was returned to Earth safely in the compromised module after 59 days. Bean was the backup commander for the joint US-Soviet Apollo-Soyuz test project, but never flew. He retired from the Navy in 1975, and from NASA in 1981. He subsequently created many paintings depicting his experiences, some of them incorporating real moondust. His 1996 self-portrait entitled 'Clan MacBean arrives on the Moon', was painted in acrylic on aircraft plywood. In 2011, he sent off a swatch of fabric with a note: *"To the Scottish Tartans Authority. This piece of MacBean tartan was flown to the moon in our Apollo 12 Command Module 'Yankee Clipper.' It was then transferred to our lunar module 'Intrepid' and was landed on the moon, November 1969. I am entrusting this valuable piece of tartan history to your care… Alan Bean, Lunar Module Pilot."*

Neil Armstrong, together with the other crew members of Apollo 11, decided not to fly in space again, but had an active 'retirement'. After the moon landing of Apollo 13 was aborted due to an onboard explosion in an oxygen tank, he was part of the investigation team and determined that the cause was an under-specified thermostat switch. He later took an academic position as Professor of Aerospace Engineering at the University of Cincinnati, where he taught extensively and designed two new graduate courses. His engineering knowledge was used again when he was asked to be a member of the teams investigating the Space Shuttle disasters of the *Challenger* launch in 1986 and the disintegration upon re-entry of *Columbia* in 2003. A keen pilot of gliders, he continued to fly them well into his 70s, and he served as a consultant or director for several commercial companies including Learjet and Thiokol. Armstrong received many honours and awards, including the Presidential Medal of Freedom, and, with his Apollo 11 crewmates, the Smithsonian Institution's Langley Gold Medal for outstanding contributions to the sciences of aeronautics and astronautics. He died in Cincinnati in 2012, aged 82, from medical complications after heart by-pass surgery. After a private funeral and cremation, his remains were buried in the Atlantic Ocean from the Navy cruiser *USS Philippine Sea*. In 2018, Alan Bean died aged 86 in Houston, Texas, after a brief illness, and is interred in Arlington National Cemetery.

The Apollo moonlandings marked the first steps of humankind in the exploration of other worlds and so were arguably the boldest and most memorable achievements of the 20th century. Although the Moon would not be visited by humans again in the next 50 years, our knowledge of planetary science was enormously increased, and technological benefits were realised in advances in computer hardware and software, materials science, and of course in spacecraft design. Perhaps even President Kennedy could not have envisaged such a rapid, determined and ingenious response to his eloquent challenge. For the Apollo astronauts, and maybe for the world in general, the most evocative legacies of reaching to the Moon were the images of our own Earth, looking distant, colourful against the blackness of space, unique, fragile, and borderless.

Part Two: Twentieth century triumphs

14   Twentieth century triumphs

The 20th century saw the emergence of science in its modern form, characterised by two major trends. First, the growth of collaborative and competitive scientific activity across the world, fostered by improved communication and greater international mobility. Second, faster practical exploitation of scientific discoveries – in medicine, pharmacology, and myriad fields of technology.

Tragically, the first half of the century was dominated by two tumultuous world wars that profoundly affected all who lived through them. Those who died perished in the cause of Empires, nationhood or political ideals which cast long shadows over the subsequent decades. Those who survived had their lives and careers forever impacted. Inevitably, the priorities of many scientists and engineers were skewed to the needs of the military combatants. The urgent imperatives to develop advanced weapons and defence systems, as typified by the races for radar, rockets and an atomic bomb, enabled electronic and computer technology, civil nuclear power, and the moon landings, arguably the greatest technological achievement of the century. High levels of military spending continued beyond the Cold War. The USA's Defence Advanced Research Projects Agency (DARPA) developed a resilient distributed communications network for computers, ARPANET, that became the phenomenon of the Internet.

In post-war Scotland, the heavy industries of steel-making, shipbuilding and coal-mining declined quickly as global competition bit hard. The demise of heavy engineering was partly offset by the discovery of new oilfields in the North Sea, and in technology, foreign investors were attracted by the opportunities afforded by a skilled workforce and the eminence of the Scottish universities. Undoubtedly encouraged by the viability of existing high-technology firms such as

Barr & Stroud in Glasgow and Ferranti in Edinburgh, from the early 1950s a swathe of American electronics companies, including Honeywell, IBM, NCR, Motorola and National Semiconductor, created manufacturing capabilities across the central Lowlands. Employment in what became known as 'Silicon Glen' peaked in the 1990s, when again international competition, particularly from east Asia, together with the late-century 'dotcom' boom-and-bust, led to its relative decline.

Somewhat insulated from the effects of the wars and economic conditions, Scotland's universities continued their steady production of well-educated scientists, medics and engineers. The traditional breadth of subjects studied in Scottish higher education, and a bias towards the technical exploitation of new knowledge, were advantageous to cross-disciplinary collaboration and inventive thinking.

The chemical engineer and businessman, Alfred Nobel, made a bequest that came into effect in 1901, to award international prizes in physics, chemistry, and medicine or pharmacology. The inaugural Nobel Prizes in those fields were awarded respectively for the discovery of X-rays and 'cathode rays' (Röntgen and Lenard), studies in molecular dynamics and osmosis (van't Hoff) and the development of serums against tetanus and diphtheria (von Behring). Scotland's scientists were well placed to compete, and soon thereafter, the country's first Nobel laureate would be addressing the Royal Swedish Academy of Sciences in Stockholm.

Noble gases and the Nobel prize: William Ramsay

The noble gases, historically sometimes called the inert gases, all share an extremely low chemical reactivity. They are also colourless and odourless, and these three characteristics make them difficult to detect. The first hint of their existence came in 1784, when Henry Cavendish showed that air contains a small amount of an unknown, unreactive gas. Nearly a century later, the first noble gas to be identified and named was helium, when in 1868, several scientists, including Joseph Norman Lockyer and Pierre Jules Janssen, observed a new element as a yellow line in the emission spectrum of the Sun's chromosphere during a solar eclipse. The mysterious inert constituent of air was eventually identified at University College London in 1895, by Lord Rayleigh and William Ramsay, who were trying to explain why the density of nitrogen extracted from air was different from that obtained by decomposing ammonia. Ramsey removed all the nitrogen from the gas extracted from air, by reacting it with magnesium to make magnesium nitride. What was left exhibited novel groups of red and green spectral lines – a new element. They named it argon, from the Greek word 'argos' meaning lazy or idle.

Idleness was not a characteristic of William Ramsay. Born within a scientific and professional family in Glasgow in 1852, he was the only child of a civil engineer, also William, and Catherine Robertson, whose father Archibald was a physician and the author of textbooks on anatomy and chemistry. William senior's father founded the Chemical Society of Glasgow; his brother, Sir Andrew Ramsay, was a director-general of the British Geological Survey; and his sister Eliza was a botanist who collected the flora of many parts of Scotland. Another brother, John, was a sugar planter in Demerara (now part of Guyana), and Uncle John's chemistry books and laboratory apparatus for testing sugar would be inherited by his nephew. Young William was fond of reading, was a strong swimmer and rower, and was good at languages and music — he amused his family by becoming a virtuoso whistler, accompanying himself on the piano. Aged eight, he broke his leg playing football, resulting in his introduction to chemistry. He wrote later, *"During my convalescence I read [Thomas] Graham's chemistry, chiefly, I must admit, because I wanted to know how to make fireworks. I remember that my father gave me small quantities of potassium chlorate, phosphorus, sulphuric acid, and some small flasks and beakers and a spirit lamp, and with these I amused myself during several weary months".* Surviving this encounter with potentially lethal chemicals, he attended the Glasgow Academy, and during summer holidays his mother took him to visit relatives in many parts of the country. Aunt Eliza had a house at Kilcreggan near the mouth of Loch Long, where the Ramsays spent much of their summers, and had a boat, in which William would make long excursions, often rowing and sailing some 18 miles, sometimes in rough water, to visit friends in Lochgoilhead.

William enrolled, aged only 14, to take the general Arts curriculum at Glasgow University, and continued performing chemical experiments at home. After two or three years, he started his formal studies in chemistry with Thomas Anderson, the subject's Regius professor at the University, while also working in the laboratory of Robert Rattray Tatlock, an alumnus of the Andersonian Institution, and the City of Glasgow's Public Analyst. Later Ramsay wrote that *"In 1869 I entered the laboratory of Robert Tatlock, who had been assistant to Professor Penny. Mr. Tatlock was (and is) an eminent analytical chemist and during the year I had with him I had a course of qualitative analysis and got through a good part of quantitative analysis."* While working in Tatlock's laboratory he also attended Sir William Thomson's lectures in physics.

In October 1870, Ramsay moved to Heidelberg to study with Robert Bunsen, but returned home after a few weeks - the Franco-Prussian War was still then in its final throes. The following April he went once more to Germany, this time to do research under the supervision of organic chemist Rudolf Fittig. In letters home, he alarmed his strict Calvinist mother by revealing that he spent some leisure hours playing baseball and billiards. She need not have worried - he received his PhD from the University of Tübingen in 1872, for his dissertation entitled *Investigations of the toluic and nitrotoluic acids'*.

When Ramsay returned again to Glasgow, he worked in the Young Laboratory of Technical Chemistry at the Andersonian, (named after James 'Paraffin' Young), and with Professor Ferguson at the University, before being selected, aged 28, for a professorship himself, at University College Bristol, in 1880. His stipend was £300 per annum, plus two-thirds of lecture fees and one-third of laboratory fees, guaranteeing him an annual income of £400. Within a year the Principal of the College resigned, and Ramsay was appointed in his place. This arrangement both saved the College the expense of recruiting a new Principal, and brought Ramsay an extra £250 of annual income. Since he had been married that year, to Margaret Buchanan, also from Glasgow, that was especially welcome. They would have a daughter and a son together. It was at Bristol that Ramsay later recalled reading Henry Cavendish's discovery of an unreactive residue of air, and made a note to himself to *"look into this."* By the time he had a chance to do it, he was the professor of chemistry at University College London, having made a success, over a period of seven years, of his triple role as a popular teacher, prolific researcher and energetic Principal at University College, Bristol, (where he started an ultimately victorious campaign to win it full university status).

At UCL, despite, or perhaps due to, the prestigious reputation of its Chairs of chemistry, Ramsay found a department in need of modernisation. He reorganised chemistry lectures so that women attended the same classes as men, introduced students to practical skills such as glass-blowing, and commissioned the construction of new teaching laboratories. In his own research, he continued his studies of the nitrogen oxides, and picked up the challenge of identifying the inert component of air. John William Strutt, Lord Rayleigh, was the second Cavendish Professor of Physics at Cambridge (having succeeded James Clerk Maxwell), and he became the Professor of Natural Philosophy at the Royal Institution in the year of Ramsay's new London appointment. In 1892 Rayleigh wrote to the journal *Nature,* saying *"I am much puzzled by some recent results as to the density of nitrogen and shall be much obliged if any of your chemical readers can offer suggestions as to the cause. According to two methods of preparation I obtain quite distinct values. The relative difference amounting to about 1/1000 part, is small in itself; but it lies entirely outside the errors of the experiment, and can only be attributed to a variation in the character of the gas."* It was Ramsay who had suggested the production of nitrogen by heating ammonia, and they both separately began to address the question by experimentation. In 1894, Ramsay removed oxygen, water vapour, carbon dioxide and nitrogen from air, the most difficult step being the absorption of nitrogen by red-hot magnesium. Rayleigh used a different method, by discharging sparks through oxygen-enriched air in the presence of potash, and had also managed to collect some of the mystery gas from the hot springs in Bath. On 4th August, Ramsay wrote to Rayleigh to say that he had isolated the gas and measured its density, and Rayleigh replied two days later saying that he believed he had too, though in *"miserably small quantities".* Ramsay suggested that a joint publication would be the best course. Over the next few days, Ramsay characterised the gas at low pressure by striking a glow discharge through it, in a so-called Plücker tube, and observed an emission spectrum dominated by a strong blue line. A preliminary announcement was made at a meeting of the British Association for the Advancement of Science in Oxford, on August 14th. On the last day of January 1895, they communicated their isolation of the new gas, argon, in a joint paper presented at an excited meeting of the Royal Society, chaired by Lord Kelvin.

Ramsey had already deduced, and had pointed out in a letter to Rayleigh, that *"there is room for gaseous elements at the end of the first column of the periodic table"*, meaning the missing atomic weights in the column containing argon. Therefore he suspected the existence other strange gases in the residue of air, and thought that if argon did form any compounds, it must be with another very rare element. The day after the Royal Society meeting, he received a letter from Henry Miers, head of the mineral department at the British Museum. It

Illustration 34: William Ramsay in his laboratory

drew his attention to a paper published five years previously in the *American Journal of Science,* by W.F. Hillebrand, *"On the occurrence of nitrogen in uraninite and on the composition of uraninite in general"*. Miers and Ramsay concluded that uraninite (pitchblende) and cleveite, the impure uranium ore from which it comes, would be shown to contain argon. On March 17th, 1895, Ramsay wrote to his father-in-law George Buchanan, with news of the gas obtained from a sample of cleveite, *"its spectrum is new, and I don't see from the method of treatment how it can be anything old, except argon, and that it is certainly not… I suppose it is the sought for krypton, an element which should accompany argon…We have settled the question of argon in the animal economy: there is absolutely no trace of argon in peas or in mice. And I have done a good deal as regards density, specific heat and expansion, a paper on which I shall send in to the R.S. for next Thursday."* In fact, it was not the 'sought for krypton', (a name meaning 'hidden one'). On closer examination of its emission spectrum, the new gas was found to be a mixture of argon and helium. This first discovery of terrestrial helium was reported at the end of March, to the annual meeting of the Chemical Society. Experiments showed that helium gas is monatomic, unreactive, and had an atomic weight of 4 (in units of the atomic weight of hydrogen).

There was a conceptual problem. The periodic table at that time, only partially populated, was arranged by the atomic weights of the elements. The concept of atomic number, that is the number of protons contained in atoms, was unknown, and the chemical behaviour of elements and their atomic weights were the only determinants of their position in the table. Argon's atomic weight was measured, in multiples of hydrogen's, as 40 - and that position in the table was already occupied, by potassium. Likewise, the occurrence of isotopes of elements, which perturbed the measured atomic weights of an element away from whole numbers, was unknown until it was proposed in 1913 by Ramsay's colleague, Frederick Soddy, by then a lecturer at Glasgow University. The term 'isotope' was coined and suggested to him by a friend, the Scottish doctor and writer Margaret Todd, after he had outlined the issue to her. In 1895, the problem of argon's correct positioning in the periodic table was merely recognised. Studies of its novel characteristics, and those of helium, for a while filled the chemical journals - together with speculations on the origin and terrestrial abundance of the two gases.

In September 1897, a grand meeting of the British Association for the Advancement of Science took place in Toronto, Canada. Ramsay was president of the chemical section, and his address focused on the relations of helium and argon, the ordering of the periodic table, and his reasoning that there should be an elementary gas with an atomic weight of 20. In *Annales de Chemie et de Physique* he concluded: *"I believe therefore that an element hitherto unknown should find a place between helium and argon. We have looked for this element in vain. However, we have not given up the search, and if we succeed the discovery would throw much light on the nature of helium and argon."*

To discover the elusive element would require new techniques. Ramsay and his colleague Morris William Travers practised to achieve the liquefaction of air, using some of the methods developed by James

Dewar, (born in Kincardine and a one-time student of chemistry under Lyon Playfair at the University of Edinburgh). From 1875, Dewar was the Jacksonian professor of experimental philosophy at Cambridge and later also the Fullerian professor at the Royal Institution. He publicly demonstrated the liquefaction of oxygen and air at the Royal Institution in 1884, based on the work of Frenchman Louis Cailletet, who had used the evaporation of ethylene and the Joule-Thomson effect to obtain droplets of oxygen and nitrogen. Dewar created liquid oxygen in large quantities, and used it in turn as a cooling agent. He succeeded in producing liquid and solid hydrogen, but did not publish his methods. He became well known for his public lectures, argumentative nature, and for his invention of the vacuum flask, which enabled the storage of liquefied gases at very low temperatures.

In May of 1898, Ramsay and Travers utilised the liquefaction of air in a hunt for the hidden element, removing the oxygen, nitrogen and carbon dioxide, and separating the residues as they boiled off. Travers recorded that the crucial experiment *"was really an incident in an investigation which we had planned to determine whether the gas which should fill the place in the Periodic Table between helium and argon, was present in the air, but in quantity too small to separate by the methods previously employed. We had made 15 litres of argon, and were proposing to liquefy it by means of liquid air...a small quantity of liquid air, brought to the College by Dr Hampson before we were ready to carry out the liquefaction of the argon, led to the experiment referred to."* They treated 750cc of liquid air to produce a residue of 26cc of gas which showed, in addition to the spectrum of argon, brilliant yellow and green spectral lines. They had found a new element, 'the hidden one' – krypton. It had a measured density indicating a monatomic weight of around 80, heavier than argon. So, unexpectedly, it was new, but not the element that Ramsay had predicted to lie in the region of atomic weight 20.

Ramsay and Travers moved on swiftly to the next step. In his biographical memoirs, Travers wrote, *"A few days after the discovery of krypton, the large quantity of argon was liquefied, the most volatile fraction of the vapour was collected... The glow from a Plücker tube filled with it was a brilliant crimson. It contained some argon, but it seemed to be certain that it consisted largely of the missing member of the Periodic Series, which should have a density 10 [i.e. atomic weight 20]. It was called neon [the new one]. The discovery was communicated to the Royal Society on 16 June 1898."* By now they were on a roll, and when they condensed the least volatile fraction of the liquid air, in the middle of July, they isolated the fifth of the noble gases, which exhibited a beautiful, eerie blue glow in the discharge tube. They named it xenon, the strange one, and determined its atomic mass to be approximately 131.

The systematic ordering of elements within the periodic table was becoming clearer. In 1902, Marie Curie isolated the salts of radium, and showed that they produced strange 'emanations'. At McGill University, Ernest Rutherford and Frederick Soddy were publishing a series of papers on radioactivity and concluding that it involved the disintegration of atoms into different atoms. They showed too that radium produced small quantities of a gas, which appeared to be chemically inert. Attracted by the expertise of the group led by Sir William Ramsay, as he had recently become, Soddy joined the team at UCL in 1903, to try to identify the gas. It showed no discharge spectrum, but oddly, after a while, the spectrum of helium appeared. Measurements of the properties of the gas proved to be extremely tricky, and determining its density required a balance with a sensitivity of 10^{-8} grams. It was the final noble gas, named at first niton, and then radon. Soon it was realised that it transformed to helium, with a half-life of 3.8 days - one of the first confirmations of the transmutability of elements by radioactive decay.

In 1904, Sir William was awarded the Nobel Prize in Chemistry, created three years previously, *"in recognition of his services in the discovery of the inert gaseous elements in air, and his determination of their place in the periodic system."* The same year Lord Rayleigh was awarded the physics prize *"for his investigations of the densities of the most important gases and for his discovery of argon in connection with these studies".* Ramsay's intellect had combined with experimentation of the highest order to clarify the structure of the periodic table and identify minute constituents of the atmosphere. The abundances of the noble gases in air are: argon 0.93%, neon 0.0029%, krypton 0.0001%, xenon 0.000009%.

Illustration 35: The noble gases from the modern periodic table, with atomic numbers and most stable mass numbers

2
He
4.00

10
Ne
20.2

18
Ar
40.0

36
Kr
83.8

54
Xe
131

86
Rn
222

As a man of many interests and huge energy, in his later life Ramsay was involved in the reorganisation of the University of London, the establishment of the Indian Institute of Technology in Bangalore, presidencies of national and international chemical societies, and the British Association. France, Italy and Prussia endowed him with their highest honours. He died in Buckinghamshire in 1916, much loved by his students and colleagues who remembered his intelligence, sociability, and humour. Frederick Soddy won the Nobel in chemistry in 1921, for his work on radioactivity and the nature of isotopes. In his obituary of Ramsay he wrote, *"At University College he was looked up to in a way that can scarcely be expressed. He was at once genial, approachable, and great — any one of which alone is an infallible passport to the student's heart — and repaid their trust and affection as complete as that of a Scottish chieftain to his clan."* Ramsay was always modest, and witty, about his achievements. Referring to the finely graduated glass test-tubes used to measure the volumes of gases, he ascribed his success to his large flat thumb, that could close off the end of a eudiometer tube, and said that *"it is all pure luck and plugging away."*

16   Head in the clouds: C.T.R. Wilson

Academic minds often become intrigued by a wide variety of subjects. That was certainly the case for Charles Thomson Rees Wilson, whose meteorological observations of clouds on the summit of Ben Nevis led to the creation of one of the most productive tools in sub-atomic physics. He was born in Midlothian, in 1869, as the youngest son of John Wilson, a sheep farmer and widower, and John's second wife, Annie Clark Harper, from Hillhead in Glasgow. When Charles was only four years old, his father died from cancer, aged 54. His mother moved the family (Charles, his slightly older siblings Helen and George, and step-sister Margret) to Manchester, where Annie's parents were living after retirement from business, with some of the step-children from her husband's first marriage. Charles went to private school, and then, with financial support from a step-brother, to Owen's College (now Manchester University), intending to become a medical doctor. Probably influenced by Balfour Stewart, the professor of physics, he studied general science, and graduated, aged 18, having won a scholarship to Sidney Sussex College in the University of Cambridge. There, he became even more interested in physics, chemistry and meteorology, and achieved 1st class honours in the Natural Science Tripos examinations of 1892.

After a spell in teaching at Bradford Grammar School, Wilson returned to Cambridge, to pursue a scientific research career at the Cavendish Laboratory, amongst a world-leading group of experimental physicists. Still interested in meteorology and in particular the nature of clouds, Wilson spent time observing in cloudy Scotland and was inspired on a visit to its tallest mountain. He later said, *"In September 1894, I spent a few weeks in the Observatory which then existed on the summit of*

Ben Nevis, the highest of the Scottish Hills. The wonderful optical phenomena shown when the sun shone on the clouds surrounding the hill-top, and especially the coloured rings surrounding the sun (coronas) or surrounding the shadow cast by the hill-top observer on mist and clouds (glories), greatly excited my interest and made me wish to imitate them in the laboratory."

Back at the Cavendish, Wilson's gifts as an experimental physicist were recognised in 1896, when the Cavendish awarded him its Clerk Maxwell scholarship. This secured his appointment for three years, and he set about trying to create clouds and to study their properties more deeply. He knew that in 1880, the Scottish engineer John Aitken had formed small clouds by jetting water vapour into a large glass jar, following the method suggested by two French researchers, Coulier and Mascart. Aitken had found that if the jar contained ordinary air, a cloud would form, but if the air had been filtered, so that it contained no particles of dust, no clouds would appear. Aitken then changed his experiment to imitate natural cloud formation by putting some water in the bottom of a sealed jar, and waiting till the air became saturated with water vapour. When he cooled the air by expansion, he confirmed that clouds condensed in normal, dusty air, but not in filtered air. Wilson began his experiments by studying and reproducing Aitken's method for producing clouds. He became an expert glass-blower and made several 'cloud chambers' to study the formation of mist and water droplets under controlled laboratory conditions. After a few months' work, he made a surprising discovery. If the expanded volume of air was greater than about 1.25 times the original volume, he could create a cloud of condensed water droplets from supersaturated, moist air, even though it was filtered and free of dust.

Through patient experimentation, Wilson found that when he expanded air that was moderately supersaturated, small water droplets were formed. When expanding air at higher supersaturations, produced at warmer temperatures, a fog filled the chamber. He asked himself why the small water droplets condensed particularly on some points of the dust-free air rather than others, and concluded that it might be to do with ionised atoms or molecules, which were thought to exist in air, since the atmosphere has a residual electrical conductivity.

There was a way to test the theory. The German physicist Wilhelm Röntgen had, in late 1895, discovered and publicised a strange phenomenon – invisible, penetrating but detectable emanations from high-voltage vacuum discharge tubes, which he called X-rays. Soon after that discovery, in an experiment at the Cavendish Laboratory, J.J. Thomson and John A. McClelland passed X-rays through volumes of various gases and showed that this produced an increase in the conductivity of the gas. Thomson and his student, Ernest Rutherford, quickly went on to prove that the 'Röntgen rays' were causing ionisation of the gas molecules. This prompted Charles Wilson to test the effects of irradiating a cloud chamber with X-rays. The result, as he suspected, was that when the chamber was irradiated, condensation of the air into droplets and fog occurred at a much lower supersaturations than otherwise. And 30 seconds after the X-rays were switched off, the air behaved as though the X-rays had never been present - the nucleation sites had disappeared. His theory that the condensed droplets were formed around charged molecules seemed to be correct. To confirm it, he applied an electric field around the chamber, which would sweep charged particles away. The result was that no clouds could be produced. He had proved that the condensation sites were ions, that normal air was slightly ionised, and that the X-rays produced more ions, and hence gave rise to denser mists under equivalent conditions in the cloud chamber.

J.J. Thomson, the head of the Cavendish Laboratory, was interested, and in March 1896, he communicated Wilson's result in a paper read to the Royal Society, *The Effect of Röntgen Rays on Cloudy Condensation.* Thomson's main interest at the time was the investigation of 'cathode rays'. These were emitted from the negative electrodes of gas discharge tubes, and he showed that they were deflected by magnetic and electric fields. Also, they travelled farther in air, and in dense materials, than would be expected for an atom-sized particle. It was the almost unanimous opinion of German physicists that the cathode rays were just that – rays, akin to Röntgen's rays. Thomson calculated from his deflection measurements that if the rays were instead composed of 'corpuscles', each carrying a negative electric charge, then they must have a charge-to-mass ratio about 2,000 times larger than a hydrogen ion. To show that the high value of their 'e/m' charge-to-mass ratio was due to their small mass, not their large electric charge, Thomson turned to Wilson's cloud

Illustration 36: C.T.R Wilson c.1927

chambers. In a series of ingenious experiments, Thomson passed cathode rays through a cloud chamber by irradiating it with radium, a known source of the rays. With his assistant, and no doubt aided by Wilson, he adjusted the conditions in the chamber to form very small clouds, of negatively-charged water droplets of known number, size and weight. Using a positively-charged plate above the chamber to 'hover' the droplets by electrostatic force against the force of gravity, the value of an individual charge, e, could be calculated. It turned out to be the same as the charge carried by hydrogen ions as determined by the electrolysis of dilute solutions. Knowing the charge, and having previously measured the charge-to-mass ratio, gave a mass for an individual 'corpuscle' of 6×10^{-28} grams, 1,700 times smaller than a hydrogen atom. This was the discovery of the electron, the first sub-atomic particle to be identified. For that, and other work on the electrical conductivity of gases, Thomson was awarded the 1906 Nobel prize in physics.

Charles Wilson's career at Cambridge continued on its upward path. He became a lecturer in experimental physics, and in 1908, he married Jessie Fraser, daughter of the Reverend George Hill Dick of Glasgow. They would have two sons and two daughters together. For a time, Wilson's main scientific interest was in atmospheric electricity and thunder-clouds, but in 1910 he resumed his laboratory experiments to see if the track of a single ionising particle could be made visible in the supersaturated atmosphere of a cloud chamber. Other types of emissions from radioactive substances had been identified, including alpha- and beta-rays, which were already suspected to consist of particles, rather than electromagnetic radiation, and Wilson was keen to explore them. In his own words, *"In the spring of 1911… it occurred to me to one day to try whether some indication of tracks might not be made visible with the rough apparatus already constructed. The first test was made with X-rays, with little expectation of success, and… while the air was exposed to the rays I was delighted to see the cloud chamber filled with little wisps and treads of clouds – the tracks of the electrons ejected by the action of the rays. The radium-tipped metal tongue of a spintharoscope was then placed inside the cloud chamber and the very beautiful sight of the clouds condensed along the tracks of the α-particles was seen for the first time. The long thread-like tracks of fast β-particles were also seen when a suitable source was brought near the cloud chamber."* More experiments and photographs of the spiky tracks of the α- and β-rays confirmed them to be particles, as they made ionising collisions with atoms in the vapour. Thomson's ex-student Ernest Rutherford, had shown that α-particles were the nuclei of helium atoms, and the β-particles were shown to be high-energy electrons.

Wilson reported his breakthrough techniques in a paper, *On a Method of making Visible the Paths of Ionising Particles through a Gas*, sent to the Royal Society in April, 1911. The paper included striking photographs of particle trails obtained in a small glass cloud chamber of only 6 mm height and 7.5 cm diameter, with an electrical potential of 8 volts applied from top to bottom. In a subsequent paper the next year, Wilson published another paper with more photographs obtained by irradiating a 16cm-diameter cloud chamber with X-rays. The results supported the view that X-rays were a form of electromagnetic radiation, and not 'corpuscular', as some physicists had supposed. His experiments were interrupted by the First World War, and when he resumed them, he produced a large number of stereoscopic photographs of great beauty

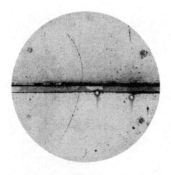

Illustration 37: Cloud chamber track of the first positron ever observed (1932). The thick horizontal line is a lead plate

as well as of scientific importance, since they confirmed predictions by the American, Arthur Compton on the scattering of X-rays from atoms, and the resultant ejection of electrons. In 1927, Wilson was awarded the Nobel prize in physics 'for his method of making the paths of electrically charged particles visible by condensation of vapour', sharing the award with Compton.

Cloud chambers became the work-horses of atomic physics for many decades. Incremental design improvements made them even more useful. The most important development was the introduction of repetitive, rapid expansion and compression of the chamber, allowing the capture of particle tracks continuously, many times per second. 'Continuous' cloud chambers were produced on a commercial basis from 1926, by the Cambridge Scientific Instrument Company. In 1932, Carl Anderson at Caltech used a cloud chamber to discover the positron, the anti-matter partner of the electron, predicted to exist on theoretical grounds by Paul Dirac three years earlier. Further discoveries of new sub-atomic particles and anti-particles, including the muon and kaon, were made using cloud chambers in later years. Ernest Rutherford, himself one of the greatest experimental scientists of all time, and who became the director of the Cavendish Laboratory in 1919, is said to have described Wilson's original cloud chamber discoveries as *"the most wonderful experiment in the world."* One of Rutherford's protégés was P.M.S. Blackett, the 1948 physics Nobel laureate who made developments in cloud chamber design, and used them in studies of cosmic rays. He said, *"There are many decisive experiments in the history of physics which, if they had not been made when they were made, would surely have been made not much later by someone else. This might not have been true of Wilson's discovery of the cloud method. In spite of its essential simplicity, the road to its final achievement was long and arduous: without C. T. R. Wilson's vision and superb experimental skill, mankind might have had to wait many years before someone else found the way."*

By the time of Wilson's retirement in 1934, as Jacksonian professor of natural philosophy at Cambridge, he was much honoured, and respected as much for his quiet

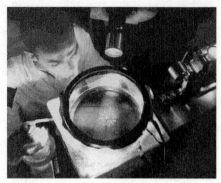

Illustration 38: A physicist studying Alpha rays in a continuous cloud chamber (c.1957)

modesty and kindliness as for his scientific achievements. He remained in Cambridge for two more years before returning to Scotland where he settled in the village of Carlops near Edinburgh, only a few miles from his birthplace. His continuing interest in atmospheric physics took him frequently back to the Scottish mountains, particularly in the Isle of Arran. In 1954, he published his reminiscences of his first trips, *Ben Nevis Sixty Years Ago.* He died in 1959, in Carlops, surrounded by his family. In 2012, the centenary of his cloud chamber discoveries, he was remembered as 'the Great Scottish Physicist' in a special meeting of the Royal Society of Edinburgh. The 'CTR Wilson Institute for Atmospheric Electricity' is a special interest group of the Royal Meteorological Society, and the Wilson Society (or 'WilSoc') continues its support for natural scientists at Sidney Sussex College, Cambridge.

17 Range and vision: Archibald Barr and William Stroud

Towards the end of the 19th century, the British Army and the Royal Navy had a problem, and sought for a solution. In the magazine *Engineering*, in the spring of 1888, the War Office posted an advertisement requesting proposals for a rangefinder for military use, that could demonstrate a range accuracy of at least 4% over 1000 yards, and preferably be usable by a single operator.

The advertisement caught the attention of two young academics at the Yorkshire College of Science, founded 14 years before, and later to become the University of Leeds. Archibald Barr, aged 32 and the professor of engineering, and William Stroud, 28, professor of physics, had already collaborated on an idea to develop a camera to produce 'lantern-slides' from printed pages. The apparatus went into production and sale, and became a standard item of equipment in colleges and universities. Barr and Stroud had become firm friends, living in adjacent parts of a semi-villa, each of them newly married, and now they were looking for another commercial opportunity. The Admiralty's rangefinder requirement was tempting, but time to submit a proposal was short – the deadline of August 1st, 1888 gave them only two months to produce a design. They were both well qualified to meet the challenge.

Barr was born in 1855 near Paisley, a centre of the weaving industry, to Jeanie Stirrat and her husband, also Archibald, who was a yarn merchant. After attending the local Grammar School, young Archibald was apprenticed as an engineer to A.F. Craig & Co., manufacturers of spinning and weaving machinery, before enrolling at Glasgow

University to study engineering. His academic ability soon brought him to the attention of James Thomson, professor of civil engineering and mechanics, and his more famous brother Sir William, later Lord Kelvin, the professor of natural philosophy. Their combined influence on him would shape his thought for the rest of his career. Barr was not just an exceptional student - he excelled as a sportsman too, and played international lacrosse for Scotland. Even before graduating, he was employed as James Thomson's principal assistant, before being appointed, aged 29, to the Chair of Civil and Mechanical Engineering at the Yorkshire College. There, as well as greatly increasing the student numbers, he showed his entrepreneurial spirit by following Sir William's dictum that *the life and soul of science is in its application* and raised £10,000 from the industrialists of Leeds, to build and equip one of the best engineering laboratories of the time.

William Stroud was a Bristolian, born in 1860, the son of a dispensing chemist in the city. As a young man he suffered from ill health, but won successive scholarships, first to University College, Bristol, then to Owen's College, an antecedent of Manchester University, and finally to Balliol College in the University of Oxford. He said later that his West Country accent and status as a scholarship student made him feel looked down upon at Balliol. Nevertheless he graduated with a double First in mathematics and natural sciences. With financial help from his mother and one of his professors, he went to Germany to study at the University of Würzburg with the physicist Friedrich Kohlrausch, and at Heidelberg with Georg Quinke. He was in distinguished company – Kohlrausch's most famous student was Svante Arrhenius, who won the Nobel prize in chemistry in 1903, while Quinke taught Albert Michelson, who won the same award in physics in 1907 for his aether-shattering measurements of the speed of light.

On his return to England, Stroud was encouraged to apply for the Cavendish Chair of Physics at the Yorkshire College. His tutor at Balliol, Harold B. Dixon, wrote a testimonial. *"My pupil William Stroud…in standing for a Professorship at the close of his University course may perhaps lay himself open to the charge of presumption... Of Mr. Stroud's special knowledge of Electricity it is not my place to speak, but... of chemistry and chemical physics, of his rapidity and manipulative skill in experiment, of his indomitable energy and power of work I can speak... Mr Stroud seems to me to possess a real genius."* Stroud passed the DSc exams of the University of London, and in July 1885, Dr. Stroud was appointed to the professorship at the Yorkshire College of Science, aged just 25. He soon met Barr, who was ensconced as engineering professor the year before, and who advised on developing Stroud's 'magic lantern' idea to produce projection slides for teaching. The other major developments that year were matrimonial. Stroud married the 17-year-old Louisa Emett, from Bristol, and Barr married Isabella Young, the 23-year-old daughter of a Paisley timber merchant.

In 1888, addressing the requirement for a military rangefinder would require fast action by Barr and Stroud, if the deadline for proposals was to be met. The state-of-the-art at the time was the Watkin Mekometer, which required two observers using separate instruments joined by a cord about 25 or 30 yards in length. The first observer sighted the target and used an 'optical square' to position the second observer at right-angles to the line of sight. The second instrument was adjusted to measure the angle to the target and its distance was read off a scale, calculated by the simple trigonometry of right-angled triangles. Needless to say, this was cumbersome, sometimes inaccurate, and problematic if the target was moving.

Range-finding 'telemeters' can be traced back to James Watt, who in 1769 devised an instrument for surveying canals, by aligning parallel hairs in the focal plane of a telescope with sliding markers on a rod held at the distance to be measured. Coincidence rangefinders, where the images from two mirrors at opposite ends of a long barrel are brought together in a single eyepiece, were first patented in Britain in 1860 by Scottish instrument maker Patrick Adie, but they were too delicate for military use. Stroud and Barr's stereoscopic design made some important improvements, using two eyepieces of different magnifications, and replacing the end mirrors with reflecting prisms. The mirrors used to combine the two images in the high magnification eyepiece were partially blanked so that the operator's procedure was to adjust the top and bottom halves of the images into coincidence, and read off the range. Encouraged by comments from Sir William Thomson, they filed a British patent application, no. 9520, on 30th June 1888, and submitted their design on time, before setting about the task of delivering a working instrument by 31st December, as mandated. With precision parts from Thomas Cooke & Sons, an optical instrument maker in York, and from Thomson's favourite supplier, James White & Co. of Glasgow, they constructed and calibrated the first rangefinder at the Yorkshire College, and Barr took it to the War Office in London just in time to meet the deadline. The following March, in Army trials at Aldershot, it was accepted for further trials in the summer, the only single operator instrument to pass the initial assessments. Stroud made a further design improvement, by introducing 'objective prisms' which had one face ground in a curve to produce lensing and a brighter image. This led to a bad decision. Already fearing the high cost of the first model, and facing the difficulty of having the new prisms manufactured, the two professors built a second rangefinder, slightly shorter than the first, and replaced the prisms with flat mirrors. This instrument dismally failed the next trials in August when the heat of the sun distorted the mirrors, and the range readings became wildly inaccurate. Their design was rejected, and the Army adopted Watkin's Mekometer as their standard equipment, to be produced by Cooke & Sons.

James Thomson, the Regius Professor of Engineering at Glasgow University, was 70 years old in 1889, and suffering from failing eyesight. He resigned the Chair, and Archibald Barr was appointed to succeed him, no doubt at the Thomsons' recommendation. Though Barr moved back to Glasgow, he and Stroud continued to work together on the rangefinder development, although it was proving expensive. Between 1888 and 1892, the pair invested nearly £743, more than their combined annual salaries, on developing the rangefinder and filing patents. Their perseverance was rewarded when another advertisement was posted in *Engineering*, which said, that the Secretary of State for War, on behalf of the Lords Commissioners of the Admiralty, *"is prepared to receive PROPOSALS from persons desirous of SUBMITTING for competitive trial, RANGE-FINDERS for NAVAL USE…"* Nine requirements were stated, including that the instrument should be usable by a single operator, be uninfluenced by normal changes in temperature or weather, while recording ranges in yards, continuously or at least ten times per minute, and transmitting those ranges instantaneously to the naval gun or guns. Preference would be given to a rangefinder that could be used at night, and a range accuracy error of a maximum of 3% was required for ranges up to 3000 yards.

This time, the entrants to the 1889 Army trials were specifically invited to trials conducted by the Admiralty starting in April 1892. Barr and Stroud submitted a five-foot long instrument equipped with additional cylindrical lenses to convert point sources of light, say a ship's lamp in the dark, into a vertical streak that could be aligned in the eyepiece, just like any daytime target. On ship-board trials against an entry from Major Watkin and another from instrument designer, Arnulph Mallock, Barr and Stroud's rangefinder proved the most impressive, and won the competition. The Admiralty asked if they would offer their patents to the British government. Astutely, Barr set a high price of £75,000 on the rights, but offered to manufacture and supply any instruments required. Early in 1893, they received an order for five rangefinders. With optical components from Adam Hilger & Co. of London, and tubes and mechanical mounts from James White in Glasgow, all five were delivered for £200 apiece by the professors' newly formed partnership, Barr & Stroud's Patents, in early 1894. The construction process was that Stroud received and tested the prisms, mirrors and lenses in Leeds, and brought them to Glasgow for assembly. Final optical adjustment was done by focusing on a target at infinity - the Moon - while lying on their backs on the roof of Barr's house. That nearly cost Stroud his life when he fell off a ladder. His absence while recuperating forced the recruitment of their first employee, an engineering student, Harold Jackson.

Barr appointed an agent, the naval shipbuilders Armstrong, Mitchell & Co. of Newcastle, to promote sales to foreign navies. A sixth rangefinder was soon sold to the Imperial Japanese Navy, followed by single orders from the navies of Argentina, Brazil, Chile, Germany, Italy, Sweden and Turkey. Barr and Stroud's Patents rented a workshop at 250 Byres Road in the west end of Glasgow, above the Hillhead underground railway station that was in construction there. Unpromising as that seemed for precision assembly of optical instruments, by November 1895 they had delivered 27 rangefinders. The next year's sales receipts were £13,409 and yielded a profit of £5,915, which was shared between Barr, Stroud and Jackson. With an expanded workforce and from new premises in Byres Road and Ashton Lane, they introduced an improved model which presented upright images rather than inverted ones, and developed 'range and order' electro-mechanical communication to naval gun platforms. By 1898, they had sold 150 rangefinders, mainly to the Royal Navy, but including many orders from Japan and 11 instruments that were sold to Spain when that country went to war with the USA in the same year.

A close, trusted and symbiotic relationship with the British Admiralty was evolving, which carried them into the new century. The partners decided to build an entirely new factory to cope with demand, and a greenfield site was chosen, and purchased for £648, at Crow Road in Anniesland, about two miles west of the old workshops. The new red-brick factory was light, airy and consisted of three floors providing 25,000 square feet of machine shops, optical grinding and polishing, fitting and adjustment areas, a drawing office, board room and a workmen's dining room. Extensions were added as soon as construction was completed in 1905. After four years, Stroud resigned his professorship in Leeds to join the company full-time, and moved his family to the Glaswegian suburbs. Barr followed suit when he resigned the Regius Chair of engineering at Glasgow in 1912, the same year the

Illustration 39: A 12-foot Barr & Stroud rangefinder (or 'heightfinder') with four operators, c.1920s

partnership became Barr & Stroud Ltd. By then, the company had an annual turnover of £190,000 and an international reputation for the manufacture of high-quality optical instruments for military markets. Some forays were made into commercial products including vacuum pumps and even synchronised electric clocks, following in the footsteps of Alexander Bain. But in the years leading up to the Great War, the growth in demand for rangefinders, and later, for periscopes, dwarfed these sidelines.

The First World War presented the company with the twin challenges of increased demand and the loss of skilled workmen to the armed forces. Hundreds of women were recruited and trained in jobs such as optical adjusting, inspection, and engraving, though by agreement with the recently-formed Industrial Committee of shop-stewards, women were not employed in the machine shop. New war-machines also required the invention of new instruments. Heightfinders were developed to determine both the height and range of enemy aircraft, and the advent of military submarines led to an Admiralty requirement for a periscope rangefinder. Barr and Stroud had already produced some small periscopes for the gun turrets of British warships.

Their component suppliers James White & Co, (who had acquired Lord Kelvin and his nephew, James Thomson Bottomley, as directors and had become Kelvin, Bottomley and Baird Ltd) had also supplied the Navy with some periscopes, which provided a good foundation of local expertise. In 1915, the initial requirement was for a rangefinder periscope for the new submarine *HMS M3*, under construction by Armstrong Whitworth on Tyneside. The periscope was to supplement a search periscope from the Navy's existing supplier, Howard Grubb of Dublin. Barr & Stroud's design was a 30-foot long periscope incorporating a 3-foot base coincidence rangefinder positioned at the top of the narrow tube. Stroud devised a way, using an internal telescope of unit magnification, to keep the top tube narrow while maintaining a bright image at every orientation. In tests, the Royal Navy were sufficiently impressed that they ordered six rangefinding periscopes in 1916, and significantly, a total of 30 search periscopes, without built-in rangefinders, the following year. Although they were not delivered before the end of the War, and the numbers were reduced after the end of hostilities, those orders established Barr & Stroud as the pre-eminent manufacturer of submarine periscopes.

Barr & Stroud's rapid development of rangefinders, periscopes, and fire-control systems continued through the War, and management's good relations with the workforce had avoided the worst of the industrial unrest which led to worker strikes in many Glasgow firms. The company founders worked also as war-time government consultants in improving anti-submarine and anti-aircraft defences. Sadly, both scientists lost a son in the conflict. In the aftermath of the War, both were offered knighthoods, which first Stroud, and then Barr, declined, believing they had just 'done their bit'.

The value of company sales from 1914-18 well exceeded £2 million, though a new Excess Profits Duty imposed on government contractors reclaimed £217,000 in 1917. The Armistice and peace brought many order cancellations, and threatened a collapse in revenue for Barr & Stroud, which, unlike some other suppliers of optical instruments, had few civilian products to fall back on. Workforce lay-offs inevitably ensued, and product diversification was explored urgently. High quality binoculars based on a prismatic design by Stroud were launched, but sales were hampered by high prices and the superior retail marketing operations of competitors, notably Carl Zeiss. A simpler and cheaper Galilean binocular was produced, but struggled for profitability in a market flooded by army surplus equipment. Cinema projectors, golf-ball impact simulators, and even a single-sleeve-valve motor-cycle

Illustration 40: Retail advertisement for binoculars c. 1935

engine were produced. The engine project was led by one of Barr's sons, Douglas, under patents licenced from a local engineer, Peter Burt and his Canadian co-inventor, James McCollum. Since the engines dispensed with noisy poppet valves, tappets and cams, they were quiet, smooth and efficient, and the design had already been adopted by Burt's employer, the Argyll motor company, which manufactured cars near Glasgow in Alexandria, Dunbartonshire. Despite success in motor-cycle racing competitions and application to electricity generation, Barr & Stroud's small 350cc engines were loss-making, and production was stopped. Another of Barr's pet projects was the 'Optophone', a clever instrument which converted printed letters into sounds, so that blind people could 'read' books by ear. Costs were high, and only 80 devices were sold. More promisingly, a range of benchtop stereoscopes was developed, used to convert aerial photographs into topographical maps.

However, Barr's and Stroud's cherished company was facing an existential crisis, and employees were put on short time, working first two weeks, then just one week, in every three. It was now that the intensively-cultivated relationships with their military clients came to the rescue. The Washington Naval Treaty of 1922, also known as the Five-Power Treaty, restricted the construction of new warships, but this put emphasis on improving the effectiveness of existing fleets. The Admiralty decided to equip Royal Navy warships with a minimum of two Barr & Stroud 'FX' 25- or 30-feet long rangefinders. Soon, British warships were typically fitted with ten rangefinders to send fire-control information to gun, torpedo and anti-aircraft stations on board. Moreover, while the USA, France and Italy depended on domestic suppliers of 'optical munitions', and Germany's re-armament was heavily constrained, the Japanese Navy continued to rely almost exclusively on Barr & Stroud, and assigned its representatives and inspectors to work in the Anniesland factory. During the 1920s, around a third of rangefinder production was destined for Japan, and Barr & Stroud's close links with the Japanese Imperial Navy continued until the early years of the next decade, when Britain's relations with Japan deteriorated sharply following the Japanese invasion of Manchuria. The largest rangefinder produced by the company was the 'FZ' 100-foot-long instrument, rotated on carriage wheels on a 50 foot diameter track. It was initially installed in a coastal defence position near Portsmouth, in 1922, and was found to be accurate to within 17 yards (0.05%) at a range of 31,000 yards. Ironically, in the 1930s it was shipped to augment the south-looking harbour defences in Singapore, which in 1942 fell to a land-based Japanese invasion from the north. The instrument was destroyed by British forces to prevent its capture by the enemy.

In perhaps the company's most significant business breakthrough of the late 1920s, Barr & Stroud became the sole suppliers of submarine periscopes to the Royal Navy, and their binoculars were also adopted as the standard for the service. Sales revenues began to rise. Less happily, Harold Jackson died in 1928, and the company lost its foremost director, ambassador and commercial negotiator. Around the same time, Barr announced that he and William Stroud wished to step back from day-to-day business, and hand more responsibility to the younger directors. Stroud was already in semi-retirement, suffering from worsening bronchial disease which meant that he spent winters abroad or in the south of England. Just as the company was triumphing in its fight for survival, Archibald Barr died, aged 76, in August 1931. Apart from his huge contributions to the British government and to Scottish industry, he was remembered with warm gratitude by Glasgow University, where he had helped to establish the Faculty of Science in 1893, and raised £40,000 from local industrialists to build the James Watt Engineering Building, opened by Lord Kelvin in 1901. He left behind his wife, a daughter, two sons, and a world-leading optical instruments company that managed to survive the Depression of the 1930s and to prosper through the 20th century. William Stroud became Chairman of the firm after Barr's death, but his declining health restricted his presence in Glasgow to the summer months. He died, aged 78, in Torquay in 1938. By then, Britain's rearmament programme was in progress, as the threat of a second world war grew ominously. Deluged by orders for rangefinders, heightfinders and periscopes, the firm's workforce grew from 2,000 in 1939 to 6,100 in 1944, and the factory managed to avoid damage from Luftwaffe bombing raids which blitzed the nearby shipyards in Clydebank.

The subsequent evolution of Barr & Stroud Ltd is a story dominated by continued, successful innovation in those twin core products of the company, rangefinders and periscopes, transformed almost beyond recognition by new technologies. Laser rangefinder development began in the early 1960s, just a few years after the invention of the laser itself. Barr & Stroud launched the world's first commercially available laser rangefinder in 1964, and development continued through successive generations of instruments deployed variously on the British Army's

Illustration 41: A Barr &
Stroud CH74 attack
periscope in a Royal
Australian Navy Oberon class
submarine

tanks and as airborne target markers. Submarine periscopes were developed with sophisticated rangefinding and infra-red thermal imaging capabilities, and night vision image intensifiers and thermal imagers became separate product lines. In the 1970s, optical tracking systems were developed for the Rapier surface-to-air missile system. In a move towards vertical integration, in 1977 the company was taken over by Pilkington, the glass-maker, which was in turn acquired the Thales Group. In 2001, Barr & Stroud became Thales Optronics, which continues to manufacture laser rangefinders, thermal imaging systems, and as sole supplier to the Royal Navy, submarine periscopes, from a new factory on the south side of the River Clyde.

The legacies of professors Barr and Stroud go beyond their entrepreneurial foundation of a successful optical instrumentation company. In the tradition of David Brewster, James Watt and Lord Kelvin, they demonstrated the practical application of scientific discovery, and the value of an intimate interaction between academia and business. Doing so, they helped to establish the strong presence in Scotland of industrial expertise in optics, electronics and precision engineering, which led to the proliferation of high-technology enterprises through the years of the 20th and 21st centuries.

18

Televisionary: John Logie Baird

Baird was born in 1888, in the small, genteel town of Helensburgh, nestled by the seaside at the mouth of the Gare Loch, some 25 miles northwest of Glasgow. He was the youngest of four children of Jessie Morrison Inglis, and the Reverend John Baird, a Church of Scotland minister. The Reverend Baird was outwardly an austere, forbidding, black-bearded man, but actually had a pithy sense of humour and a healthy scepticism for the Old Testament. Reputedly, while tutoring a young student of theology, Willie Milne, the Reverend Baird asked, *"Now Willie, you believe in the literal truth of Jonah and the Whale?"* which prompted the reply *"I do indeed, Sir"* from the devout pupil. *"Aye Willie"*, said the Reverend, *"you and the whale rival each other in swallowing capacity."*

From an early age, John junior's fascination with engineering was evident, as was his lack of interest in traditional schooling. When he was only 14, he learned how to assemble telephones, complete with a small exchange that he built in the family home, *'The Lodge'*, to connect with the houses of four school friends. That project came to grief when an overhead wire, displaced by a storm, caught the local horse-and-cart cab driver round the neck and threw him into the gutter. In another enterprise, Baird installed electric lighting in *The Lodge* using an old engine, a dynamo and home-made accumulator cells. More significantly for his future inventions, he commandeered the kitchen range to try to make a photoelectric cell from melted selenium, which he knew to have light-sensitive conductivity. He said the outcome was mainly *"bad smells and burnt fingers"* but he learned that the current from a selenium cell was tiny. In the days before the invention of vacuum-tube valves, his attempts to amplify the current came to nothing. Other mischievous forays into glider construction, photography and pigeon-rustling were undertaken with his best friends, Jack Buchanan, who became a star of stage and film, and Guy Fullerton Robertson, nicknamed 'Mephistopheles' or 'Mephy', who would participate in many of Baird's future experiments.

Baird's parents were tolerant of his escapades. No rebuke came from his father even when Baird's increasing certainty of the absurdity of religion had him trying to convert visitors, including clergymen, to his agnosticism. So it could have come as no surprise when he rejected his father's request to enter the ministry, and chose instead to study engineering at what soon became the Royal Technical College, the descendent of Anderson's Institution, and the forerunner of the University of Strathclyde. Part of the requirement was to spend time in industry, and Baird had three placements, including at the motor-car works of Argyll's of Alexandria, where he met a Belfast-born apprentice called Oliver Hutchinson, destined for the Army, who he would meet again later in life.

At the Royal Technical College he encountered John Reith, a fellow student, the future Lord Reith, who as its first Director-General would become the driving force of the British Broadcasting Corporation. Baird and Reith had in common that they were both sons of the manse – Reith's father was a Free Kirk Moderator – but there the similarities ended. Though Reith trained as a civil engineer, his real interests lay elsewhere. Of his first sight of Reith, Baird recounted, *"I met him for the first time in rather unfavourable circumstances. I was, and still am, very short-sighted and at the beginning of one of the classes, the Professor asked if those who were short-sighted and wanted front seats, would hand in their names… three large impressive students were talking to him. They talked in terms of equality; in fact there was a distinct aroma of patronage… they boomed with heavy joviality at the poor professor who was distinctly embarrassed…I interrupted, timidly, and handed him a piece of paper with my name on it. As I did so, the heaviest and most overpowering of the three 'heavies' turned round and boomed at me, 'Ha ! What's the matter with you? Are you deaf or blind?'…This was the first time I saw Reith. I did not see him again for twenty years."*

When he left the Royal Technical College with his Associate's diploma, Baird was 26 years old. After a few months study at Glasgow University, he took a supervisory job with the Clyde Valley Electrical Power Company. He tried to enlist in the Army in April 1916, but was declared unfit for service and spent the remaining years of the Great War at the Clyde power company. The work was arduous, and often involved emergency call-outs in the middle of cold nights to oversee repairs to cables or sub-

Illustration 42: John Logie Baird c.1917

stations. He was frequently ill, and decided to follow his own advice, written under the pseudonym 'H$_2$O' in one of his many articles in the Royal College magazine. It was entitled *'How to Make Money'*.

His first idea was to make artificial diamonds by applying intense heat and pressure to carbon. He was probably inspired by a short story called *'The Diamond Maker'* by H.G. Wells, a favourite author of his, and by the experiments of another inventor, the chemist and metallurgist James Ballantyne Hannay, a former pupil of Baird's same Larchfield School in Helensburgh, who had sensationally claimed to have synthesised diamonds in 1880. The French chemist, Henri Moissan, who won the Nobel Prize for the isolation of fluorine, later claimed to have achieved the same feat using an arc-furnace. Following this logic, Baird attempted to fuse carbon with the electric current from the bus-bars of the Clyde Company's power station. That resulted in a loud bang. Circuit breakers tripped, and part of Rutherglen was rendered briefly without electricity. Baird was not fired, but was deemed a dangerous, unreliable character, not least because of his frequent illnesses.

The next venture was advertised as *The Baird Undersock: Medicated, Soft, Absorbent. Keeps the feet warm in winter and cool in summer. 9d. per pair, post free.'* The technical breakthrough was to sprinkle factory-bought socks with borax (sodium borate) to absorb moisture. The 'Baird Undersock Company' operation soon came to the unhappy attention of the directors of the Clyde Valley Power Company, and Baird had to resign his position there. Twelve months after leaving, he fell ill again and sold the sock business having made around £1,600, equivalent to 12 years' salary in his engineering job.

Next, Baird decided to expand his fortune while improving his health in the warm West Indies. In November 1919, aged 31, he embarked for Trinidad with trunks of personal belongings, books on light, sound and electricity, and samples of safety pins and cotton goods that he hoped to sell to the inhabitants. Sales were not abundant, but his main plan was to establish a jam and chutney factory, exploiting the plentiful sugar and tropical fruit on the island. The factory consisted of three bamboo huts and a large open cooking pan, which soon became a paradise for insects, who turned out to be his most enthusiastic customers.

On his return to Britain, with savings dwindling fast, he stayed initially in a dowdy boarding house in London where Mephy was also a resident, before moving on. He hatched another business idea when he saw an advertisement for two tons of resin soap at a knock-down price. He placed an order for one ton, rented a single-room office in Water Lane, and hired an elderly gentleman to recruit and manage salesmen for 'Baird's Speedy Cleaner'. The soap was poor, being mainly caustic soda, but it was cheap, and orders flowed in. Business grew, but soon competition appeared in the form of 'Hutchinson's Rapid Washer', promoted by none other than Oliver Hutchinson, one-time apprentice at the Argyll Motor Works. He and Baird agreed to cooperate. The next day, Baird fell ill again and was advised by a doctor to vacate London as soon as possible, to improve his health. The soap business was sold at a profit, and Baird moved to Hastings, on England's south coast. After experimenting with several inventions, including pneumatic shoes and glass razors, his mind went back to his *"early work on television"* and he focused on the aim of transmitting moving images.

He knew that he needed three fundamentals: first, a photoelectric cell to convert incident light to electrical current, and amplification of its output; second, a way to scan the subject with sufficient speed to capture its motion; and lastly a method to reconstruct and rapidly display the images at the receiver. His chosen scanning method was one invented and patented by Paul Gottlieb Nipkow in 1885. Decades before that, Alexander Bain had used electrically-connected, synchronised pendulums to create line-by-line transmission of documents in the world's first telegraphic facsimile machine. Nipkow realised that much faster scanning could be achieved with a spinning wheel, perforated by a spiral of holes, where each hole in the spiral tracked a single line of the subject. Nipkow's patent outlined how the disc could be used to transmit images, though he did not at that time implement his invention.

In 1907, the Russian scientist Boris Rosing had suggested that cathode-ray tubes could be used as television displays, and the next year, the Scottish engineer, Alan Archibald Campbell-Swinton, was the first to propose an all-electronic television system, using cathode-ray tubes for image capture and transmission and as well display. In his letter to *Nature*, Campbell-Swinton wrote that *"the problem of obtaining distant electric vision can probably be solved by the employment of two beams of kathode rays (one at the transmitting and one at the receiving station) synchronously deflected by the varying fields of two electromagnets placed at right angles to one another and energised by two alternating electric currents of widely different frequencies...The real difficulties lie in devising an efficient transmitter, which, under the influence of light and shade, shall sufficiently vary the transmitted electric current so as to produce the necessary alterations in the intensity of the kathode beam of the receiver..."*

Knowing all this, but in the absence of much money, and readily-available electronic solutions, Baird worked in various private locations in London, Folkestone, Helensburgh and Hastings to construct a prototype television system, using Nipkow disc scanning. In July 1923,

Baird applied for a British patent for *A System of Transmitting Views Portraits and Scenes by Telegraphy or Wireless Telegraphy*. The system, described in patent GB222604, used a lens to focus the scene to be transmitted onto a rotating Nipkow disc, and a selenium photocell to generate the signal current, which was boosted by a valve amplifier. At the receiver, a synchronously-revolving copper brush arm passed over a series of contacts to illuminate an array of electric lamps to reconstruct the scene, an approach chosen with a view to scaling up the display to full cinema-sized screens.

Baird applied for another patent at the end of 1923, describing a system intended for domestic use, this time involving a spinning disc receiver that was now fitted with lenses. Many practical problems remained. The response times of the photocells and the lamps were long, and the signal-to-noise ratio from the selenium cell was low. Nevertheless Baird gave a demonstration of the system to the press and in January, 1924, the *Hastings and St Leonard's Observer* reported that *"A Scotsman has come south, in fact he has come to Hastings, and this particular Scotsman is now engaged upon perfecting an invention which at some not very distant date may enable people to sit in a cinema and see on the screen the finish of the Derby at the same moment as the horses are passing the post…"* There was a long way to go. At that time, the images being transmitted were simple silhouettes of subjects such as cardboard crosses.

In April 1924, Baird accepted an offer from a cinema owner, Wilfred Day, of £200 for a one-third share in the exploitation of his patents. Day's solicitor made Baird sign an agreement very detrimental to his interests, obliging him to pay all development costs and patent expenses, worldwide. Fortunately for Baird, the document was badly drafted, and found to be illegal, while Day and Baird were increasingly in dispute with each other. Day's interest in the patents was soon acquired by JLB's old acquaintance, Captain Oliver Hutchinson, who became Baird's business manager.

Technical progress continued, and seeking publicity in London, Baird had several encounters with Fleet Street newspaper editors who regarded his claims of 'seeing by wireless' as madness and branded him as a possibly dangerous crank. There were certainly dangers in Baird's laboratory. He survived a 2,000 volt electric shock, and in attempting to improve the performance of his system he later wrote in his memoirs, *"Light, how to provide more light was the most serious problem with which I was faced. The photoelectric cells then available were quite unresponsive to the light given by my apparatus..."*

At some point in 1924, he acquired from America a state-of-the-art 'Thalofide' photocell made from thallium sulphide, which exhibited a faster response than selenium, but he continued to wrestle with the problems of photocell performance. In his twelfth patent application, number GB270222, in October 1925, Baird described a clever technique to overcome the time lag in the selenium photocells, by using differential amplification to add a current to the output of the photocell, proportional to its time rate of change. The same month, everything came together in Baird's new laboratory at Frith Street, Soho, when the front-illuminated image of the face of his favourite subject, a stucco plaster dummy head known as 'Stooky Bill', formed itself on the screen with what Baird said was *"unbelievable clarity... I ran down the little flight of stairs to Mr Cross's office and seized by the arm his office boy William Taynton, hauled him upstairs and put him in front of the transmitter...I saw the flickering but clearly recognisable image of William's face - the first face seen by television - and he had to be bribed with half a crown for the privilege of achieving this distinction."*

Public demonstrations followed quickly. In early 1926, about 40 members of the Royal Institution, some with guests, attended the Frith Street rooms, six at a time, invited to see a working system. The transmitter used a lensed Nipkow disc, and 30-line moving images, about 3 inches square, of both Stooky Bill and live volunteers were received by wireline and projected by a neon lamp onto a ground-glass screen via a synchronised scanning disc. Baird was very careful not to divulge the detail of certain parts of his equipment, which were often shrouded from prying eyes. He had moved away from using solid selenium photocells in his transmitter, and now used either cooled thallium sulphide ('Thalofide') cells, or 'colloidal' selenium cells of his own invention.

Baird and Hutchinson announced their intention to sell 'Televisor' receivers commercially, and to apply for a British broadcasting licence using medium wavelengths, and a signal bandwidth of 10kHz, to provide live moving images of radio presenters. The publicity succeeded in attracting private investors, and worldwide attention. The *New York Times* devoted a page to the subject, commenting that, *"No one but the Scottish minister's son has ever transmitted and received a recognisable image with its gradations of light and shade... Baird was the first to achieve television."* The formidable resources of AT&T's Bell Telephone Laboratories were brought to bear, and they conducted wireline television transmissions from Washington DC to New York in April, 1927. A number of papers detailed their progress in the *Bell System Technical Journal*, six months later. The Bell Labs transmitter used sensitive potassium hydride photoelectric cells, and a Nipkow disc to create a 'flying spot' of light to scan the subject scene, a method that Baird had also used to avoid the need to flood the scene with bright light, but which had the disadvantage of requiring a darkened room to work well.

Baird was also coming to the notice of the British government, not least for his experiments in detecting radio waves reflected from distant objects, which had potential military applications. However, admiration for his work was not universal. Campbell-Swinton, (who was by now a member of the Broadcasting Board, a Fellow of the Royal Society, and had introduced Guglielmo Marconi to the British Post Office to accelerate the development of radio telegraphy), continued to be prominent in doubting the long-term viability of 'mechanical' television, and in touting the promise of all-electronic cameras and receivers based on cathode ray tubes. In *Nature* he recalled some *"not very successful"* experiments of his own, back in 1908, but extolled the virtues of CRTs as the way to dispense entirely with moving parts in televisions. His view was shared by some companies who would be Baird's most dangerous competitors, including Electric and Musical Industries (EMI) in Britain, and the Radio Corporation of America (RCA).

As well as forming two new companies – the Baird Television Development Company, in 1927, and Baird International Television Ltd the following year – Baird produced a stream of patents covering his numerous developments in night vision, colour television, video recording, and interlaced scanning. 'Noctovision' was based on the use of optical filters combined with thallium sulphide photocells, sensitive to infrared wavelengths. Visitors to Baird's laboratory in Long Acre included the British Prime Minister, Ramsay McDonald, who was initially sceptical of Baird's ability to televise a subject who was in complete darkness, but was quickly convinced. The armed services were interested too. Over several years, Noctovision trials were undertaken with the Admiralty, but they concluded that more sensitive photo-detectors would be needed for military use.

Another Baird invention was a system for recording vision signals on a gramophone disc, using either two separate grooves for audio and video, or using both the bottom and side-walls of a single groove. He patented the idea and made several 'Phonodisc' recordings in this way, including the first video recording of a human face, but he judged the quality to be poor and abandoned the method.

Oliver Hutchinson succeeded in raising £100,000 from investors in the new Baird Television Development Company (BTDC), and Sir Edward Manville, Vice-President of the Confederation of British Industry, and head of the Daimler Company, became its inaugural Chairman. Baird, as founder and a Managing Director, had no patience for board meetings, but the directors were aware of Baird's unique inventiveness and value to the Company, and of his poor health. His life was insured for £150,000 for one year, at a premium of £2,000.

The Bell Labs demonstrations posed a challenge that required some response. As the source of much of the investment in the Company, Glasgow was chosen as the venue to receive television transmissions via wireline from London. Baird's receiver was placed in an upstairs room of Glasgow's Central Station Hotel, attended by the leading scientists and dignitaries of the city. After the viewings, Baird gave a public address from the St Andrew's Hall, the largest in the city. The event was set in motion by the Duke of Montrose, who said proudly, though not entirely accurately, *"Scotland has introduced many great pioneers. We have given the world James Watt, the inventor of the steam engine, Henry Bell, the pioneer of the steamboat, and tonight we have with us John Logie Baird from the same town as Henry Bell... and the inventor of the great marvel of the age – television."*

Baird was now a celebrity, and enjoying the new lifestyle afforded him by his role in the BTDC. Seeking still more publicity, he fixed his sights on a transatlantic transmission of television that would be carried wirelessly. He employed a technician, Benjamin Clapp, who owned a London-based amateur radio business, including a 2 kilowatt, 6.6 MHz transmitter in his house at Coulsdon, Surrey. Clapp was sent to New York in early October, 1927, with a Baird Televisor receiver. After many tests and some failures, the first successful transatlantic television transmission was made on February 9th 1928, featuring the head of Baird rather than that of the glamorous actress, Elissa Landi, whose anticipated countenance the night before had failed to appear in New York due to technical problems. The Baird Company, with only a few personnel, had won the race to demonstrate the world's first transatlantic television transmission, against the odds and despite the superior resources of AT&T and RCA. A few days later, Clapp and Hutchinson left America on the Cunard liner *SS Berengaria,* and with the enthusiastic approval of the captain, set up the receiver equipment on board. On the 6th of March, recognisable images were received in mid-Atlantic, including that of the chief wireless officer's fiancée, who had been specially invited by the Baird Company to sit before the transmitter in London.

These world firsts were impressive and generated good publicity, but they did not persuade Britain's authorities that television was sufficiently developed to provide a public service, and they were aware of the views of Campbell-Swinton, who was increasingly sceptical and regarded

Baird and Hutchinson as rogues. Nevertheless, tests and demonstrations were conducted, and an experimental trial was set up from a BBC broadcasting station, with Baird Televisor receivers, to determine the achievable quality of reception. In September 1928, three different models of Televisors were exhibited at the Radio Exhibition in Olympia and at Selfridge's in Oxford Street, who sold the first Televisor kit for £6-10s-0d to a customer on the promise that a future broadcast service was being planned. The BBC was reluctant to see any value in the proposition, but began negotiations with the BTDC, as represented by Oliver Hutchinson and a new, influential Baird Company investor and publicist, Sydney Moseley.

In the same year, Baird achieved another world first – the production of colour television images. The transmitter used the 'flying spot' technique where a Nipkow disc with three spirals of red, green and blue filters scanned the scene, which was reconstructed at the receiver by neon tubes and mercury/helium vapour lamps, plus appropriate filters. An observer, Dr Russell, reported in *Nature* that, *"The coloured images we saw… were quite vivid. Delphiniums and carnations appeared in their natural colours and a basket of strawberries showed the red fruit very clearly."* Colour television was demonstrated at a British Association meeting in Glasgow in September 1928, together with another development, stereoscopic television, to render the scene in 3-D.

Worldwide interest was aroused by the demonstrations of transatlantic television transmission and Baird, Hutchinson and Moseley were invited to Berlin to meet representatives of the German Broadcasting Corporation. Experimental transmissions from the capital took place in May and June of 1929, and subsequently a new company, Fernseh AG, was formed in equal partnership by BTDC, Zeiss-Ikon, Bosch Magneto Company, and the Loewe Radio Company. Around the same time, the Baird Television Corporation was established in the USA and systems were displayed in New York. No doubt piqued by the foreign interest, John Reith's BBC overcame their frosty reservations about Baird, and agreed to their first experimental television broadcast, from London, on September 30th, 1929.

The programming began with speeches from Sydney Moseley and Sir Ambrose Fleming, inventor of the thermionic vacuum valve, lauding Baird's achievements, followed by a

Illustration 43: A Baird 'Televisor' with Nipkow disc, c.1930

succession of two-minute solo performances including a rendition of the song *'He's Tall, Dark and Handsome'* from Miss Lulu Stanley. The 30-line transmitter used a specially-constructed Nipkow disc, made in Germany, and projected a flying spot of light from a 1 kW lamp through a 12 x 6-inch aperture in the wall which divided the studio from the control room. Receivers were few in number. Aside from three sets, one each at Baird's home, the BBC and the headquarters of the General Post Office, there were around half-a-dozen commercial sets in Britain, with some additional receivers, home-built by amateur enthusiasts. Since the BBC had allocated only a single transmitter, the performers were televised for two minutes before the acts were repeated before a microphone and the matching sound was transmitted. Subsequently the BBC provided another transmitter and extended the available hours, so that sound and vision were synchronised on different broadcast wavelengths. A Baird receiver was installed at 10 Downing Street, and Ramsay McDonald was effusive in his praise for *"the most wonderful miracle...being done under my eye."* After concluding final negotiations with the BBC, public transmissions from Broadcasting House began in August 1932. By then, commercial Baird receivers were on the market priced at 25 guineas, or 16 guineas for a home-assembly kit. Programmes of comedy, song, and magic tricks were broadcast for 30 minutes, starting at 11 pm, on four evenings each week.

The subject of Baird's first patent application in 1923 was large-screen television, using a display consisting of an array of lightbulbs, intended to enable cinema audiences to view live events. This system was demonstrated on the roof of the Long Acre building, in July 1930, to a select audience including the booking agent for the Coliseum Theatre. He was sufficiently impressed that the large display, consisting of a rectangular screen containing 70 rows each of 30 bulbs, was featured in all performances at the London Coliseum for a period of two weeks. The content transmitted from Long Acre was a series of talking heads, including Moseley's, involving live questions and answers. The public was enthused. With a team of four engineers, the equipment was taken on a European tour to cinemas and theatres in Berlin, Paris, and Stockholm, displaying transmissions from within the cities.

Improvements were soon made to the large-screen display, which originally used direct modulation of the lightbulbs by signal current, as each bulb was connected in rapid sequence. By using Kerr cell electro-optic variable attenuators, the light source could be left permanently on, while the signal modulated the attenuation through the cells, which took advantage of their fast frequency response. Other transmitter innovations followed. To televise outdoor scenes, Baird dispensed with Nipkow discs and introduced revolving drums of mirrors instead. Using that system, an experimental outside broadcast of the 1931 Epsom Derby was made, back to Long Acre via a BBC transmitter from a Baird television van parked near the finish line. The following year, Baird again televised the finish of the Derby through the BBC transmitter and also by three parallel land-lines, each carrying one-third of the picture, to a large screen in the Metropole Theatre in London, while simultaneously the central 30 line portion of the image was broadcast in the usual way. The combination of a small mirror drum and a Kerr cell was later also used to develop domestic television receiver displays.

Baird's personal and romantic life was as unconventional as his approach to business. During his days selling undersocks in Glasgow, he had fallen in love with a young woman, Alice Bain, only to find on his return from Trinidad that in his absence, she had married, and was now Mrs Wise. Undaunted, he travelled north to Scotland and persuaded her that she should return to him. He subsequently agreed a novel arrangement with her husband, that she would be shared between them. In the early days of television, Alice lived in Hastings with Baird and Mephy, and she continued to alternate between Baird and her husband for many years. In 1931, Baird decided that he needed a wife of his own, and he arranged for the Baird Company to audition for concert pianists, so that he could observe possible candidates from behind a curtain. He was smitten by a 24-year-old from South Africa, Margaret Albu, and fortunately the attraction turned out to be mutual. They were married in November that year, in Baird's New York hotel suite while he was on an American business trip. As was often true, Baird had the flu, and *"struggled out of bed into a dressing-gown and slippers for just long enough to tie the nuptial knot."* Later that day, he and the new Mrs. Baird spent hours drafting a letter to inform Alice, sympathetically, of the new situation. It did no good, as she learned of the marriage, to her shock, in the next day's British newspapers. Margaret and JLB had their first child, Diana, in the autumn of 1932, just a few days before the death of the Reverend Baird back in Helensburgh.

Competition in television grew fiercer. Bell Labs developed their systems and built some small broadcasting stations in America. At RCA, Vladimir Zworykin invented a cathode ray tube display he called the 'Kinescope', and an electronic camera, the 'Iconoscope' which used an electron beam to scan photoelectric cells and 'read' their state of charge. In Britain, the BBC received an approach from EMI, proposing a higher definition 'telecine' service based on capturing images from celluloid film, transmitting at around 120 lines but therefore requiring higher frequency broadcast channels than the BBC had provided to Baird. EMI demonstrated the transmission of a number of silent films over a distance of two miles on a 6m wavelength. Baird protested to John Reith, that Baird Television Ltd (BTL) could provide 240 line pictures, using both cathode ray and mechanical scanning, if the short broadcast wavelengths were made available. Baird was allowed to demonstrate high-definition television, transmitted by wireline, to 3-inch x 3-inch cathode ray tube receivers, though Reith, and the BBC generally, believed EMI's system to be superior.

BTL needed more resources, and Baird and Moseley were keen to merge with the Marconi Wireless Telegraph Company. This was overruled by Baird's new chairman, Sir Harry Greer. Sydney Moseley was forced to resign, and JLB was increasingly isolated by his own board of directors. Engineering management of Baird Television Ltd was given to a new technical director, Captain A G D West, formerly head of research at the BBC. He and Baird got on well, but Baird had less and less to do with the management of BTL, in favour of working in his private laboratories at his home in Sydenham, or at the nearby BTL workshops and studios rented within the huge glass structure known as the Crystal Palace. West corrected a previous deficiency of the Company by strengthening its complement of professional engineers and physicists, and soon Baird Television was competing on almost equal terms with EMI's team of 'Oxbridge' graduates and PhDs – except that BTL was disadvantaged by new corporate mergers. In May 1934, EMI and Marconi formed a new joint venture, the Marconi-EMI Television Company, which inherited EMI's scientists and had access to patents of Marconi, EMI, General Electric, Telefunken, and RCA. The Baird Company pursued a different approach, by acquiring an electronic camera called the 'Image Dissector', developed by an independent American inventor, Philo Farnsworth. His inventions and patents, dating from 1927, gave Zworykin technical inspiration and later, RCA cause for litigation on patent priority issues. JLB met Farnsworth in England in 1932, and he continued to experiment with the Image Dissector camera for several years.

The Nazi government in Germany was aware of the potential power of television, and BTL was forced to relinquish its 25% stake in Fernseh AG. In March 1935, the German Broadcasting Service launched broadcasts operating at 180 lines and 25 frames per second, using mechanically-scanned cameras. They then televised the 1936 Olympic Games at 375 lines using Iconoscope and Image Dissector electronic cameras, transmitting on wirelines to special viewing halls across the country, that were equipped with CRT receivers projecting on large screens. In Britain, the BBC closed down the Baird system of 30-line public broadcasts in September 1935, to the annoyance of viewers nationwide. Competitive trials were conducted between Baird and Marconi-EMI systems to provide television at higher definition, therefore requiring larger signal bandwidths and higher transmission frequencies, which meant an inherently shorter wireless broadcast range. Little difference was discernible in the picture quality of the two trial systems, though the technical specifications were quite different, and EMI made great progress with their 'Emitron' all-electronic cameras.

On November 30th 1936, the Baird Company suffered an enormous setback when a huge fire at the Crystal Palace destroyed most of their facilities, including technical records and about £100,000 worth of their most advanced equipment. Baird is said to have suspected sabotage, but an accidental cause is more likely. The next year, Britain's Television Adviser y Committee chose the Marconi-EMI system as the basis for future television transmissions at 405 lines, with EMI's electronic cameras an important factor in the decision. Baird regarded this as a bitter blow. Baird Television, from which he had been side-lined for several years, were more sanguine. The Company had continuously lost money on transmissions, and believed that the profits lay in the sales of CRT receivers.

Baird continued to work on colour and stereoscopic television, focusing particularly on large-screen displays for cinemas. In February 1938, he demonstrated 12-foot x 9-foot colour television pictures transmitted wirelessly to the Dominion Theatre in London. A new company called Cinema Television, with JLB as President, was formed with the help of Isidore Ostrer, president of the Gaumont-British Picture Corporation and the chairman of BTL by virtue of its acquisition by Gaumont-British in 1932. Technical developments and commercial negotiations with the Post Office and the BBC were abruptly halted in September 1939, by the outbreak of the Second World War. All television services in Britain were ceased, and technical staff and transmission frequencies were re-assigned to military functions. Baird Television suffered cancellations of receiver set orders, and was soon put into liquidation. Its assets were acquired by Cinema Television, which in turn was also owned by Gaumont-British.

Baird evacuated his wife, daughter Diana and son Malcolm to Cornwall, while he continued to research and develop colour and 3-D television in London. He suffered a heart attack in May 1941, but recuperated, while using the time to dictate his memoirs. Some sources indicate that he was involved in consulting on the wartime development of radar, and he was certainly recruited as a technical consultant for Cable & Wireless, which provided him with some badly-needed income during the war years. Working from his private laboratory, he developed a double electron-gun colour television display, the 'Telechrome', and exhibited it in 1944. Using a large spherical vacuum tube and a double-sided screen coated with cyan and orange phosphors, it reproduced skin tones well, and Baird's recommendations were chosen by Churchill's 'Television Committee' as the standard for a post-war UK national colour TV service. Further development of Telechrome from a two-colour to a full three-colour Red-Green-Blue system was ongoing when Baird died from a coronary thrombosis in June 1946, two months short of his 58th birthday, and a week after the BBC resumed its black-and-white television service.

About 180 patent applications were filed by Baird over the course of his career. His visionary inventions ranged from mechanical and electronic scanning systems and colour CRT displays, to infrared cameras, video recording, and volumetric 3-D displays. Had the Second World War not intervened, his contributions to television development would have been even greater, and his early death robbed him of the honours and wealth which could have followed. Margaret Baird ensured that he was buried in his home town of Helensburgh, and she returned to South Africa to continue her career as a concert pianist and lecturer in music, into her seventies. Baird's son Malcolm became his biographer and a professor of chemical engineering at McMaster University in Canada. JLB's own vivid memoirs, entitled *Sermons, Soap and Television*, were published in a limited edition by the Royal Television Society in 1988, to mark the centenary of his birth. Later editions, published as *Television and Me*, include a short final chapter written by Margaret two years after the death of her pioneering husband.

19 The race for radar: Robert Watson-Watt

In Great Britain, the credit for the development – even for the 'invention' – of radio detection and ranging is usually given to the Scottish engineer, Robert Watson-Watt, born in Brechin in 1892. However, the roots of radar are deep and convoluted, and since many of the technical advances were made rapidly during the Second World War, much of the information on its development was kept secret. A few years before Watson-Watt's birth, Heinrich Hertz first detected the electromagnetic waves predicted by the theory of James Clerk Maxwell, by using spark-gap transmitters to generate electrical oscillations with wavelengths of around one metre. It was fundamental to Hertz's experiments that radio waves could be reflected by metallic objects, which he used to create standing waves, and to focus radio-frequency energy onto wire-loop detectors. Hertz had only the intention of verifying Maxwell's theoretical prediction, and when asked about the potential applications of his discovery of radio waves, he is supposed to have said, *"It's of no use whatsoever... this is just an experiment that proves Maestro Maxwell was right - we just have these mysterious electromagnetic waves that we cannot see with the naked eye, but they are there."*

Another German scientist, the inventive Christian Hülsmeyer, used radio wave reflections to detect distant metallic objects, and showed the feasibility of revealing the presence of large ships in fog. In 1904, he filed patents in Germany, quickly followed by a British patent for a system he called a *'telemobiloscope'*, which emitted pulses in a directed beam on a 50 cm wavelength and could detect reflections from ships at ranges of up to 3 km, though without the capability to measure the distance to the ships, without a little trigonometry. In demonstrations, shipowners were not sufficiently impressed, and were nervous of breaching Marconi's radio patents. Hülsmeyer's invention was taken no further.

In 1914, Robert Alexander Watson Watt was 22 years old and had graduated in engineering from University College Dundee, then part of the University of St Andrews, having won medals in electrical engineering and applied mathematics. He was a post-graduate assistant to the College's professor of physics, William Peddie, who encouraged his interest in wireless telegraphy and radio waves. Robert was the youngest of the seven children of Mary Ann Matthew, a temperance reformer and a feminist, and Patrick Watson Watt, a carpenter and joiner, whose mother was a Watson and whose father was a Watt, claiming descent from the famous James Watt. On the outbreak of the First World War, Robert joined the Meteorological Office at Farnborough, and was asked to develop radio detection to locate thunderstorms that posed a risk to aircraft. He was married in 1916, to Margaret Robertson, from Perth, who was a teacher in Dundee and had been an evening class student in metalwork and jewellery-making at the University College. They reputedly began their married life living in a wooden hut between Aldershot and Farnborough, using a second hut for Robert's research work, where Margaret helped by soldering connections and repairing the apparatus. During the Great War, she also transcribed messages received from Paris in Morse code, and passed them onto the British High Command in Aldershot.

Watson Watt's idea was to use rotatable loop antennas and earphones to identify the compass bearing of short wideband radio bursts emanating from lightning. He found that the British Admiralty already had a network of longwave radio direction-finding stations that could in principle take multiple bearings to pinpoint locations, but the very short durations of the signals presented a problem. A fast-response method of signal detection was needed, and Watson Watt was aware that oscilloscopes (then called oscillographs) offered a solution, and proposed to use them although the underlying technology of cathode-ray tubes was immature. It was not until 1922 that he obtained two examples of an early commercial oscilloscope, from Western Electric in America. One was shared with Edward Appleton at King's College London, and Appleton and Watson Watt used it to study radio ionospherics, advised and inspired by C.T.R. Wilson and his studies of thundercloud electricity. With the other oscilloscope, Watson Watt developed and patented improved time-base circuitry, which he used to demonstrate the feasibility of determining the direction of received radio pulses as short as 1 millisecond, as described in his paper entitled *'An instantaneous direct-reading goniometer'*. The focus of these investigations, and Watson Watt's main interest, was still on meteorological phenomena. In 1923, accompanied by Margaret, he conducted radio-atmospheric studies in Egypt and Sudan. Others were thinking of wider applications for radio location.

In late 1926, John Logie Baird submitted an ingenious patent application, no. GB292185, which extended his thinking beyond visible light and infrared radiation, to the reception and visualisation of radio signals. His system proposed scanning a target 'illuminated' by short radio waves, with rectification, light conversion and synchronous scanning at the receiver to render an optical image of the object on a display screen. The system was based on electro-mechanical scanning, and was impractical for long-range imaging, but it aroused the interest of H.E. 'Harry' Wimperis, Director of Research at the British Air Ministry, who would later become influential in the development of Britain's air defences.

Watson Watt's research was put into practice in the summer of 1927, with the installation of two 'radio direction-finding' (RDF) units at Radio Research Stations in Slough in Berkshire and Cupar in Fife, interconnected by telephone to facilitate near-simultaneous observations. The stations were reasonably successful in locating thunderstorms, and were increasingly used to establish the bearings of commercial and naval radio signals. The same year, the Meteorological Office was merged with the UK's National Physical Laboratory, and

Watson Watt was appointed to head the expanded Radio Research Station at Slough.

Exploration of radio direction-finding was also ongoing in the USA, France, Germany, Japan and the Soviet Union. In 1930, Albert Hoyt Taylor, Leo Young and Lawrence Hyland, working at the US Naval Research Laboratory (NRL), used radio equipment to detect the presence (but not the range or direction) of passing aircraft and filed a US Patent for a *'System for detecting objects by radio'*. Their system worked by comparing the signals received directly from the transmitter with the 'sky waves' reflected and re-radiated by the moving object. Hoyt Taylor became chief physicist at the NRL, and Hyland went on to become the President and CEO of the Hughes Aircraft Company, leading its transformation into a major corporation.

One obstacle to technical progress in RDF was the lack of a source of high-power radio waves that could be emitted directionally. A promising answer was provided by a new device, the magnetron. It was originally invented in 1917, at General Electric in the USA, to develop improved high-frequency valve amplifiers, while circumventing the 'triode' patents of Lee de Forest by controlling the vacuum tube's electron current using a magnetic field, rather than a voltage applied to a third electrode. Magnetrons were used by German and Czech researchers to produce microwaves with frequencies of around 1GHz, and in 1929, the Japanese engineers, Hidetsugu Yagi and Kinjiro Okabe, used a magnetron to produce radiation at 10cm wavelengths (a frequency of 3 GHz). The first magnetron applications were in the construction of high-frequency radio communication links, but by the mid-1930s, commercially-produced devices had been used in radio detection trials in Germany, Holland and the USA. In France, the ocean liner *SS Normandie* was equipped with an obstacle detection system based on 10cm wavelength radio reflections, but restricted to short range by the low power of the magnetrons then available.

In the UK, Watson Watt was now the head of a new radio research department of the National Physical Laboratory, and in 1935 he was asked by Harry Wimperis to investigate whether high-power radio beams could be used as 'death rays' to damage enemy aircraft, by frying their metallic components – or their crew. Watson Watt delegated the feasibility study to an assistant, Arnold 'Skip' Wilkins, asking him to calculate the amount of radio energy that would need to be emitted to raise the temperature of 8 pints of water from 98°F to 105°F at a range of 5km. Wilkins showed, as expected, that the idea was completely impractical, and Watson Watt fed back the conclusion to the Air Ministry, writing, in his notoriously convoluted way, *"Meanwhile attention is being turned to the still difficult, but less unpromising, problem of radio detection and numerical considerations on the method of detection by reflected radio waves will be submitted when required."* Further calculations showed that the reflected energy could be enough to enable detection at useful distances, and Watson Watt wrote again in February, 1935: *"I enclose, herewith, a memorandum on the 'Detection of aircraft by radio methods'. It turns out so favourably that I am still nervous as to whether we have not got a power of ten wrong, but even that would not be fatal."* The memorandum estimated the strength of the radio signal reflected by aircraft and discussed the optimum radio wavelength, noting that wavelengths similar in size to the aircraft resulted in stronger received signals. It outlined how the range of the target could be measured by the use of short pulses, and its location fixed by the use of three range measurements. Watson Watt recommended that cathode-ray oscilloscopes should be developed to display the target's bearing and elevation.

The British government's new 'Tizard' committee for the scientific study of air defence, formed at a time of growing international tension in Europe, asked for a demonstration. In February 1935, Watson Watt and Wilkins used the BBC's 10kW, 49m wavelength transmitter at Daventry to detect the presence of a Heyford bomber, flying at 6,000 feet, several miles distant. The signals received from two dipole antennas were fed in phase opposition to a cathode-ray display tube such that signals arriving directly from the transmitter produced no response, but signals from the target, arriving at a different angle, were not cancelled and produced a vertical deflection on the screen. The Air Ministry observer, A.P. Rowe, reported back, comparing the result to existing sound detection methods, *"It was demonstrated beyond doubt that electromagnetic energy is reflected from the metal components of an aircraft's structure and that it can be detected. Whether aircraft can be accurately located remains to be shown. No one seeing the demonstration could fail to be hopeful of detecting the existence and approximate bearing of aircraft approaching the coast at ranges far in excess of those given by the 200 ft (sound) mirrors."*

The success led to the establishment of a new research station at Bawdsey Manor on the Suffolk coast, near Felixstowe. Directed by Watson Watt, its mission was to develop a radio direction finding and ranging capability for Britain's air defence. A prototype pulsed system was quickly built, based on Appleton's and Watson Watt's work on analysing reflections from the ionosphere, and testing began on the sandy peninsula of Orfordness in the summer of 1935. A high-power 50m wavelength transmitter was designed by Edward Bowen, producing 25µs pulses with a 25Hz repetition rate. In tests on June 17th, the system successfully measured the direction and range of a 'Supermarine Scapa' flying-boat at a distance of 17 miles, in what is generally recognised as the first demonstration in Britain of radar – though the acronym was coined four years later by the US Signal Corps. Further tests targeting aircraft from RAF Martlesham Heath improved the range to 100 miles with sufficient resolution to distinguish echoes from separate aircraft in formation. With commendable alacrity, the British government's Treasury assigned £60,000 for the construction of five RDF stations called *'Chain Home'*, guarding the approaches to the River Thames and London. Watson Watt's team of engineers and physicists had the first stations of the system built and operational by 1938, transmitting pulses of between 100kW and 1MW of peak power, on wavelengths between 7 and 14 meters. It was the first early-warning radar network in the world.

Elsewhere, teams of engineers were also racing to develop viable radar systems, using both short pulses and a continuous-wave approach based on detecting radio interference and Doppler shifts in the returned signals. Hoyt Taylor's team at the US Naval Research Laboratory demonstrated a prototype pulsed radar operating at 28.6 MHz (about 10m wavelength) to track aircraft at ranges of 25 miles. A shorter-wavelength and higher-power system was tested aboard the *USS Leary* in 1937, and after further development with the Radio Corporation of America, was installed on the *USS New York* two years later. In Germany, the Telefunken and GEMA companies were developing metric and decimetric wavelength systems. A successful demonstration to the German Navy in 1935 led to the wartime deployment of the *Seetakt* (50cm wavelength) and *Freya* (1.2m) systems, respectively by the Kriegsmarine and the Luftwaffe. The shorter wavelengths enabled smaller antennas, which were more mobile, and easier to rotate, and the *Freya* system was superior to the *Chain Home* stations in resolution and its ability to detect smaller targets. However, its complexity meant that at the outbreak of World War II in 1939, only eight *Freya* stations were in place, leaving large gaps in coverage, when by then the *Chain Home* network covered all of Britain's east coast, and most of the south.

France too had been racing to prepare for another war. At the Laboratoire National de Radioélectrité, Pierre David had developed a radio-detection method called the *barrage électromagnétique* which was based on continuous wave transmissions at 75 MHz (4m wavelength) that could detect Doppler interference from aircraft flying at 7,000 metres and up to 10km distant. Installations were made in Cherbourg, Brest, Toulon and Bizert in northern Tunisia. The system could indicate the presence of an aircraft, but not its instantaneous speed or direction, and tests in 1936 showed that too many aircraft were missed. David switched his attention to pulsed radar. He experimented with magnetrons developed at the CSF company earlier in the decade, but designed a 50MHz system, with a peak power of 12kW. Stations were deployed at Toulon and in Paris, with a ranging capability of up to 55km, but too late to impact the overwhelming German invasion of France in 1940.

Illustration 44: The Chain Home tower at Gt. Baddow, Chelmsford

A few days before the fall of Paris in June 1940, Maurice Ponte, a senior CSF scientist, crossed the English Channel and presented two highly-advanced magnetrons to the GEC Laboratories in London. The devices used split anodes and efficient oxide-coated cathodes to produce a peak power of 1kW, demonstrating the solution for producing high-power, short-wavelength pulses without 'burning out' the electrodes. GEC had already been asked to make engineering improvements to a 'cavity' magnetron developed by two physicists at Birmingham University, John Randall and Harry Boot. The combination of resonant-cavity anodes and oxide-coated cathodes enabled the rapid production of cavity magnetrons producing 15kW at 10cm wavelength. The technology was in turn shared with the Americans. Cavity magnetrons became the key components in the development of Britain's *H2S* and *ASV Mk III* airborne, surface-scanning microwave radars which guided bombing raids and attacks on U-boats in the last years of the War.

Britain's resistance to that point depended greatly on Watson Watt's *Chain Home* (CH) radar defence stations, and their successors, known as *AMES Type 7* stations, which afforded a 360 degree scan around each installation, and enabled aircraft interceptions to be plotted directly from the display, a method known as ground controlled intercept (GCI). As the Air Ministry's Director of Communications Development, Watson Watt led studies on the operation of the network and liaised with the Royal Air Force to ensure that optimal use was made of radar technology. Air Marshal Sir Raymund Hart was attached to Bawdsey Manor in his early days, and after the War he said, *"The Battle of Britain was fought and won on information passed from the original CH chain, for that was in fact the original major development that the Bawdsey Research Establishment produced... when I was Chief Air Signals Officer at Supreme Headquarters, Allied Expeditionary Force, with General Eisenhower at the latter end of the war, I had an opportunity to interrogate General Baumer, who was my opposite number on the German side. He told me that he*

Illustration 45: Sir Robert Watson-Watt, c.1944

was convinced that one of the primary reasons why we won the Battle of Britain against the Germans was that the Germans lost faith in their intelligence organization, by virtue of the fact that, whereas they had been told that the opposing force was of a certain size, when they came to attack this country they invariably, or very nearly invariably, found that they were met by a force of a strength, and in a position, that was competent to do battle with them. Their calculations according to the size of the British Air Force at the time was that that was literally impossible. Mr. Watson-Watt and his scientists had in fact made it possible."

The official history of the RAF puts the context: *"The hostile bomber, holding the initiative, had the choice of time, target and approach; and no place in England was more than twenty minutes' flight from the nearest coast. In such circumstances how could the fighter, which might spend ten minutes merely in climbing to its operational height, intercept before the bombs dropped... Only with a truly gigantic fighter force could this be done — a force so enormous that it would leave us few resources for guns, tanks or ships, and none at all for bombers. . . . With the advent of Watson-Watt there occurred, in an incredibly brief period, nothing less than a revolution in the science of air defence."*

Watson Watt was elected a Fellow of the Royal Society in 1941, and the following year he acquired both a knighthood and a hyphen in his name. After the War, he received many other honours and awards, including the US Medal of Merit, and led the British delegations to international meetings on radio navigation for ships and civil aviation. He set up an engineering consultancy practice, Sir Robert Watson-Watt

& Partners, and moved to Canada for several years. In a talk broadcast in 1948, he was unjustifiably self-deprecating: *"A sixth-rate mathematician, a second-rate physicist, a second-rate engineer, a bit of a meteorologist, something of a journalist, a plausible salesman of ideas, interested in politics, liking to believe there is some poetry in my physics, some physics in my politics. Thirty years a Civil Servant, now a socialist in 'private enterprise'".*

In 1952, the Royal Commission on Awards for Inventors gave a tax-free sum of £87,950 to the Bawdsey team, of which Watson-Watt's share was £52,000. He and Margaret divorced, and she returned to live in Perth. The same year, he married his second wife, Jean Wilkinson, a Canadian eight years his junior, and the widow of a historian, Professor George M. Smith. While in Canada, on collecting a speeding ticket awarded by a radar trap, Sir Robert rhymed ruefully,

Pity Sir Robert Watson-Watt, strange target of this radar plot
And thus, with others I can mention, the victim of his own invention.
His magical all-seeing eye enabled cloud-bound planes to fly
but now by some ironic twist it spots the speeding motorist
and bites, no doubt with legal wit, the hand that once created it.

Between 1958 and 1960, Watson-Watt took part in five international meetings of scientists, called for by the Russell-Einstein Manifesto of 1955, to discuss the dangers posed to humanity by nuclear weapons. The first conference was held in Pugwash, Nova Scotia, and gave rise to successive Pugwash Conferences on Science and World Affairs. Watson-Watt supplied the meetings with papers on many topics strictly outside of their remit, for example, on the problem of global food shortage. He was increasingly concerned that the world should avoid another war, and his book, *'Man's means to his end',* emphasised the dangers of uncontrolled technical progress. His Canadian engineering consultancy went bankrupt in 1960, and he is said to have relied on Lady Jean to settle debts with creditors. During the Cold War, it seems that his precarious finances, anti-nuclear views, and associations with Soviet scientists brought him to the attention of the intelligence services in Britain and the USA.

Lady Jean Watson-Watt died in 1964, and Sir Robert returned to live in Scotland. He began a relationship with Dame Katherine Trefusis Forbes, a successful businesswoman who had been the wartime Commander of the Women's Auxiliary Air Force. They were married in 1966, when she was 67 years old, and he was 74. They lived at 'The Observatory', Katherine's summer home in Pitlochry, and spent their winters in London. She died after five years of marriage, and Watson-Watt died in 1973, in Inverness. He was buried with Katherine in the Episcopal Church at Pitlochry. His unsuccessful business dealings meant that he died by no means a rich man, and despite three marriages he had no children; but he is revered as the 'father' of British radar, and the winner of the race to build the world's first effective air defence network.

20

Penicillin, the first antibiotic: Alexander Fleming

The First World War battlefields of the Western Front in France were an important training ground for a young bacteriologist, Alexander Fleming of the Royal Army Medical Corps. In treating the grievous wounds of Allied soldiers, Lieutenant Fleming observed that the application of antiseptics to deep, infected lacerations often worsened the injuries, sometimes resulting in death from sepsis, completely contrary to accepted wisdom since the work of Joseph Lister at the Glasgow Royal Infirmary. Fleming focused his attention on an antiseptic, flavin, which was supposed to be one of the most effective, and least harmful. In a series of clever experiments performed in 1917 at an Army base hospital at Boulogne-sur-Mer, he showed that in fact flavin was more effective in killing protective white blood cells (leucocytes) than in killing bacteria, and reported his findings in *The Lancet*. More generally, he realised that while antiseptics worked well on the surface of skin, deep wounds could shelter anaerobic bacteria and keep them out of antiseptic reach. His findings were clear, but flavin continued to be used during the remaining course of the War. After demobilisation, Fleming returned to work at St Mary's Hospital, London, and resolved to find antibacterial substances that were not harmful to animal tissue.

Alexander was born to a farming family in Ayrshire, near Darvel, in 1881, the third of four children of Hugh Fleming and Grace Morton. His father was a 59-year-old widower when he wed Grace, his second marriage, and he died when Alexander, known as Alec, was just seven. A bright student, Alec won a scholarship to the venerable Kilmarnock

Academy before moving to London when he was 14, to live with a step-brother, Thomas, who was an ophthalmologist, and he continued his education at the Polytechnic Institute. After four years working as an apprentice clerk, he started his studies in medicine, funded by a scholarship and a legacy of £250 from his Uncle John. He graduated as the top medical student at the University of London, in 1908, and took a temporary position at St Mary's Hospital, where he had done clinical training. In the laboratory of the Inoculation Department, he assisted the eminent immunologist Sir Almroth Wright, who had developed an anti-typhoid vaccine that was proved effective during the Boer War, and would save the lives of thousands of British troops in World War I. Wright was formidably intelligent, yet he espoused various untenable theories that female brains were unsuited to public duty, that micro-organisms were mere vehicles of disease rather than a cause, and that scurvy was caused by eating poorly preserved meat. He railed against the women's suffrage movement, and his opponents nicknamed him 'Almroth Wrong' and 'Sir Almost Wright'.

After leaving St Mary's, Fleming established a successful private practice as a venereologist, and was one of the first doctors in Britain to treat syphilis with a new drug, arsphenamine, known as 'Salvarsan' or '606', developed by the German bacteriologist, Paul Ehrlich. The drug contained arsenic, and was given by intravenous injection, an unusual procedure at the time. It was the first drug devised to overwhelm an invading microorganism without harming the host, and it ushered in a new era of 'chemotherapeutics'.

Through the early years of the century, Fleming was an active sportsman, swimming, golfing and rifle-shooting, and he was a part-time soldier in the London Scottish Regiment of the Volunteer Force. On the outbreak of the Great War, he was initially commissioned as a Lieutenant, then promoted to Captain, in the Royal Army Medical Corps. He worked as a bacteriologist in the Boulogne field hospital set up by Almroth Wright, to study and treat the bacterial infections of the terrible wounds inflicted by high explosives, and where he made his observations on the hazards presented by the careless use of antiseptics.

On leave from Army duty in 1915, Alec Fleming married Sarah McElroy, an Irishwoman known as Sareen, who with her twin sister Elizabeth ran a nursing home in Baker Street. The marriage came as a surprise to Fleming's friends and colleagues, who had been unaware that there was a woman in his life. His brother John later married Elizabeth, further strengthening the close ties between the families and the siblings.

After the end of the War, Fleming remained in France for a while, trying to identify the cause of the 'Spanish Flu' epidemic that caused an estimated 20 million deaths in the country, which was already devastated by the conflict. Eventually unsuccessful, he returned to England and with Sareen, purchased a Georgian house they called the 'The Dhoon' as a country home in Barton Mills, West Suffolk. He re-joined St Mary's Hospital as assistant director in the Inoculation Department, where in later years he would succeed Almroth Wright as director in what became the Institute of Pathology.

His awareness of the human body's physiological defence mechanisms prepared his mind for his first remarkable discovery, made in late 1921. While making daily cultures from the nasal secretions of a patient suffering from a common cold, he found that one of the plates had been contaminated with bacterial spores from the air – not unusual in Fleming's laboratory, which was notoriously untidy. In this case, he found that the nasal mucus (which was actually his own) had prevented growth of the bacteria and created a circular 'killing zone' of about 1cm radius around the spores. He confirmed the bactericidal effect of the mucus on bacteria grown in liquid suspension, and went on test the effect of tears, contributed by his colleagues. His research student and co-worker, V.D. Allison recalled, *"For the next five or six weeks, our tears were the source of supply for this extraordinary phenomenon. Many were the lemons we used (after the failure of onions) to produce a flow of tears... The demand by us for tears was so great, that laboratory attendants were pressed into service, receiving threepence for each contribution."* Even more extraordinarily, they further demonstrated that the same bactericidal agent was present in blood, saliva, semen, pus, and even in the white of hens' eggs. Fleming named the agent 'lysozyme', and showed that it was present also in non-human animal tissue, and had a bactericidal effect on a range of microbes including *streptococci* and *staphylococci*. Yet when Wright reported these findings to the Royal Society in 1922, on Fleming's behalf, there was little reaction. Not until the last decades of the 20th century was lysozyme generally recognised as a key component of the innate immune system. It is an important constituent of human breast milk, and low lysozyme levels are associated with chronic lung disease in newborn infants. The discovery of lysozyme was no great act of genius, but it illustrated Fleming's acute powers of observation and deduction, given that hundreds of bacteriologists all over the world had been studying nasal secretions for many years in the hope of finding the cause of the common cold.

A few years later, in September 1928, these powers would come into play again in a similar way. While making some daily observations of *staphylococcus* colonies growing on agar plates, Fleming noted greatly inhibited growth around some spots of contaminating mould, presumed to have arrived in the laboratory through an open window. In fact, the plates were likely contaminated from the mycology laboratory run by a young Irish doctor, C.J. La Touche, on the floor below Fleming's lab. La Touche initially identified the mould as *penicillium rubrum*, a multicellular fungus mostly found indoors in damp buildings, but it seems that he really meant *penicillium rubens* (also called *penicillium notatum*) which is now known to be one of the very few strains that produce antibacterial 'juice'.

For the next six months, Fleming tested a range of mould secretions for their toxicity to a number of harmful bacteria, hoping that he had found a group of naturally occurring antiseptics. He cultured and examined eight strains of *penicillium*, and other moulds including *Botrytis cinerea*, the 'noble rot' sometimes encouraged on grapes to make sweet

Illustration 46: Alexander Fleming at work in his laboratory

wine, and *cladosporium,* responsible for tomato leaf mould. The test results were slightly disappointing. Only the one strain of *penicillium* produced a secretion that inhibited bacterial growth – the same as the original mould from the contaminated plate. He called his mould broth filtrate 'penicillin'. In the laboratory, the action of the mould juice was evident but slow, and when applied to the infected wounds of animals, it lost potency quite quickly after application. It was ineffective against many bacteria, such as Pfeiffer's bacillus, but was strongly toxic to others including strains of *pneumococci, staphylococci* and *streptococci,* even when highly diluted. Just as importantly, penicillin's toxicity to animals was very low, as shown by injecting mice and rabbits with the penicillin filtrate, which caused no harmful effects. In his 1929 paper published in the *British Journal of Experimental Pathology,* Fleming concluded that, *"A certain type of penicillium produces in culture a powerful antibacterial substance…the active agent is readily filterable and the name 'penicillin' has been given to filtrates of broth cultures of the mould…It is suggested that it may be an efficient antiseptic for application to, or injection into, areas infected with penicillin-sensitive microbes."*

Fleming's ground-breaking paper was met with complete indifference, against a general background of scepticism about the use of antiseptics for anything other than local infections. He himself seems to have had in mind only the topical application of penicillin, but he was convinced of its importance and the need to purify the extract and produce it in quantity. He approached the UK Medical Research Council Laboratory at Hampstead, whose director was uninterested, and then Harold Raistrick, a chemical expert at the London School of Tropical Hygiene and Medicine. Raistrick's team failed to purify the active substance and declared *"the production of penicillin for therapeutic purposes...almost impossible."* Fleming continued to supply mould samples to researchers who requested them, but he put his discovery aside to focus on his other work, in immunology. With G.F. Petrie of the Lister Institute, he co-authored the influential 1935 textbook *Recent Advances in Vaccines and Serum Therapy.*

Illustration 47: Sample of the penicillium mould, 1935

Penicillin remained interesting only to bacteriologists, and of no great practical importance, until the work of an Australian pathologist, Howard Florey, and the Russian-German chemist Ernst Chain, at the University of Oxford. In 1938, Florey started a systematic study of naturally occurring antibacterial substances, beginning with comparisons of lysozyme extracted and purified from egg-white, cats and humans. Moving on to substances produced by micro-organisms, Florey and Chain selected penicillin, and succeeded in producing it in a much-reduced but highly purified form which prevented the growth of *staphylococci* even in dilutions of 1 part per million. They then took a step which Fleming had not, by testing the antibacterial properties of penicillin when injected to animals *in vivo*. They injected eight mice with haemolytic *streptococci*, followed by timed and measured injections of penicillin to four of the mice. The lucky four treated with penicillin survived, and their untreated fellows swiftly died. Hundreds of mice as well as rats and cats were tested during the summer of 1940, and the outcomes, reported in *The Lancet*, caused excitement in research groups around the world: *"The results are clear cut, and show that penicillin is active in vivo against at least three of the organisms inhibited in vitro. It would seem a reasonable hope that all organisms inhibited in high dilution in vitro will be found to be dealt with in vivo. Penicillin does not appear to be related to any chemotherapeutic substance at present in use and is particularly remarkable for its activity against the anaerobic organisms associated with gas gangrene."*

Fleming was excited too, and he visited Oxford to discuss the results. Further tests in humans initially showed mixed outcomes. The first British patient to be treated, a young woman with terminal cancer, reacted with a fever that was attributed to remaining impurities in the penicillin. Albert Alexander, a policeman with an infection of his face, was treated and showed improvement until the supply of penicillin was used up, and he died. In America, Karl Meyer, Henry Dawson and others at Columbia University were inspired to extract penicillin from mould and succeeded in purifying enough, they hoped, to treat two patients. However, the administered doses were too small to evoke a cure. Trials later in 1941 were more successful – the Oxford group made enough penicillin to treat five more patients with persistent bacterial infections and very poor prognoses, and three were saved.

The press and news media at first presented penicillin as an accidental discovery by Fleming that had been recognised and developed as useful by the Oxford team. Fleming maintained that he had always seen its potential as a systemic antibacterial drug. Relations between Fleming and the Oxford group became strained; but in the summer of 1942, he received a call from his brother Robert regarding a friend called Harry Lambert, who was dying of streptococcal meningitis, and he asked Florey for penicillin to treat him. Florey generously obliged with almost his entire supply. Fleming injected it into Lambert's spinal canal, the first such 'intrathecal' use of penicillin. The patient recovered within a week, and *The Times* published the news that the man had been saved from certain death. At the end of August, 1942, Almroth Wright wrote to the editor: *"Sir, In the leading article on penicillin… you refrained from putting the laurel wreath for this discovery round anyone's brow… it should be decreed to Professor Alexander Fleming of this laboratory. For he is the discoverer of penicillin and was the author of the original suggestion that this substance might prove to have important applications in medicine."*

That prompted journalists to descend on St Mary's Hospital, beginning the process of Fleming's lionisation, and launching what he later self-effacingly called 'the Fleming Myth'. Another letter was published in *The Times,* from Sir Robert Robinson, an Oxford University chemist. *"Now that Sir Almroth Wright has rightly drawn attention to the fact that penicillin was discovered by Professor Fleming and has crowned him with a laurel wreath, a bouquet at least and a handsome one, should be presented to Professor H.W. Florey, of the School of Pathology at this university. Toxic substances are produced by the mould alongside penicillin and Florey was first to separate 'therapeutic penicillin' and to demonstrate its value clinically."*

Meanwhile, in the middle of the chaos of World War II, Howard Florey had realised the importance of scaling up the production of penicillin. He secured funds from the Rockefeller Foundation and left Britain for the United States with his colleague Norman Heatley, leaving behind a very disgruntled Ernst Chain. The Florey children were spending the War in New Haven, Connecticut, with an old friend of Florey's, the Yale University clinician John Fulton. Two of Fulton's patients had already been saved by the injection of scarce samples of Oxford penicillin sent to him by Florey. With Fulton's network of contacts, it was agreed that Heatley would work at the US Department of Agriculture facility in Peoria, Illinois, to share the Oxford experience and develop techniques for the mass-production of penicillin. The choice of location was extremely fortunate. A successful production method was developed using deep fermentation of mould filtrate with corn-steep liquor, a by-product of the manufacture of corn-starch that was in plentiful supply in Illinois. Florey succeeded in overcoming initial disinterest and persuaded a consortium of American pharmaceutical firms, including Abbott Laboratories, Merck, and Pfizer, to produce penicillin in huge quantities. By the end of 1943, the stock was sufficient to supply all the armed forces of the Allied nations in the War, and 2.3 million doses were manufactured in preparation for the D-Day landings of June 6th, 1944.

Until that point, back in England, Ernst Chain and the team continued to research the chemical structure of penicillin and improve its purity. While the drug remained scarce, Florey and his wife, Dr Ethel Florey, successfully treated more than 170 patients with penicillin, and

Ethel was seen regularly riding her bicycle in Oxford having collected urine from patients, in order to reclaim the precious substance from the excretions, in a journey known as the 'P-patrol'. Chain wanted to patent his purification methods, but the Medical Research Council, and the president of the Royal Society, dissuaded him on the grounds that the discovery was for the benefit of all mankind. The American companies were not so high-minded, and when the War ended, British scientists were incensed to learn that they were asked to pay patent royalties to use techniques they had discovered.

Fleming and Florey were knighted in 1944, and the following year they and Chain were awarded the Nobel Prize in Physiology or Medicine for the 'discovery of penicillin and its curative effect in various infectious diseases'. It was the first of the 'antibiotics', substances with immense antibacterial power, derived from organisms, and harmless to the body – although Fleming regarded lysozyme as the first antibiotic he discovered. The term was introduced by the Russian-American microbiologist Selman Waksman who co-discovered many antibiotics including streptomycin and neomycin, and who himself was awarded the Nobel in 1952. The deadly 'white plague' of tuberculosis was largely overcome by the widespread use of streptomycin in the 1950s.

For his discoveries, Sir Alexander Fleming was universally acclaimed, and received numerous awards and honours, including the French Légion d'Honneur. Fleming was a gregarious man, but taciturn, with a reputation as a terrible lecturer, and afflicted with an almost pathological lack of light conversation. Yet he and Sareen enjoyed travelling extensively and were warmly received by international statesmen and famous hosts, including the British Royal family, Marlene Dietrich, President Roosevelt, and the Pope on three occasions. For all of his life, Fleming retained a sense of playfulness, and after the Nobel award he created 'fungal novelties' – samples of *penicillium* mould in glass medallions – which he presented as gifts.

Sir Almroth Wright retired in 1946, and Fleming assumed his position as Principal of the newly-renamed Wright-Fleming Institute of Pathology. Sareen was taken ill while accompanying Alec on a trip to Spain, and her health declined steadily until her death in 1949. In the following years Fleming continued to travel, touring the world as a celebrity, while the younger Howard Florey returned to his laboratory. Some tension between them remained. Fleming was elected Rector of the University of Edinburgh in 1951, and two years later he was re-married, to

Illustration 48: Sir Alexander Fleming during the 2nd National Congress on Antibiotics, Milan, 1950

Amalia Koutsouri-Vourekas, a 39-year-old bacteriologist who had joined the Institute in 1946.

Sir Alexander resigned as Rector of Edinburgh University in January 1955. Two months later he became ill just as he was due for a lunch at the Savoy with Eleanor Roosevelt and the film-star Douglas Fairbanks Jr. Amalia telephoned a doctor, but before he could arrive, Fleming died of a coronary thrombosis, three months short of his 74th birthday. He was survived by Amalia and his son with Sareen, Robert, who became a medical practitioner.

Fleming's discovery of penicillin has been described as the single greatest victory ever achieved over disease, though as he acknowledged, the credit was shared with many others, and he foresaw the risks and potential problems of emerging bacterial resistance to antibiotics. As a mark of the esteem in which he was held, Fleming's ashes were interred in St Paul's Cathedral with Nelson, Wellington, and Wren, among the pantheon of great British heroes.

21 Scientific refugees: Charlotte Auerbach and Hans Kosterlitz

Nowhere in Europe were the horrors of World War Two more extreme than in Nazi Germany and the territories occupied by the Third Reich. State-sponsored persecution of Communists, homosexuals, and 'non-Aryans', specifically Jews, began soon after the appointment of Adolf Hitler as Chancellor in 1933, and intensified quickly. Within a few weeks, Hitler passed the *'Law for the Restoration of the Professional Civil Service'*, which meant that Jews and members of opposition parties were dismissed from their posts as lawyers, doctors, teachers or professors. Such educated members of the proscribed classes could read the writing on the wall, and left in droves. One of them was a 34-year-old biologist, Charlotte Auerbach, who in the year of Hitler's accession fled Germany to become a researcher at Edinburgh University's Institute of Genetics. Another was Hans Kosterlitz, a young doctor and radiologist, who was in contact with John J.R. Macleod, the Nobel Laureate, co-discoverer of insulin, and Professor of Physiology at the University of Aberdeen. Macleod was fluent in German, and was aware of Kosterlitz's publications on carbohydrate metabolism. He told him, *"come to Aberdeen...but no guarantee of a secure job."* With financial support from the UK's Academic Assistance Council and Imperial Chemical Industries (ICI), Kosterlitz arrived in Aberdeen in March 1934.

Auerbach, known as Lotte, was born into a Jewish family in 1899. Her father was a physical chemist, and her grandfather discovered 'Auerbach's plexus', a group of autonomic nerve cells found in the intestine. Lotte was greatly influenced by her father but became intrigued when her biology teacher at school spent an hour explaining chromosomes and their replication through cellular mitosis – topics that were not on the official curriculum. It was she said, *"one of the few great spiritual experiences of my school life."* At the University of Berlin, she studied biology, chemistry, physics, and to some extent the philosophy of David Hume, which she admired for its wonderful clarity. She started and then abandoned postgraduate research to become a biology teacher, and when she arrived at Edinburgh University, she had little money and qualifications that were initially regarded inadequate to begin a PhD. Nevertheless she was soon enrolled at Edinburgh's Institute of Genetics under the supervision of Professor F.A.E. Crew, who guided her to study the genetics of the tiny fruit fly, *Drosophila*, and he largely left her to get on with it.

Lotte's thesis on the development of *Drosophila* legs was accepted, and she began post-doctoral work in Crew's team of lively researchers, which included guest scientists such as Julian Huxley and the colourful character J.B.S. 'Jack' Haldane, a brilliant pioneer of genetics and evolutionary biology, who claimed that his Y chromosome could be traced back to Robert the Bruce. Most importantly for Auerbach, another scientific refugee, Hermann J. Müller, joined the 'crew' in 1937. Müller was in fact a third generation American, who arrived in Edinburgh via Germany, which he left in 1933, and then the Soviet Union, which despite his Communist sympathies rejected him four years later, for opposing the state-sponsored genetic dogma of Lysenko. In a series of experiments in the 1920s, Müller had demonstrated that exposure to X-rays caused genetic mutations in *Drosophila*, a discovery which would earn him a Nobel Prize in 1946. While at Edinburgh, he encouraged Auerbach to consider other possible drivers of mutagenesis, saying *"if you want to come nearer to a gene, you need to understand what happens when it mutates, just as if you want to know something about a substance, you must make it react."*

Auerbach, assisted by Crew, became a naturalised British citizen in 1939. Two weeks before the outbreak of World War Two in September, Lotte's mother fled from Berlin and arrived, with no baggage or money, to join her in Edinburgh. They lived in two cramped rooms in the south of the city, sharing facilities with other refugee families.

Sometime in 1940, Auerbach had a meeting with the Professor of Pharmacology, Alfred J. Clark, and a member of his department, J. M. Robson, born in Belgium to a Russian Jewish family as John Michael Rabonovitch and known as 'Rab'. It was suggested that Auerbach should test for possible mutagenic effects of mustard gas, which had killed or maimed around 150,000 British soldiers in the First World War. Clark knew its effects to be long-lasting, producing wounds that were slow to heal and prone to recurrence, similar to the effects of over-exposure to X-rays, and Rab had a hunch that it could be mutagenic. They agreed that Auerbach and Robson should expose *Drosophila* flies to mustard gas and test them for the presence of gene mutations.

The flies were in vials exposed to mustard gas in an open vessel, and the vials were afterwards removed manually. This was hazardous, and all the people doing the work developed burns on their hands. Auerbach was warned that she could develop serious wounds, and she noted, *"We used up a lot of technicians. All of them got allergic to mustard gas."* Rab was equally casual, and the dosage of mustard gas applied was never precisely monitored. When the pre-exposed flies were examined using a technique developed by Müller, the results were striking. Lethal mutations in X-chromosomes were common, compared to the untreated controls. Auerbach's hero Müller telegraphed from America, *"We are thrilled by your major discovery opening great theoretical and practical field. Congratulations you and Robson."* Confirming the result proved difficult due to the haphazard experiments, but it was conclusively reported to the British government in 1942, and eventually published in a 1946 letter to *Nature*, postponed until after the end of World War Two because of wartime secrecy. The result showed for the first time that genetic mutations can be caused by a chemical agent.

Auerbach received much international credit for the work, and in 1947 she was awarded the 'Keith' Gold Medal, the most prestigious prize given by the Royal Society of Edinburgh. The award annoyed Robson, who thought the prize should have been shared, and many years later he said, *"I discovered the mutagenic action of mustard gas... I suggested to Müller that he should do it... He suggested that I should approach Lotte Auerbach."* She agreed with the sentiment, saying that she accepted the

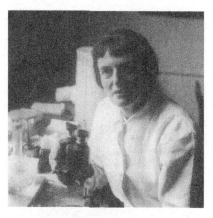

Illustration 49: Charlotte Auerbach in her Edinburgh University laboratory (1953). Courtesy of the Royal Society.

prize only because she needed the money (£50, almost a third of her then annual salary), though she recalled that it was Clark who had suggested the experiments. In any event, Robson broke off contact between them.

Though Charlotte Auerbach is remembered mainly for the first demonstration of mutagenesis by a chemical agent in 1941, her subsequent work on genetics was important too. Working initially at a time when genes were still thought to be proteins, before the discovery of DNA, her research discovered the existence of 'mosaics' of mutant and non-mutant cells, and she showed how chemical agents affected genes differently according to their specific locations on the chromosome. Among many other honours, she was elected as a Fellow of the Royal Society in 1957, and she summarised many of her 91 published papers in six books, including *Genetics in the Atomic Age* (1956) and *Mutation Research* (1976). She never married, but she informally adopted two sons, and worked on into her late seventies. She died in Edinburgh in 1994, two months short of her 95th birthday.

...

Auerbach's compatriot refugee, Hans Kosterlitz, spent his entire career at the University of Aberdeen, having quickly secured a place in the laboratory of John J.R. Macleod, who gave him great support and encouragement. Macleod's untimely death in 1935, after a long illness, left Kosterlitz in some degree of scientific isolation, but he qualified in medicine and gained a PhD for his thesis on the biochemistry of the liver. Thereafter he succeeded in winning research grants from the Diabetic Association and the UK's Medical Research Council. His personal loneliness was assuaged by the arrival in Scotland of his girlfriend, Hanna Grosshöner. Hanna left her job in Berlin to take a role as nanny to the prosperous Shanks family, famous for the production of vitrified enamel bathroom fittings, and who resided in Barrhead near Glasgow. Hanna was not Jewish, and when she and Hans were married in 1937, any prospect of a return to Germany was ended. They settled in Aberdeen, and would have a son, John Michael. Just before the start of World War Two, Hans's parents and younger brother Rolf also migrated to Britain, and settled in Oxford. During the war, Hans and Rolf were both interned on the Isle of Man for several months, and Hanna's internment was only prevented by the intervention of Sir William Hamilton Fyfe, Principal of Aberdeen University.

When he returned to Aberdeen, Kosterlitz focused his research on human nutrition, helped by the proximity of the Rowett Research Institute, founded in 1922 by John Boyd Orr. By studying liver cells, Kosterlitz determined the nutritive value of protein in the diet, and published guidelines for protein intake during pregnancy. From there, his interests became wide-ranging, and he researched the effects of chemical agents (including barbiturate anaesthetics) on the autonomic nervous system, spending some months on study leave at Harvard University with support from the Carnegie and Fulbright trusts.

Prompted by discovering an old research paper published in 1917 by the German pharmacologist Paul Trendelenburg, Kosterlitz next turned to the effect of low doses of opiates, particularly morphine, in paralysing the autonomic nerves that activate muscles in the gastrointestinal tract. It is this 'myenteric plexus', discovered indeed by Charlotte Auerbach's grandfather and known as Auerbach's plexus, which is responsible for the peristaltic transport of food through the gut. The standard thinking of the time was that morphine simply anaesthetised nerves, stopping the peristaltic reflex and giving pain relief. Using the isolated intestinal nerves of guinea pigs, Kosterlitz and his Aberdeen co-workers showed that this occurred only at high morphine concentrations. At low, sometimes very low, concentrations of morphine, the effect was different. Morphine inhibited the release of neuro-transmitting chemicals from the nerves of the gut, blocking muscular reflex signals at source. Kosterlitz made a further discovery: the inhibitory effect of morphine could be neutralised by nalorphine, its close structural relative.

Of course, like other opiates, morphine can be addictive, and the discovery of its effect at low dosage was intriguing, and useful in quantifying the potency of the drug. Trying to understand in more detail how morphine works, Kosterlitz travelled to the USA, in 1962, to get up-to-date with the latest work on narcotic analgesics – pain-killers.

He visited the National Institutes of Health where withdrawal from heroin addiction was being researched, and the University of Michigan, where Maurice Seevers was studying a colony of morphine-dependent monkeys. After Kosterlitz had delivered a seminar on the discoveries made at Aberdeen, Seevers queried whether the results could be believed, having been obtained using just *in vitro* samples of animal tissues. A challenge was offered and accepted. Seevers would send eight anonymous compounds to Aberdeen to be tested for their effect on electrically-stimulated samples of cat and guinea-pig nervous tissue. On testing, one compound was easily identified as morphine, and compound number 5 was found to be active in blocking the effect of morphine, and also capable of inhibiting the release of neuro-transmitters itself – a so-called 'partial agonist'. When the code was broken, compound 5 was found to be nalorphine. In meeting the challenge, and in showing that the effects of the compounds were similar *in vivo* and *in vitro*, Kosterlitz and the Aberdeen team gained worldwide esteem. Consequently they were frequently asked by pharmaceutical companies to assay new compounds, which often proved to have analgesic effects without leading to addiction. As another practical outcome, by the mid-1960s a derivative of nalorphine called naloxone was available as a medication to reverse the effects of opioid overdose.

At the University of Aberdeen, some thought that Hans Kosterlitz was long overdue for a promotion, and it eventually arrived in 1968 when at 65 years of age, he was appointed to the University's Chair of Pharmacology. This belated recognition seemed in contrast to the respect in which Kosterlitz was held by his colleagues, nationally and globally. He was active in founding the International Narcotics Research Conference, which held its first meeting in Aberdeen in 1971, and his enthusiasm attracted new staff members to work in his department. When he was obliged by his age to 'retire' in 1973, he set up the Unit for Research on Addictive Drugs, in an old, dilapidated space in a University building. Yet the discovery for which he is best remembered was still to come.

Kosterlitz reasoned that the molecular receptors in the tissues of guinea-pig intestines and cat eyelids were so sensitive to 'foreign' opioids that the receptors must have a more intrinsic physiological function in animal bodies. Furthermore, research in the USA and in Finland showed that fragments of brain membrane tissue also reacted to narcotic analgesic drugs. Surely it had to be the case that the body itself must produce a morphine-like factor. With one of his newer and younger colleagues, John Hughes, Kosterlitz decided to search within the central nervous system for 'natural' endogenous compounds that acted like opioids.

They knew that the search was likely to be a difficult one, and initial experiments using extracts of pig brains (obtained from a local abattoir) showed no results when tested on myenteric plexus preparations from guinea-pigs. However, more sensitive tests on *vas deferens* tissues of mice were more promising. Work proceeded using extracts of rat and guinea-pig brains tested on *vas deferens* mouse tissue. The critical test was that stimulated mouse tissue contractions should be inhibited by the opioid factor in the extract, and that the inhibition could be reversed by naloxone. In the summer of 1973, in a last-ditch test before moving their equipment, Hughes and Kosterlitz had a positive result. Something in the brain tissue was an opiate-like substance.

Biochemical tests on the crude extract showed that the active molecule was a small peptide – a short chain of amino acids. Kosterlitz then astonished and infuriated Hughes by revealing their preliminary findings at a planning meeting for a Neurosciences Research Programme (NRP) conference in Massachusetts. Hughes was invited to speak at the forthcoming event, but he was well aware that Kosterlitz had triggered a race for glory and grants with competitive American researchers keen to identify the molecule.

At the NRP conference near Boston in May, 1974, Hughes presented his evidence for the existence of an endogenous opiate in the brain, and tried to avoid answering probing questions in too much detail. Several other speakers described their own findings that pointed in the same direction, and the competition to identify the opiate grew fiercer. The Aberdeen team co-operated with a peptide chemist, Barry Morgan at the food company Reckitt and Colman, to use their plant in Hull to extract and analyse brain tissue from some 500 pigs, a necessary precaution to handle safely the large volume of acetone that was used as a solvent in the process. By the end of the year Hughes and Kosterlitz were ready to announce their results, definitively showing the presence of an opiate in the brain tissue. The paper was published in the journal *Brain Research* in May, 1975. Surprisingly, at the last moment Kosterlitz removed his name from the paper, saying that Hughes should receive the full credit for the work. He and Hughes decided to name the substance enkephalin, from the Greek meaning 'within the head'.

A stream of research publications followed quickly, and by the end of the year, an expanded team, now including Linda Fothergill and Terry

*Illustration 50: Hans Kosterlitz.
Courtesy of INRC*

Smith at Aberdeen and Howard Morris at Imperial College London, had both sequenced and synthesised the enkephalin peptide. Furthermore, Morris showed that there were two closely similar enkephalin variants, and the team published their findings in *Nature*. A tsunami of research papers followed, including the discovery at the University of California of a third endogenous opiate, produced mainly in the pituitary gland, which was named beta-endorphin, from *endo*genous and m*orphine*. Subsequently other endorphins were identified and the Kosterlitz team clarified that there are three different types of opioid receptor in the body. The enkephalins and endorphins are now known to play crucial roles in the physiology of the body. In addition to inhibiting pain, they are variously responsible for producing pleasurable neural responses to eating, exercise, music, and sexual activity, and in combating the effects of anxiety and depression.

For leading the discovery of the natural opiates of the brain, while in his mid-seventies as a 'retired' professor, Kosterlitz was elected a Fellow of the Royal Society and honoured in the same year with the 1978 Lasker Award for Basic Medical Research, shared with John Hughes. The third recipient, Solomon Snyder, was honoured for his work on opiate receptors, but the award was criticised for omitting his postgraduate student. The controversy was said to have deterred the Nobel committee from considering a further award for the discoverers of the endogenous opiates.

Hans Kosterlitz continued working and publishing research into his nineties, and recorded his memories in an article called 'The *best laid schemes o' mice and men gang aft agley'*. He was famously hospitable, fond of good food, drink, and conversation, and loved Scotland and all things Scottish. In 1996, he died at the age of 93, in Aberdeen.

The Kosterlitz story does not end there. His discoveries of the natural opiates of the body set in train a stream of research that continues to reveal unexpected results, including the finding that real morphine is produced endogenously in vertebrate and invertebrate animals. In 2010, the University of Aberdeen opened the Kosterlitz Centre for Therapeutics, which was later joined by the Kosterlitz Centre for Industrial Engagement, intended to foster relationships between the University and the life sciences industry. And in 2016, Hans and Hanna's son John Michael was awarded the Nobel Prize in Physics, for discoveries in the theory of phase transitions in condensed matter and 2-dimensional thin films, leading to improved understanding of superconductivity and the possibilities of quantum computing. John Michael and his Nobel co-laureate, David Thouless, originally from Bearsden near Glasgow, became the second and third Scots-born physicists to achieve that distinction.

22 Nourishing science and peace: John Boyd Orr

In his Nobel address of 1949, having just been awarded the organisation's Peace Prize, John Boyd Orr said, *"In this lecture I wish to consider the possibility of eliminating the causes of war and bringing in a new era of world unity and peace by the intelligent application of the new knowledge and new powers over the forces of nature which modern science has given mankind... The history of our civilization has been one of intermittent war... Science has produced such powerful weapons that in a war between great powers there would be neither victor nor vanquished. Both would be*

Illustration 51: John Boyd Orr, in 1949

overwhelmed in destruction. Our civilization is now in the transition stage between the age of warring empires and a new age of world unity and peace."

These were not the thoughts of a naïve, unworldly dreamer. As a teacher, scientist, soldier, and politician, Boyd Orr had more than enough real-world experience to understand the difficulties in achieving a new international order and an end to war. Lord Boyd Orr, as he was by then, had been elected President of the World Union of Peace Organisations, the British National Peace Council, and what became the World Federalist Movement. Through his fierce intelligence and force of personality, he brought drive and insight to all those initiatives.

John Boyd Orr was born in 1880 at Kilmaurs, Ayrshire, the fourth of seven children of Annie Boyd and Robert Orr, a ship owner and quarry master, a committed member of the Free Church of Scotland,

and a widely read, clever man. But when a ship owned by Robert was lost at sea, the family were forced to sell their home and moved to West Kilbride, where young John was educated at the local school before winning a bursary to the Kilmarnock Academy, fifteen miles away. The decline in the fortunes of his father's business meant that the bursary fees were welcome and necessary, but John's stay at the Academy was brief, since he spent much of his time with the men at his father's nearby quarry, where he learned *"a wonderful vocabulary of swear-words"*. Boyd Orr returned to West Kilbride where he soon became a pupil-teacher, and then won a scholarship to train in teaching at Glasgow University, graduating in 1902. He was posted to a school in the inner city, and his observations of the slums in Glasgow's poorest districts stayed with him all his life. Rickets was common among the children, and the widespread malnutrition, squalor, destitution and disease were shocking to the young man from the countryside. In his autobiography, *'As I Recall'*, he wrote later, *"These experiences gave me an intense hatred of unnecessary hunger and poverty and affected my subsequent life much more than any lectures I listened to on philosophy."*

After three years of teaching in an almost equally deprived part of the seaside town of Saltcoats, Boyd Orr returned to the University of Glasgow to study biology and medicine. It was there that he encountered the distinguished teachers and mentors who were the greatest influencers on his later life: Noel Paton, the Regius Professor of Physiology, who *"believed in science for science's sake"*; Edward Provan Cathcart, head of the department of Physiological Chemistry; Sir Robert Muir, Professor of Pathology and Bacteriology; Sir William Macewen, considered to be the father of neurosurgery; and perhaps above all, the philosophically inclined paediatrician Samson Gemmell, Professor of Clinical Medicine, who Boyd Orr said was *"the man with the widest outlook on medical and world affairs generally that I have ever met."*

Halfway through his medical course, even with the help of his bursaries, and having used up his savings, Boyd Orr had difficulty financing his studies. His family could have helped, but aged 27, he wanted to retain his independence. He arranged a mortgage and an overdraft to buy a tenanted block of flats, which he rented out for about £30 per year, enough for his living expenses and tuition fees. When he graduated in 1912, he sold the flats and for four months took a job as a ship's surgeon in the Merchant Navy, sailing between Liverpool and West Africa, to pay off his remaining £50 overdraft. Still restless, he worked briefly as a locum in general medical practice in Saltcoats, before accepting a Carnegie Scholarship to work back at Glasgow with Professor Cathcart, as a researcher in biochemistry. Their studies of malnutrition and the metabolism of proteins and creatine were interrupted after a year, when Cathcart was invited to head up a new Nutrition Institute at the University of Aberdeen, and he asked Boyd Orr to join him. Cathcart then turned down the position but recommended Boyd Orr, who, to his astonishment, was offered the job at a salary of £360 a year, after he had made a perfunctory application and despite telling the interviewing committee that he was not adequately qualified for the post.

The well-funded laboratories at Glasgow University, and their proximity to the Western Infirmary where he studied malnourished medical patients, made Boyd Orr reluctant to leave. He agreed a deferment of six months on going north, and arrived in Aberdeen in April, 1914. He was still undecided whether he would stay. *"On 1 April—All Fools' Day !—1914, I arrived in Aberdeen, and enquired where the Nutrition Institute was. I was told there was no Institute. All they had was an approved scheme of research… The scheme provided for a total expenditure of £5,000 to be spent in building and equipping a wooden laboratory on the College of Agriculture's farm about five miles from Aberdeen. The recurrent expenditure was never to exceed £1,500 a year…*

The scheme was a shock for me. To leave the well-equipped laboratories in Glasgow, where about a dozen people were doing research, to work in isolation in a wooden laboratory in the wilds of Aberdeenshire, was a gloomy prospect which demanded an agonising re-appraisal. My first impulse was to resign immediately and go back to Glasgow to finish my research scholarship."

Instead, he proposed a new plan for a granite building and research equipment costing together £50,000, and asked the funding committee to approve it. In a poor compromise, the committee members accepted that the £5,000 capital sum might be used for a granite building. By the time they agreed it, they discovered that it was already half-built, and Boyd Orr had proceeded anyway on his own authority. Before it was completed, the First World War had begun.

Boyd Orr was given a leave of absence to join a civilian branch of the Royal Army Medical Corps. As the officer in charge of hygiene and sanitation at Army training camps, he did not hesitate to go above the heads of more senior officers to make the improvements needed to safeguard health. When he was assigned as the Chief Medical Officer to the 1st Battalion of Sherwood Foresters at the Western Front, the realities of warfare soon destroyed his faith in press and headquarters reports on the progress of the War.

The Battalion was decimated in the Battle of the Somme, and Boyd Orr recalled, *"At night, we were relieved by another division, and what was left of us moved back to the reserve trenches... My officer friends were nearly all dead. While what was left of a first-class battalion travelled back I heard a piper of a Highland regiment which had suffered a like fate playing 'The Flowers o' the Forest are a' wede away'. I have never in my life felt so unutterably sad. My friends and comrades were nearly all gone."*

For his devotion to duty and his courage under fire, Boyd Orr was awarded the Military Cross for his actions at the Somme, and the Distinguished Service Order after the Battle of Passchendaele. At a place near Passchendaele nicknamed 'Stirling Castle', his younger brother James, a clergyman, was killed.

In 1918, Boyd Orr resigned from the Army and joined the Royal Navy, initially at the naval hospital in Chatham, and then as a junior surgeon aboard *HMS Furious*, one of Britain's first aircraft carriers. Out of the blue, the Royal Society requested that he be seconded to assess the food and nutritional requirements of the Army and the civilian population. He was excused from naval service and given an Army commission to allow him to do the work. From then until the end of the War, he noted wryly, he was the only officer, apart from the King, who could appear in either a Navy or Army uniform. During the War, he achieved another goal – he married his teenage sweetheart, Elizabeth Callum, whom he had met in West Kilbride. They had a daughter, also Elizabeth, born in 1916, and they would have another, Helen and a son, Donald. His wife was his constant and irreplaceable partner for the rest of his life.

His war duties completed with high accomplishment, Boyd Orr returned to Aberdeen in 1919, now with a wife and daughter, to resume his campaign to build a substantial institute for research in animal (including human) nutrition. Soon, the basic Institute building was complete, and the first few researchers were recruited. The following year, the government agreed to fund half of Boyd Orr's investment plan, if he could find private finance for the remainder. He persuaded a successful businessman, John Quiller Rowett, who had made his fortune in wines and spirits, to fund half the cost of the expansion, and in 1922 the Rowett Research Institute was opened by Queen Mary. Much of the Institute's research was initially on animal nutrition, but quickly Boyd Orr's interests were focused on human nourishment and dietary health, and he visited, with Elizabeth, many foreign countries in an official capacity to study their social conditions and public health standards.

Successive studies of malnutrition, starting with the work of James Lind in the 18th century, showed that deprivation of certain foodstuffs was clearly a cause of disease. In 1912, a Polish biochemist, Casimir Funk, working at the Lister Institute in London, isolated a water-soluble complex of micronutrients from rice-bran that he called 'vitamine' (from 'vital amine'). It seemed to be important in preventing the debilitating disease beriberi, and is now known as thiamine, or vitamin B_1. Funk proposed that other diseases such as rickets, scurvy and coeliac disease could be cured by vitamins. The 1929 Nobel Prize in Physiology or Medicine was awarded for the discovery of thiamine, though strangely, Casimir Funk was not a recipient.

Against this background, Boyd Orr was characteristically independent of thought, writing later that, *"The establishment of the Institute coincided roughly with the discovery of vitamins and the newer knowledge of nutrition. At first, when a certain food was found to improve health, the improvement was regarded as being due entirely to its vitamin content... I wrote a paper showing that the improvement attributed to an unknown vitamin in some experiments might be correlated with the mineral content of the added foodstuff! This brought the Institute into conflict with some of the vitamin work promoted by the Medical Research Council."*

Sir Frederick Hopkins, who was one of the recipients of the 1929 Nobel Prize, visited Aberdeen to spend a day at the Institute and eventually agreed with Boyd Orr that the dietary importance of minerals had been neglected. A new Medical Research Council committee on nutrition was set up and Boyd Orr was invited to join. He suggested research to demonstrate the nutritive value of milk, and the Rowett Institute was given a grant to pursue it. Controlled trials were made on school children in the seven largest cities in Scotland, and in Belfast. The results showed marked improvements in the health and rate of growth of the milk-fed children, confirmed by further trials. Dr Walter Elliot, the Unionist Member of Parliament for Glasgow Kelvingrove and at that time the Under-Secretary for Health for Scotland, had been a researcher at the Rowett during parliamentary recesses. He moved a Private Member's Bill that introduced free school milk in Scotland, which was expanded soon afterwards to the rest of the United Kingdom.

Boyd Orr was elected a Fellow of the Royal Society in 1932, proposed by the co-discoverer of insulin, J.J.R. Macleod, and three years later he was knighted. He continued to point out the poor state of health and nutrition of British people, and lobbied for a national food policy. He privately published a ground-breaking study, *'Food Health and Income'*, which the government had declined to publish. In it he showed the links between poverty, malnutrition and the under-achievement of school children, and revealed the appalling levels of malnourishment in the general British population, concluding that the diet of the poorest 10%, *"comprising 4 and a half million people, is… deficient in every constituent examined. The second group, comprising 9 million people, is adequate in protein, fat and carbohydrates, but deficient in all the vitamins and minerals considered."* The study was supported by Harold Macmillan, the future British Prime Minister and chairman of his family's publishing company, which published it in 1936.

Of course, the problems of malnutrition and food shortage were shared by many other countries. Sir John Boyd Orr joined a committee of the League of Nations to construct a World Food Plan, and 22 countries, including the USA and the USSR, met harmoniously in conference to devise a new world food policy. But as the omens threatened a second world war, the work stopped. Boyd Orr advised Churchill's wartime Cabinet Food Committee and Lord Woolton, the Minister of Food, on methods to avoid wartime malnourishment and food shortage, and as a result new measures were introduced in Britain to encourage production of food at home, and for the distribution of milk, orange juice and cod-liver oil to mothers and children. During the War, in 1941, Elizabeth and John Boyd Orr's only son Donald, 20 years old, was shot down and killed in action in the RAF's Coastal Command.

In 1942, Boyd Orr accepted a request to visit the USA and take part in renewed discussions on a World Food Plan. He addressed a meeting in Chicago and met Henry Wallace, the American Vice-President, and Dean Acheson the Under-Secretary of State, who were both supportive, as was the First Lady, Mrs. Eleanor Roosevelt. By then America had joined the Second World War, and a 'Combined Food Board' was agreed by President Roosevelt and Winston Churchill, which co-ordinated food strategy between the UK, the USA and Canada. In 1943, Roosevelt invited all the Allied nations to a conference in Hot Springs, Virginia, to put into effect the third of his 'Four Freedoms' – namely, the 'Freedom from Want'. Boyd Orr did not attend, and the British delegation did not share his optimistic enthusiasm for a global Food Plan, but the conference agreed to set up a 'Food and Agriculture Organisation' (FAO) to co-ordinate worldwide action.

At the end of World War Two, Boyd Orr was 65 years old, and he retired from the Rowett Institute and Aberdeen University. He was elected both as the Rector of the University of Glasgow, and as the Independent Progressive Member of Parliament for the Scottish Universities. In the House of Commons, he surprised himself by developing an admiration for the 'Red Clydeside' MPs, Jimmy Maxton and Willie Gallacher, sharing their hatred of deprivation and poverty. His tenure in both elected roles was cut short when, in 1945, he accepted an invitation to be the first Director-General of the new Food and Agriculture Organisation, the first official international agency of the United Nations, and based in Washington D.C. He set a time limit of two years on his tenure and defined an ambitious goal – nothing less than the creation of a World Food Board to plan and co-ordinate agricultural production, storage and distribution across the globe. With the help of the US Department of Agriculture, he focused on gathering information and statistics on population trends, food production outputs, and trade patterns. Under his direction, the FAO set up regional offices in Cairo and Bangkok, and it established an International Emergency Food Council, with 34 member nations, including the USA and Canada, to tackle post-war food shortages. It became the only body through which certain foods for export could be bought, and at fixed prices. It recommended food allocation according to need rather than purchasing power, and in Boyd Orr's estimation saved millions of lives from death by starvation.

In attempting to build on this, and raise support for a longer-term, more comprehensive food plan, Boyd Orr travelled the world, lobbying national governments. In 1946 a major conference in Copenhagen unveiled the plan for the World Food Board, with the apparent approval of the major food-producing countries. But within twelve months the USA and the UK had repudiated their support, with the respective governments of President Truman and Prime Minister Attlee believing that the immediate post-war crisis had been averted, and that food supply should be governed by market rules under the International Trade Organisation. Recalling the annual FAO conference in Geneva in 1947, Boyd Orr wrote, *"Here the British delegation, all civil servants, excelled themselves in opposing everything that involved any international cooperation or giving any authority to FAO even in minor activities."* He was furious, and of his address to the conference one delegate said, *"The director-general rose with a face white with anger. He had the fire of God in his belly, and he belched."* Boyd Orr was bitterly disappointed, and increasingly exasperated by the FAO's lack of authority and funding. He resigned his Director-Generalship in 1948, and continued to lobby for international cooperation and world government.

The following year, he was made a Life Peer as Lord Boyd Orr of Brechin, and his award of the Nobel Peace Prize cited 'his lifelong effort to conquer hunger and want, thereby helping to remove a major cause of military conflict and war.' He donated the entirety of his financial award of £10,000 to various organisations promoting peace and global cooperation, including the National Peace Council, and the Paris-based Movement for World Federal Government, of which he became President. The French government appointed him a Commander of the Légion d'Honneur.

In his 'retirement', Boyd Orr continued to be active in the House of Lords and in many other duties. He became the Chancellor of Glasgow University in 1946, and served until he was 90 years old, while managing his farm near Edzell in Angus, and continuing his promotion of world peace. In 1960, he was elected as the first president of the World Academy of Art and Science, an international network concerned to avoid the misuse of scientific discoveries. He died in 1971, in his 91st year, survived by his wife and daughters. Today, the Boyd Orr Building is perhaps the most prominent in Glasgow's University Avenue, and the University's Boyd Orr Centre for Population and Ecosystem Health is named for him. His passionate and energetic commitment to science, peace and international cooperation was undimmed throughout his life. He was particularly concerned to assimilate Russia and China in a new world order, and in his autobiography he wrote, *"The most important question today, when the terrific advance of modern science has shaken the economic systems of the twentieth century, is whether man has attained the wisdom to adjust the old systems to suit the new powers of science and to realize that we are now one world in which all nations will ultimately share the same fate."*

23

DNA and the chemistry of life: Alexander R. Todd

Since the middle of the 20th century, the acronyms RNA and DNA have become part of our common language and deeper understanding. Ribonucleic acid and deoxyribonucleic acid are often referred to as the 'building blocks of life'. They are each composed of four of the five still more fundamental building blocks called 'nucleotides', labelled C, G, A, T, and U. Each nucleotide contains one of five nitrogen-containing 'nucleobases': cytosine (C), guanine (G), adenine (A) thymine (T) or uracil (U). Even before the double-helix structure of DNA was determined in 1953, through the work of Francis Crick, James Watson, Rosalind Franklin, and Maurice Wilkins, nucleotides and related compounds were the subject of intense study, particularly by the biochemist Alexander R. Todd. In his account *'DNA – the secret of life'*, Watson wrote of the precursors to the double-helix realisation. *"In Cambridge, England, the canny Scottish chemist Alexander Todd rose to the challenge of identifying the chemical bonds that linked together nucleotides in DNA. By 1951, his lab had proved that these links were always the same, such that the backbone of the DNA molecule was very regular."*

Alexander Robertus Todd was born in 1907, in Cathcart, a suburb of Glasgow. He was the second of three children of upwardly mobile, working-class parents who prized hard work and education, and he attended Allan Glen's School – the self-styled 'Glasgow High School of Science', founded in 1853 by the will of a local carpenter who believed in the paramount importance of a scientific education. For many years, Allan Glen's governors decreed that no Greek should be taught, in distinction to Glasgow's other selective high schools, where Classics featured prominently in the curriculum. At the School, Alexander excelled in all subjects except drawing, leading his art master to comment that his parents *"certainly had a sense of humour"* in giving him the initials A.R.T.

Since receiving the gift of a home chemistry set at the age of eight, Alexander's prime interest was in that subject. He graduated with first-class honours in chemistry from the University of Glasgow in 1928, and within a year had published his first scientific paper, co-authored with the professor of organic chemistry, Thomas Stewart Patterson. A Carnegie scholarship enabled Todd to work with Patterson for a while, before he moved on to the University of Frankfurt-am-Main to pursue doctoral research on the structure of cholic acid, a constituent of bile. He completed what he called his apprenticeship in research as a post-doctoral scholar at the University of Oxford, working with Britain's leading organic chemist, Robert Robinson, who would later win the Nobel Prize for his research on plant dyes and alkaloids.

Todd's interests turned to the compounds important to animal life, and with the help of a Medical Research Council grant he moved to the University of Edinburgh in 1934, to study the structure of vitamin B1, thiamine, the anti-beriberi factor that was the first 'vitamine' to be discovered. There, Todd developed a method for the commercial synthesis of thiamine for the Swiss pharmaceutical business Hoffmann La Roche, with the result that the company became a major presence in the market for manufactured vitamins, and an important source of Todd's research funding.

While in Edinburgh, Todd met his future wife, Alison Dale, who was then a post-doctoral researcher in pharmacology. She was the eldest daughter of the distinguished physiologist and pharmacologist, Sir Henry Hallett Dale, a founding trustee and chairman of the Wellcome Trust. Alison and Alexander were married in 1937, and they would have a son and two daughters. Sir Henry's guidance had a considerable influence on Todd's career. Alexander became recognised as the most innovative and productive of young British organic chemists, moving first to the Lister Institute in London where he helped to determine the structures of vitamin B12 and cannabinol, and then to the University of Manchester to take its prestigious chair of chemistry, in 1938.

It was in Manchester that Todd began his studies of the nucleic acids, but his work was interrupted by the Second World War, when he was assigned to the Ministry of Supply's chemical defence research department to study chemical warfare agents which, happily, were never used. He worked also on the joint British-American programme to produce penicillin in large volumes, though no method for its artificial synthesis was discovered.

Todd's earlier work on vitamin B1 had led him to realise that it, and other vitamins, acted as 'co-enzymes' in metabolic processes. Enzymes are proteins that act as catalysts in biological reactions, and co-enzymes are organic molecules which bind to certain sites in enzymes to increase their catalytic effect. Nearly all metabolic processes at the cellular level need enzyme catalysis to proceed at a rate fast enough to sustain life. Todd had the insight that the B-group vitamins were closely related to the fragments of nucleic acids – the nucleotides that contained cytosine, guanine, adenine, thymine, and uracil – and that began his career-long interest in the nucleic acids.

Towards the end of World War II, Todd was appointed professor of organic chemistry at Cambridge University. He took with him eighteen Manchester colleagues, and set about organising the sorely-needed modernisation of the Pembroke Street laboratories. Gas lighting was replaced by electric lights, and later he supervised the design and construction of entirely new laboratories. He launched an ambitious research programme to understand the structure of nucleotides and their roles in the nucleic acids, DNA and RNA.

Around the same time that Todd was moving to Cambridge, a truly revolutionary experiment was being conducted at New York's Rockefeller Institute Hospital by Oswald Avery, Colin MacLeod, and Maclyn McCarty. The focus of their study was a mutation of the bacterium that causes pneumonia, responsible for millions of deaths during the Spanish Flu pandemic of 1918-19. Two strains of *streptococcus pneumoniae* were known, labelled 'rough' (R) and 'smooth' (S) due to their appearance under the microscope. The R strain was harmless, while the S strain was highly virulent and when injected into laboratory mice, they died in a few days. Avery, MacLeod and McCarty's interest stemmed from an experiment in 1928 by the British bacteriologist Frederick Griffith, which had yielded a remarkable result. When virulent S-strain bacteria were killed by heat and injected, they were harmless as expected. But when killed S-strain and harmless R-strain bacteria were injected together, the mice died. From the blood of the dead mice, Griffith was able to isolate both R-strain and live S-strain bacteria. A strange 'transforming principle' had changed some of the R-strain bacteria to the lethal S form, somehow using the dead S-strain material.

The transforming agent which enabled the bacterial mutation was unidentified. In Oswald Avery's team at the Rockefeller Institute, Michael Dawson and Richard Sia confirmed Griffith's findings and succeeded in repeating the transformation also *in vitro*. In 1933, following in their footsteps, James Alloway went one step further by breaking open the cells of the S-form bacteria and extracting aqueous solutions of the transforming principle. Colin MacLeod joined the Rockefeller lab a year later, and over several years he developed purified solutions to the point where they could be produced reliably, and the transforming agent could be chemically characterised. Avery, MacLeod and McCarty systematically removed components of the transformative solution to determine which of its constituents was the chemical which mutated the bacteria. The answer was deoxyribonucleic acid – DNA.

Their conclusions were published in 1944 and were met with surprise, and disbelief, from many fellow scientists. Although DNA is found in every chromosome, so are proteins. With their 20-letter alphabet of amino acids, proteins were always considered to be the very likely conveyors of complex genetic information, rather than DNA, with its simpler 4-letter ACGT alphabet of nucleotides. Avery's own colleague at the Rockefeller, the protein chemist Alfred Minsky, was particularly vehement in his rejection of DNA as the genetic substance, and we now know that Avery's nomination for the Nobel Prize was repeatedly blocked by the Swedish chemist Einar Hammersten, who continued to oppose the idea well into the 1950s.

At Cambridge, Alexander Todd's research produced copious results. His team synthesised co-enzymes including ATP (adenosine triphosphate), the energy-carrying molecule found in the cells of all living things. By determining the detailed internal structure of

Illustration 52: Alexander Todd in 1957

nucleotides, then synthesising them, and breaking down nucleic acids to yield identical nucleotides, they confirmed that both RNA and DNA contain polynucleotides, linked to specific nitrogen atoms. Todd made a presentation of the findings on the structure of nucleic acids at the 75th annual meeting of the American Chemical Society in 1951, and became an immediate candidate for an award of the Nobel Prize in chemistry. His work was the crucial step towards the complete determination of the structure of DNA, made finally by Crick and Watson in Cambridge the following year. Todd was among the first to be invited to see their model of the double helix structure. Watson wrote, *"That the nature of the gene was so simple both surprised and pleased him. Later, however, he must have asked himself why his own lab, having established the general chemical structure of the DNA chains, had not moved on to asking how the chains folded up in three dimensions. Instead the essence of the molecule was left to be discovered by a two-man team, a biologist and a physicist, neither of whom possessed a detailed command of even undergraduate chemistry."*

Todd's Nobel award was confirmed in 1957, his fiftieth year, for his work on nucleotides and nucleotide co-enzymes. He finished his Nobel lecture by saying, *"To-day the nucleotides occupy a prominent place in chemical, biochemical and biological research and new vistas are opening before us which may in a relatively short time lead to a far deeper understanding of the mechanisms of the living cell than seemed possible only a few years ago. And this is surely a matter of profound importance to humanity in its ceaseless struggle against disease."* Crick, Watson and Wilkins received their own, more famous Nobel award in 1962, 'for their discoveries concerning the molecular structure of nucleic acids and its significance for information transfer in living material.'

In his later career, Todd continued to develop the Cambridge department's international reputation and recruited many researchers from overseas. He became one of science's statesmen, and was the chairman of the British government's Advisory Council on Scientific Policy, for twelve years from 1952 in succession to Sir Henry Tizard. Todd himself was knighted in 1954, and was ennobled as Lord Todd of Trumpington in 1962. He was elected as President of the Royal Society in 1975, and received the Order of Merit in 1977, sharing those distinctions with his father-in-law, who had also received a Nobel Prize, for his work on neurotransmitters, in 1936. Todd's height, over 6 feet 6 inches tall, combined with an athletic build, patrician demeanour and somewhat elitist attitudes, led to occasional accusations of arrogance, and made him the subject of humorous undergraduate limericks, such as:

Doesn't it strike you as odd
That a commonplace fellow like Todd
Should spell, if you please,
His name with two D's
When one is sufficient for God?

Todd avoided press and media attention when he could, but privately, he was a sociable, gregarious and affable man. Among his many other awards, university associations and honorary degrees, he served as Chancellor of the University of Strathclyde from 1975, where, in yet another accolade, the bar in the Students Union building was named 'The Lord Todd'. Alison, his wife and lifelong companion, died in 1987 and he died ten years later, in Cambridgeshire, in the ninetieth year of his highly accomplished life.

24 Evidence-based medicine: Archie Cochrane

How can we determine the degree of effectiveness of medicines? Or even if they are effective at all? The expectations of patients and doctors can fundamentally impact treatment outcomes, and a placebo pill can improve health in the absence of any medicinally active ingredients. Carefully monitored clinical trials are needed to assess the efficacy of drugs, and the 'gold standard' is the double-blind randomised controlled trial, where neither doctor nor patient knows if the medicine is real or not, until the eventual 'unblinded' results are compared with control groups receiving either a placebo, or just no treatment. However, since James Lind conducted what is often deemed to be the first reported clinical trial in 1747, in searching for a cure for scurvy, the quality and scale of clinical trials has been highly variable, and the resulting data can be hard to interpret.

Since late in the 20th century, arguably the best worldwide assessments of clinical trials have been provided by the Cochrane Collaboration, an international not-for-profit organisation founded in 1993 and named after the Scottish doctor, Archibald Leman Cochrane. He was born in Galashiels, the eldest son of a family of tweed makers, who were wealthy and the largest employers in the town, but no strangers to misfortune. Archibald's father Walter, a Captain in the King's Own Scottish Borderers, was killed in the 2nd Battle of Gaza in 1917 when Archie was only eight years old. His young brother Walter died soon afterwards, from infant tuberculosis.

Archie was an excellent sportsman and student, and won a scholarship to the exclusive Uppingham School in Rutland before winning a second scholarship to King's College Cambridge. It was while at Cambridge that he was shocked by the death of his brother Robert in a motorcycle accident. Their grandfather died at around the same time, so that Archie inherited a small private income. He graduated with a double first-class degree in natural sciences in 1930, and decided to study medicine, attending medical schools in Vienna, Leiden and London, but his studies were prolonged and interrupted by a distressing discovery. In his own words, *"Sexually I matured late and my first affairs were postgraduate ones revealing a disturbing problem. To my horrified surprise, I discovered I was incapable of ejaculation, despite desire and erection."* In seeking medical advice, he said he found the reactions of doctors *"singularly unsympathetic and unhelpful"*, and he turned to psychoanalysis as a possible solution. In Berlin, he began consultations with the eminent psychiatrist Theodore Reik, one of the most successful students of Sigmund Freud, and followed Reik to Vienna and then The Hague when Reik's Jewish affiliations forced him to flee Nazi persecution. Two-and-a-half years of psychoanalysis did not cure Cochrane's sexual dysfunction, which he later attributed to the liver disorder porphyria, though his childhood tuberculosis may have been an additional factor. Whatever the cause, the failure of his psychoanalysis prompted Cochrane to become interested in the scientific basis of therapies and in treatments proven by evidence to be effective.

When he returned to Great Britain in 1934, having developed strong anti-fascist sentiments, Cochrane joined the Socialist Medical Association, and interrupted his studies for the second time to spend two years working as an ambulance assistant and triage manager to the democratic forces in the Spanish Civil War. More convinced than ever on the need to combat fascism, he returned to complete his medical training at London's University College Hospital in 1938.

During World War II, Cochrane was recruited to the Royal Army Medical Corps and was captured by Wehrmacht troops during a shambolic military raid on Crete. As a doctor fluent in German, he was used as chief medical officer in a huge prison camp in Salonika, where he had to deal with typhoid, diphtheria, malaria and a mysterious outbreak of oedema – severe water retention and swelling – of the lower legs, which affected many prisoners including Cochrane himself. He speculated that this was caused by malnutrition resulting in 'wet beri-beri', and in the footsteps of his medical hero, James Lind, he designed a clinical trial. The patients were allocated alternately into two groups of ten, with one group as a control given a daily tablet of smuggled vitamin C, and the others given daily supplements of yeast – in fact the yeast paste called 'Marmite' – that Cochrane bought from the prison camp black market. In what he subsequently described as *"my first, worst, and most successful clinical trial"*, Cochrane noted, *"I convinced myself that there was less oedema in the 'yeast' ward. I made careful notes of the trial and I immediately asked to see the Germans. Since I had become chief medical officer I had been making strong and frequent complaints, with minimal results, so I had little hope. I gave them a short talk, mentioning James Lind, then presented the results of my trial and argued that there was a major 'epidemic' due to a diet deficient in vitamin B. I said that it was possibly wet beri-beri. I asked for a lot of yeast and more food."* Surprisingly, yeast was provided for all the prisoners, and the incidence of oedema fell away. Many years later, Cochrane reflected on the trial in the *British Medical Journal*, noting that it was too small, too short, with outcomes too poorly measured – and that, after all, the cause of the oedema was not wet beri-beri. For his 'gallant and distinguished' service in various prisoner of war camps, Cochrane was awarded the MBE by the British government.

In the post-war period, Cochrane's interest in the evidential basis of medical treatments and in randomised controlled trials (RCTs) was intensified by studies at the London School of Hygiene and Tropical Medicine. He was especially influenced by the lectures on epidemiology and RCTs delivered by the professor of statistics, Austin Bradford Hill, who was the statistician in the randomised controlled trial of streptomycin in treating pulmonary tuberculosis, and with Richard Doll, the first in Britain to document the association between cigarette smoking and lung cancer.

Illustration 53: Archie Cochrane in 1949. Courtesy of the Cardiff University Library Cochrane Archive, U. Hospital Llandough

With the aid of a Rockefeller Scholarship, Cochrane spent a year at the Henry Phipps Clinic in Philadelphia, where he studied the reliability of X-rays in the diagnosis and prognosis of pulmonary tuberculosis. That convinced him of the ubiquity and importance of observer error. He returned once again to Britain in 1948, and joined the Pneumoconiosis Unit of the Medical Research Council (MRC). At Llandough Hospital in Cardiff, he used comparative studies to investigate the effects of coal dust in miners from the Welsh valleys, and established a long-term programme of high-quality clinical studies called the Rhondda Fach Scheme, which revolutionised the design of epidemiological studies. The scheme X-rayed almost the complete valley community of around 19,000 miners and non-miners, and determined the high prevalence of tuberculosis in the population. Cochrane and his team persuaded 92% of the underground workers to volunteer for radiography, and follow-up studies over 10, 20 and 30 years made clear the extent of excess mortality in the miners, chiefly through pneumoconiosis and gastric cancers.

In 1960, Cochrane was appointed by the Welsh National School of Medicine to the David Davies Chair of Tuberculosis and Diseases of the Chest, and became honorary director of a new epidemiology unit founded in Cardiff by the MRC. His sociable and gregarious nature – and the hospitable parties he hosted – made him popular with medical students and colleagues alike. He directed numerous randomised controlled trials on a variety of conditions, gaining the unit a worldwide reputation for the high quality of its innovative studies, and making the

Vale of Glamorgan epidemiologically the most well-mapped area in the United Kingdom.

As they became increasingly interested in the performance of health systems as well as of clinical practices, Cochrane and his colleagues published several ground-breaking studies in quick succession. In reviews and analyses of the value of pro-active screening for conditions such as cancer, tuberculosis and hypertension, they clearly laid out the criteria that any successful screening programme must meet. A study with his colleague Peter Elwood indicated the effectiveness of a daily 300mg dose of aspirin in reducing the mortality of heart-attack patients. And in an echo of the 19th century concerns of James Young Simpson about 'hospitalism', the phenomenon whereby hospital patients fared less well than patients with similar conditions treated at home, Cochrane wanted to know if heart-attack patients recovered better at home or in a hospital cardiac unit. He proposed a randomised clinical trial to test the question, against the opposition of many cardiologists who regarded such a trial as reckless and dangerous. After debates in several ethics committees, approval was given and Cochrane, with the trial leader Gordon Mather reported back after about six months. The results showed a slight advantage for those patients who had been treated at home, though the difference was not statistically significant. Cochrane wickedly compiled two reports, one of which reversed the numbers of deaths in the two groups in the trial. Just before formally reporting to the adjudication committee, Cochrane showed the false report to some cardiologists, who abused him vociferously for endangering patients, before he apologised and showed them the real results, and challenged them to conclude that coronary care units should be closed immediately. When concluded, the trial results showed that for the group of patients with normal blood pressure, those treated at home experienced a 4.4% lower mortality than those treated in hospital.

Cochrane's professional focus was disturbed by a highly personal crisis when in 1965 his elder sister Helen, aged 58, was admitted to a mental hospital in the Scottish borders suffering from weakness, partial paralysis and hallucinations. Travelling there hastily, Cochrane discovered that the diagnosis was acute senile psychosis, which he seriously doubted. In her moments of lucidity, Helen pleaded to be removed from the mental hospital, and after a discussion with her husband, Cochrane signed the discharge form, hired a private ambulance and had her transferred to the Edinburgh Royal Infirmary, where he slightly knew the professor, Ken Donald. Urine tests quickly confirmed a diagnosis of porphyria, an inherited disorder of liver enzymes which affects the biosynthesis of haem in the blood and is often dormant until later life. Its name comes from *porphyra*, the Greek word for 'purple', in a reference to the colour of urine often presented during an attack. Helen very nearly died, but she recovered almost fully after an extended convalescence thanks to the care of Donald and his Edinburgh team, and a world expert in porphyria, Abraham Goldberg from the University of Glasgow.

Knowing that the chances of inheriting porphyria from a parent were 50:50, in typical style Cochrane hosted a sherry party in Galashiels to inform close family, and organised the testing of urine and faecal samples for them and their extended family across the world. Cochrane himself was among the family members who tested positive for latent porphyria. His sceptical nature surfaced again when Helen, who enjoyed the occasional glass of sherry, was medically advised to become teetotal. He tested himself over three months, first drinking alcohol normally, followed by a month of abstinence, ending with a month of increased consumption, just before Christmas. At no time did he measure changes in the level of porphyrin in his faecal samples, and he informed his sister that her sherry tipples could be resumed. Cochrane recorded that one wit among his Cardiff colleagues observed to him that when he retired from his professorial Chair, *"there would always be my stool to continue the interest!"*

Perhaps Cochrane's most influential views were summarised in a monograph, *Effectiveness and Efficiency: Random Reflections on Health Services*, which was published in 1972 after a fellowship award from the Nuffield

Provincial Hospitals Trust. The social injustices that Cochrane saw in the 1930s had made him naturally sympathetic to the UK's National Health Service, which he believed to be *"the best of a very poor lot"*, but he was not uncritical of it. He was predictably concerned about the then lack of a scientific basis for many immunisation and screening programmes (including cervical smear testing to prevent cancers) and equally critical of the failure to reduce cigarette smoking, or to promote more active birth control. Throughout, he emphasised the need to assess cost-effectiveness, and to test medical practices objectively, ideally through randomised controlled trials wherever possible.

Cochrane retired from his professorship in 1974, and was succeeded by Peter Elwood, whose leadership maintained the Cardiff unit's position at the forefront of epidemiology and the design of RCTs. In his later years, Cochrane's health declined as he suffered a recurrence of earlier cancers and a cardiac arrest in 1981. Throughout his life he challenged medical dogma and criticised therapies that were unverified by scientific testing. He died in 1988, at the age of 81. Never married, he left no offspring, but is regarded by many as 'the father of evidence-based medicine'. Five years after his death, the Cochrane Collaboration was founded as a charitable organisation to provide systematic reviews of RCTs, and to establish the Cochrane Library of evidence to guide medical practice worldwide. Its founder, Iain Chalmers, became the coordinator of the James Lind Initiative, which encompassed the James Lind Library and the James Lind Alliance. The Collaboration, now much larger and known simply as 'Cochrane', has become a global source of systematic reviews of the effects of medical treatments. It has official relationships with Wikipedia and the World Health Organization. A more fitting legacy from the life and work of Archie Cochrane can hardly be imagined.

25 Radiating energy: Sam and Joan Curran

Married couples are rare in physics, and few have made such important contributions as Sam and Joan Curran, who met and fell in love in the summer of 1938, at the famous Cavendish Laboratory of the University of Cambridge. They went on to work together on the Manhattan Project, and each of them made inventions that were crucial in the World War Two. Subsequently, they helped to drive Britain's post-war establishment of technological universities, and after the birth of their first child, they established the Scottish Society for the Parents of Mentally Handicapped Children, known now as Enable Scotland.

Samuel Crowe Curran was the second of four sons of John Hamilton Curran, a steelworks foreman from Kinghorn in Fife, and Sarah Crowe, who briefly left Scotland for Ballymena in 1912, to ensure that Sam was born in Northern Ireland, her ancestral home. The family lived in Lanarkshire, and after Wishaw High School, Sam attended the University of Glasgow, gaining a first-class honours degree in mathematics and 'natural philosophy'. He joined the physics department as a research student in 1934, and was awarded his PhD for a thesis on '*Diffraction of Beta rays by thin films*'. Not content with a single doctorate, Curran gained a Carnegie Scholarship to study for a further PhD at the Cavendish Laboratory, where he used his Glasgow experience in repairing Geiger counters to improve the Laboratory's radiation detectors. With the Czech, Vaclav Petrzilka, he used the new Cavendish particle accelerator to study the capture of protons by carbon nuclei, which supported the 'carbon-oxygen-nitrogen' cycle theory of Hans Bethe as the mechanism whereby the brightest stars generate their fusion energy.

When Petrzilka returned home, he was replaced in the research group by a young PhD student, Joan Strothers. Born in Wales in 1916, she had qualified with honours in physics at Cambridge in 1937, eleven years before the University officially awarded degrees to women. She excelled as an experimental physicist, but her doctoral research was halted on September 3rd 1939, when Britain and France declared war on Germany.

The research group head, Philip Dee, moved his team briefly to the Royal Aircraft Establishment in Farnborough, then to Exeter, where Joan and Sam worked on 'proximity fuses' that used miniaturised radio devices to detect when the distance to the target was less than a pre-determined value. Limited production capacity in Britain was overcome by the 'Tizard Mission' to America, which enabled the USA to produce around 20 million proximity fuses over the next few years. They became important in destroying enemy aircraft and particularly in the destruction of most of the V1 rockets which attacked southern England toward the end of the War.

Sam Curran and Joan Strothers were married in November of 1940, and moved to work on the development of centimetric radar systems at the Telecommunications Research Establishment (TRE) in Dorset. Sam Curran's experience of designing pulse amplifiers for radiation counting enabled the TRE team to develop high-power, centimetre-wavelength pulsed radars capable of 2kHz repetition rates, which became the basis of the '*H2S*' system that was used by the RAF in precision night bombing raids, and the '*ASV*' system used to locate U-boats. Meanwhile, Joan Curran worked in an adjacent laboratory on radar counter-measures, developing one of the ideas of R.V. Jones, who in peacetime became the professor of physics at Aberdeen.

Jones had considered two types of defence against enemy radio guidance and radar systems, and he led on the development of both. 'Jamming' was used to confuse and deflect the radio signals guiding Luftwaffe bombers, in a spiralling race between German innovation and British counter-measure that became known as 'the Battle of the

Beams'. To screen British aircraft from detection by German radar defences, Jones proposed another approach which would be called 'chaff'. The idea was to use strips of metallic foil, cut to the length of one half-wavelength of the probing radar, which would reflect, resonate and re-radiate the radio energy. Joan Curran made the idea practical and devised a scheme for dumping packets of lightweight metallised paper strips, 27cm long by 2cm wide, from bombers to generate clouds of false radar echoes. The head of the TRE, A.P. Rowe, named the project 'Window', and after initial reluctance, RAF Bomber Command used chaff successfully to reduce aircraft losses in major raids, and to create decoy radar echoes during the D-day landing operation. Sam said of this period: *"When my wife was working at TRE on radar intelligence and countermeasures she carried out personally very early in 1942 the first experiment on 'Window' and this proved to be an experiment of truly major importance. I remember that at home she cut up a large amount of metal foil with her household scissors and then she organized the dropping of the thin metal foil strips from an aircraft sent up from Christchurch aerodrome. She had arranged that observation at the radar detection stations on the ground should be done. The effects on the radar screens were truly amazing and it looked as if a large fleet of aircraft was present. This first demonstration of 'Window' was clearly of outstanding importance to the whole of radar science."*

In 1944, the Currans were assigned to the University of California at Berkeley, where plutonium had been discovered four years earlier, to work with Ernest Lawrence as part of the development of an atom bomb – the Manhattan Project. By the time the Currans arrived in California, Britain's early lead in nuclear research, and an informal agreement between Winston Churchill and President Roosevelt to exchange relevant information, had been superseded by American progress and vastly superior funding. A formal agreement to co-operate, known as the Quebec Agreement, was signed in 1943.

The Manhattan Project mission of the Berkeley group was to develop a process for the separation of uranium isotopes, to provide enough fissile U-235 for use in an atomic weapon. Guided by

Lawrence's expertise in designing cyclotron particle accelerators, the team developed electromagnetic separators they called *calutrons*. Their construction consumed huge amounts of scarce materials, including silver, obtained as bullion from the US Treasury. The first few hundred grams of enriched uranium was shipped from Berkeley to Los Alamos in March, 1944.

At Berkeley, Sam Curran continued to think about ways to detect ionising radiation with high sensitivity, because within the Manhattan Project there was an immediate requirement to measure the radioactivity of very small quantities of uranium. The answer was prompted by remembering an invention by the physicist William Crookes, who in 1903 had observed that the radioactive emissions of radium produced minute flashes of light in a zinc sulphide phosphorescent screen. Crookes developed the *'spinthariscope'*, which consisted of a small zinc sulphide screen mounted within a microscope lens, specifically designed to view the scintillations. Curran realised that the light flashes could be used to count radioactive particles, and developed a device that coupled a scintillating phosphor crystal with a sensitive photomultiplier tube of the type developed by the Radio Corporation of America (RCA). That arrangement produced a pulse of current for every scintillation event, which could be measured and recorded electronically. 'Scintillation counters' became a standard for radiation measurement across the world. However when Curran showed his invention to the head of the Berkeley laboratory, Professor Lawrence was not impressed. He reminded Curran that his job was uranium isotope separation, and instrumentation was in the remit of the Chicago project team. To Curran's annoyance, he classified the invention 'Secret', so that it was only later that scintillation counters became generally available, and Sam made no financial gain from his innovation. In the 1950s Curran wrote a book, *'Luminescence and the scintillation counter'* and sent a copy to Lawrence, reminding him good-humouredly how he had brushed aside the invention.

While living in California, Joan and Sam had their first child, a daughter, Sheena. Sadly, she was severely mentally disabled, and for the rest of their lives, the Currans would devote time, money and energy in the cause of handicapped children. They went on to have three sons, and Joan's attention was progressively focused on their growing family.

When World War Two was horribly but decisively ended by the atomic bombs detonated over Hiroshima and then Nagasaki in 1945, the Manhattan Project was soon dissolved and nuclear research in the UK and the USA again became largely mutually independent. Sam Curran declined Lawrence's offer of a position at the University of California and the Currans returned to Scotland, where Sam took up a post at Glasgow University, offered by Philip Dee who was installed as professor and head of the Department of Natural Philosophy. Curran helped to realise the University's 300 MeV synchrotron particle accelerator, but again his true interest was the instrumentation, and he developed refined 'proportional counters' capable of measuring the energy spectrum of ionising particles as well as their flux intensity. One of his research students was Ronald Drever, who would go on to initiate the University's programme of gravitational wave detection, and who co-founded the LIGO laser interferometer project that was ultimately successful in the first observation of gravity waves.

Curran was elected a Fellow of the Royal Society in 1953, and two years later he was invited to join the Atomic Weapons Research Establishment at Aldermaston to assist in the development of a British hydrogen bomb. Tests were conducted successfully at Woomera in Australia and at Christmas Island, and by 1957 Britain had its own nuclear bomb. The following year, the American government repealed the McMahon Act of 1945 which had forbidden their scientists to discuss nuclear physics with researchers in other countries. Information exchange resumed between the USA and the UK, and Curran spent much time in visits to America, while running a team of several hundred engineers and scientists based at Aldermaston. When in 1959 the UK Atomic Energy Authority decided to concentrate research on nuclear fusion at its Culham laboratories, 34 miles distant, Curran chose to leave and eagerly accepted the offer to return to Glasgow, as Principal of the city's Royal College of Science and Technology, with a mandate to take it through to full university status.

The attraction was the opportunity to create a new kind of university, the first technological university in Britain. As Curran pointed out to the amazed chairman of the University Grants Committee, Sir Keith Murray, the Royal College was producing more than 10% of all technology graduates in the United Kingdom, and more than all four of the ancient Scottish universities put together. Those universities were not keen on extra competition, and Murray was wary of the political and financial implications of a new university. In particular, the University of Glasgow had a long-standing resistance to a second university in the city, dating from the founding of John Anderson's Institution, the antecedent of the Royal College, in 1796. With persistence and negotiating skill, Curran overcame the numerous obstacles, and in the spring of 1961, Murray informed him that the new university would be formed, and to prepare its Charter and Statutes. The question of the university's title arose and 'The Andersonian University' was proposed. It was rejected by the University Grants Committee which favoured a geographical name. The Currans were at the time living in Helensburgh, requiring Sam to drive to work through Dumbarton, the self-proclaimed 'Capital of the ancient kingdom of Strathclyde'. Thus the 'University of Strathclyde' was finally awarded its Royal Charter in 1964, with Curran as its first Principal and Vice-Chancellor. With Sir Keith, Curran defined the profile of the ideal first Chancellor for the University: a distinguished scientist, perhaps a Nobel Laureate; a Scot, if possible a Glaswegian; someone of influence in British higher education. They agreed that one candidate met all the criteria, and Alexander Todd, Lord Todd of Trumpington, accepted the position.

Under Curran's leadership, the University of Strathclyde expanded rapidly, and in 1966 its Centre for Industrial Innovation was built, a forerunner of science parks where academia and industry co-operate in research and development. Ever energetic, Curran chaired the committee of Scottish universities which persuaded the UK government to build a 100kW nuclear research reactor at the National Engineering Laboratory in East Kilbride, and he served on countless industrial boards, public bodies and government committees. He was knighted in 1970, and Sir Sam remained as Principal of Strathclyde University until his retirement ten years later, by which time more than 20 major buildings had been constructed on about 24 acres of city centre campus. His retirement was spent clock-making, resulting in several patents; golfing, with his scientific interest exemplified by a published article on 'the physics of the golf swing'; and above all in supporting the Enable charity that the Currans had co-founded. Sir Sam died in 1998, and Lady Curran passed away twelve months later, survived by their daughter and three sons.

26 Seeing with sound: Ian Donald and Tom Brown

Illustration 54: Ian Donald. Courtesy of NHSGGC

The images of a fetus in the womb are now a routine and reassuring part of pregnancy for most women. Obstetric ultrasound imaging began with efforts of two very different characters. Ian Donald was the Regius Professor of Midwifery at the University of Glasgow, and the beneficiary of an education at exclusive private schools. Red-headed, tall, forceful, inventive, and the occasional wearer of a monocle, his ideas were regarded by some as quite mad. Tom Brown was a talented, geeky young engineer, not long out of his apprenticeship, who heard that Donald was trying to use ultrasound in obstetric medicine, and offered to help. Their complementary skills combined to create one of the most valuable diagnostic tools ever invented in the history of medicine.

Ian Donald was born in 1910, the eldest of four children in a medical family - both his father and grandfather were general practitioners in Paisley. His mother, Helen, was a concert pianist. Ian was educated first at a preparatory school in the Scottish borders, then at the Fettes College boarding school in Edinburgh, which he heartily disliked. His father, John, had tuberculosis which prompted the family to move to the warmer climate of South Africa, where Ian completed his secondary education at the Diocesan College near Cape Town. Tragically, the family's emigration had did not avoid health disasters. In 1927, two of

Ian's siblings and his mother contracted diphtheria. Helen's heart was weakened, and she died of a cardiac arrest. John's death followed three months later. The family's house-keeper was left in charge of a trust fund to care for the children, and Ian successfully ensured that the family stayed together.

Deciding to follow his paternal line in a medical career, Ian took a BA in Arts at the University of Cape Town and degrees in medicine at St Thomas's Hospital and the University of London, planning to specialise in obstetrics and gynaecology. He married Alix de Chazal Richards, daughter of a farming family in the Orange Free State, but all their plans were disrupted by the Second World War. Donald was drafted into the Royal Air Force in 1942, where his courage in rescuing airmen from a burning bomber was mentioned in dispatches, and he received the MBE for bravery in 1946. Having been intrigued by mechanical gadgets and technical devices since childhood, Donald became interested in the RAF's use of radar and sonar while posted as a medical officer to the Hebridean island of Benbecula.

When he returned post-war to St Thomas's Hospital, Donald worked long and exhausting hours in obstetrics, and with a specialist in perinatal physiology, Maureen Young, to study respiratory ailments in infants. Together they designed an improved negative-pressure respirator, and when Donald moved on to the Hammersmith Hospital, he continued to make improvements to it. His next two inventions were the 'trip spirometer', a device which measured the respiratory efficiency of new-borns, and a positive-pressure 'servo respirator', known as 'the puffer', which could be quickly used to send a stream of oxygen mixture to a baby's face-mask.

While at the Hammersmith, Donald met the Anglo-American inventor, engineer and surgeon John J. Wild, who described how he had used ultrasound at the University of Minnesota to detect abnormal lumps in the human breast. Ultrasound was already being used for the non-destructive testing of various materials, including the identification of cracks in metals. Wild was not alone in wondering if it could be applied to living tissue, and in 1951 he demonstrated the safe use of pulsed-echo ultrasound at 15 MHz to detect differences in the thickness of tissue, and the presence of nodules in the breasts of two trial patients. A year later, Wild and Reid devised a method to scan the ultrasound transducer in synchronism with the sweep of a cathode-ray tube display to obtain crude two-dimensional 'echograms' of kidney tissues in the laboratory and thigh muscle in a real patient.

In 1954, Ian Donald applied for the vacant Regius professorship of midwifery at Glasgow University, and had a slightly bizarre interview, over tea, with the Principal and Vice-Chancellor, Sir Hector Hetherington. After some inconsequential questions, Hetherington said, *"I believe you are interested in art. I would like you to come and see a picture we have recently acquired for the Glasgow Art Gallery. It will be closed now, but don't worry, I'll have it opened."* Donald was duly taken down to Kelvingrove to see Salvador Dali's 'Christ of St. John of the Cross', and was reputedly just as impressed by Hetherington's display of academic power and influence. He accepted the offer of the professorship when it eventually came, and arrived in Glasgow bringing with him the nickname bestowed by his London colleagues – 'Mad Donald'. His textbook *Practical Obstetric Problems* appeared the next year and was anything but mad – it found widespread and lasting favour with students and professional obstetricians alike, internationally, over many editions.

Donald's interest in ultrasound was heightened by a visit in 1955 to the famous Clydeside boiler fabrication company, Babcock and Wilcox, who used the technology routinely to examine the integrity of welds. On the visit, Donald took with him a large ovarian cyst, and a number of recently excised fibroids, to see if the Babcock equipment could differentiate the tissues. Many years later he recalled, *"All I wanted to know, quite simply, was whether these various masses differed in their ultrasonic echo characteristics. The results were beyond my wildest dreams and even with the primitive apparatus of those days clearly showed that a cyst produced echoes only at depth from the near and far walls, whereas a solid tumour progressively attenuated echoes at increasing depths of penetration. Furthermore, lower frequencies – for example 1½*

MHz instead of 2½ MHz – were necessary to penetrate the denser types of tissue, such as an ovarian fibroma."

The manufacturers of the ultrasound equipment were the Kelvin and Hughes Scientific Instrument Company, who had been producing marine echo-sounders since 1923, and were in the forefront of developing industrial ultrasound machines. Donald acquired a Kelvin Hughes Mark IIb 'supersonic flaw detector' from the Royal Cancer Hospital in London, where attempts to use it in brain imaging had been unsuccessful. He found that it was incapable of detecting anything within a range of 8cm from the face of the transducer. In the spirit of Heath Robinson, Donald improvised to fill the void with glass tubes and balloons full of water, but the poor echoes produced were useless for his purpose.

Luck intervened in late 1956 when some young Kelvin Hughes staff were installing a new 'shadowless' light bulb in a Western Infirmary operating theatre. They learned of Donald's fruitless ultrasound experiments and mentioned them to Tom Brown, a 23-year-old Glaswegian research engineer, a product of Allan Glen's School, who had helped to develop the Kelvin Hughes ultrasound equipment. Brown telephoned Donald and offered to help. Donald told him that he had all the technical assistance he needed, but he was welcome to come along to see what was going on. When Brown examined the old Mark IIb machine, a couple of things were immediately obvious to him. It had been manufactured not by Kelvin & Hughes, but under sub-contract, and it had been converted from a double-probe to a single-probe transducer, used for both send and receive, which explained its 8cm 'blind spot'. Brown contacted his boss, Alex Rankin, who quickly gifted a new double-probe Mk IV machine, described by Brown as *"a brute of an instrument",* which was installed in Donald's gynaecology unit.

Donald described the difference in performance as *"chalk and cheese".* A new registrar, John MacVicar, originally from Argyllshire and not yet

Illustration 55: Tom Brown. Courtesy of BMUS

30 years old, joined his obstetrics team and started experimenting with surgical specimens immersed in water, and then with live volunteers. Soon they had scanned 250 patients, trying to understand how particular organs and tissue masses produced ultrasound echoes. The returned signals were displayed as one-dimensional echograms that were captured on an oscilloscope and recorded on photographs in so-called 'A-mode'. The echogram blips clearly showed the difference between fluid-filled cavities and solid tissue, useful in differentiating between cysts and tumours.. But there were usually many echoes that appeared simultaneously, fluctuating wildly in size and number, with slight movements of the patient or the ultrasound probe. What was really needed was a system that produced good two-dimensional images.

Against some scepticism, Brown persuaded his directors that he should be allowed to spend a half-day per week working with Donald and MacVicar, and £500 was allocated to develop a better machine. He devised a system to measure the position of the ultrasound probe in an X-Y plane using potentiometers, and a synchronised dual-timebase oscilloscope display which showed the intensity of echoes on a grey-scale to build a long-persistence two-dimensional image. Much clever signal processing was needed, both to filter out spatial 'noise' and to display a very wide dynamic range of echo signal amplitudes of more than 100 to 1. The scan displays were recorded photographically. Brown recalled, *"The frequency used was 2.5 MHz, corresponding to an ultrasonic wavelength of 0.6mm This was chosen partly because it was one of the standard frequencies on the Kelvin & Hughes industrial machines, and partly because it was quickly found to give a good trade-off between range and resolution, with the available technology of the day. Patents were applied for by Kelvin & Hughes prior to publication of our early results in 'Lancet' in June 1958. I was named as inventor, though commercial rights were assigned to the company."*

This so-called 'B-mode' or bed-table scanner was built largely from government-surplus equipment, and the supporting frame even included bits of 'Meccano', but it was used, mainly by John MacVicar, to obtain reasonable images. In further improvements, Brown automated the X-Y scanning movement and also introduced what he called a 'plan-position-indicator' display by mounting the probe in a steel ball and rocking it through different angles while keeping it in light, lubricated contact with the patient's skin during the whole scan. This enabled good imaging of pregnant wombs for the first time, as published in *the Lancet* in 1958, clearly showing fetuses and in one case, twins. Kelvin Hughes were approached by a young Swedish obstetrician, Bertil Sundén of the University of Lund, to supply another machine, which was delivered with a better control panel and much improved ergonomics, devised by Dugald Cameron, a student in industrial design at the Glasgow School of Art. The result was a very elegant machine, the first-ever obstetric ultrasound scanner to be sold, and which became the basis for the inelegantly named *Diasonograph* that went into production in 1965, the world's first commercial obstetric ultrasound machine. Just twelve were built, and Dugald Cameron remembered, *"We were due to get a Design Award, one of the very first ones, for the Diasonograph. Unfortunately, when the evaluation team came up to see it the actual machine was covered in notes and whatnot, and I think Professor Donald was showing the full range of its activities and it frightened the life out of them. In fact, had it been a nurse or someone using it, we perhaps would have got the Design Award. There was a lot of early ergonomic thinking that went into the design, particularly for the design of the Sundén machine, which preceded the Diasonograph."*

The early 1960s were eventful. Kelvin & Hughes had struggled to finance the onward development of medical ultrasound scanners, which was now being undertaken by a team of 25 engineers in Glasgow, led by Tom Brown. Ian Donald's determined advocacy and fund-raising campaigns elicited several sustaining research grants amounting to some

£20,000 over several years. In 1964, the company was completely acquired by its major share-holder, Smiths Industries. Tom Brown found himself *"at the mercy of a bunch of American-management-style whiz kids"*, and quickly moved on to become chief engineer at Honeywell's medical equipment division.

Meanwhile, Ian Donald continued to combine his clinical practice with an increasingly heavy load of administrative work. He was asked to design a new maternity hospital for Glasgow, which he did, and construction started in 1960. Its many innovations included separate delivery rooms for each woman, and a dedicated ultrasound examination room. However, his own health was far from perfect. On a lecturing trip to New York in 1961, he collapsed with atrial fibrillation, a consequence of chronic heart problems stemming from a childhood infection with rheumatic fever. He went back to the Western Infirmary for a mitral valve replacement, and went through three major heart operations in the next few years. His enthusiasm for ultrasound scanning was undiminished, and his diagnostic use of ultrasonic scanners led to their widespread adoption by the end of the decade. At the new maternity hospital, which Donald named The Queen Mother's Hospital, he encouraged others to use the new technology. His colleague Stuart Campbell published a landmark paper, *'An improved method of fetal cephalometry by ultrasound'* in which he described his use of both A-mode and B-mode scans to measure the diameter of fetal heads, a technique that quickly became standard practice.

As the pioneering team split up, John MacVicar took a secondment to the University of East Africa in Nairobi and to establish a new department of obstetrics and gynaecology. He returned to the UK to become the foundation professor at the Leicester Medical School, where he remained until his retirement, many years later.

Around 1967, Smiths Industries closed the old Kelvin Hughes factory in Glasgow and pulled out of Scotland. The decision corresponded with a ruling of the US Supreme Court in a patent dispute with Automation Industries of Denver, which acquired the title to the

Smiths patents on ultrasound, including Tom Brown's patents on two-dimensional contact scanning. Nevertheless, and under pressure from the UK Department of Health, Smiths sold their medical ultrasound business to the Edinburgh subsidiary of a Canadian company, Nuclear Enterprises, with a 'paid up' licence to the Brown patents, so that manufacture could continue. A new

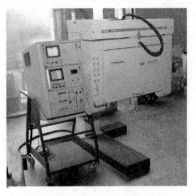

Illustration 56: An NS 4102 Diasonograph machine.

model was developed with semiconductors replacing valves in the electronics, and the *'NE 4102 Diasonograph'* became a successful and ubiquitous instrument, used in most British and European hospitals. Ten years later, most of Nuclear Enterprises was acquired by EMI, who were particularly attracted by the ultrasound scanning business.

Tom Brown did not stay long at Nuclear Enterprises, but moved on again, via a research position at Edinburgh University, to join a small company called Sonicaid, a manufacturer of fetal monitoring equipment, who were eager to enter the medical imaging market. There, Brown was in the strange position of having to invent his way around the protections of his own patents. He did this by developing a stereoscopic 3-D ultrasonic imaging system which circumvented his previous 2-D patents. The development was successful, but it was the last of the 'static' machines which used a relatively low pulse repetition rate to slowly build up a scanned image on some form of storage device. They were superseded from the mid-1970s by fast real-time scanners, enabling the probes to be hand-held.

Ian Donald, whose supposedly 'mad' ideas had started the whole project, spent much of the rest of his career in Glasgow at the new Queen Mother's Hospital that he had specified and named, and he made sure that it had a fully-functioning diagnostic ultrasound department.

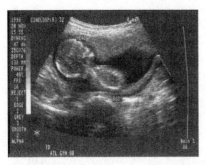

Illustration 57: An ultrasound image of a fetus at four months

Ian Donald was appointed a CBE in 1973 and received many other national and international honours. Survived by his wife Alix and their four daughters, he died in 1987. The production of medical ultrasonic scanners continued in Edinburgh under the aegis of EMI, and then Fischer Ultrasound, until 1995, when the cost advantages of manufacture in Asia became irresistible.

27 Blockbusting pharma: James W. Black

The creation of one revolutionary drug is usually sufficient to guarantee fame and honours for any pharmacologist, but the invention of two of the most effective new drugs of the 20th century was a towering achievement. 'Invention' is the operative word, because James Black pioneered a novel approach to drug development. Rather than synthesising new compounds and then testing hopefully for their effects on various diseases, Black took the logical and practical approach of targeting specific conditions and tailoring molecules to suit. He described it as creating *"drugs crafted round a natural template"*.

While working at the University of Glasgow in the 1950s, Black became interested in the effect of adrenaline on the human heart, and its relationship to heart disease, and in disorders of the gut, including stomach ulcers. In his crafting of drugs to address these conditions, he created whole new classes of pharmaceuticals, and he was awarded the Nobel Prize in Physiology or Medicine in 1988.

James Black was born in Uddingston, Lanarkshire in 1924, and was brought up mainly in Fife. He was the fourth of five sons of Walter Black, a mining engineer and colliery manager, and Catherine Whyte, a seamstress. James had childhood interests in music and mathematics, and despite the family's lack of wealth, all of the sons of the Black-and-Whyte union graduated from university. At the age of 15, encouraged by his teachers, James won a residential scholarship to the University of St Andrews, and entered the next year. Later, under the dual influences of his elder brother William, who had graduated in medicine from St Andrews, and the prodigious polymath, Professor D'Arcy Wentworth Thompson, he matriculated at the University's medical school which was then housed in University College Dundee. Just as importantly, at a Student Ball he met a biochemistry student, Hilary Vaughan. They married in the summer of 1946, soon after James graduated, and they would have a daughter, Stephanie. In his Nobel biographical text Black described Hilary as the best student he ever had, and wrote, *"Had she chosen a sectarian approach to study she would have become a visible star but her eclectic pursuit of knowledge and her unwavering support for her family led her to study law and choose poetry as a distillate of her wisdom. Intellectually she was the most exciting person I have ever known and, quite simply, the mainspring of my life until she died..."*

As newly-weds, Hilary had her final year of studies to complete, and James took a research job with Professor Robert Garry in the physiology department, where he studied how the intestinal system is able to absorb sugars selectively. Then, faced with the debts incurred during his medical training, Black took a lecturing post in Singapore, where he said *"he learned how not to do experiments",* and the couple spent a happy three years before returning to Scotland. Robert Garry, by now at the University of Glasgow, facilitated Black's appointment to its veterinary school, where he was asked to establish a new department of physiology. While recruiting staff and commissioning new teaching and research laboratories, Black focused his own research on two important topical questions, given the prevalence in humans of heart disease and stomach ulcers. First, what is the biochemistry underlying the stomach's secretion of gastric acid? Second, how could oxygen supply to the heart be improved in patients with narrowed coronary arteries?

Black had two crucial insights. Experiments on dogs showed that the small amine molecule, serotonin, was effective in reducing gastric acid secretion. Serotonin has important roles in the brain as a neuro-transmitter, but it is primarily found in the gastro-intestinal (GI) tract. His team's discovery of the effect of serotonin (and its pre-cursor) on stomach acid was published in *Nature* and attracted the attention of the pharmaceutical division of Imperial Chemical Industries (ICI).

In thinking about the second problem, Black calculated that improvements to heart oxygenation could be achieved using vasodilatory drugs to increase blood flow, but that their effect would be marginal and temporary. He turned the problem on its head and favoured an alternative strategy, which was to lower the oxygen demand of the compromised heart, by reducing the stimulus of the 'stress response' of the sympathetic nervous system. His interest was also personal – Black's father had suffered from angina, and died from a heart attack following a car crash. In the stress response mechanism, the hormones adrenaline and noradrenaline are crucial, causing blood pressure to rise and the heart to pump harder and faster. Black recalled a neglected 10-year-old paper by the American pharmacologist, Raymond Ahlquist, which proposed that there are two types of receptors for such stimulating hormones, because of their differing response to stimulation. Ahlquist called them 'alpha' and 'beta' adrenotropic receptors, and postulated that those in the heart and bronchi were of the beta type. Black surmised that if the hormones acted selectively on tissues, then perhaps selective blocking drugs could be developed to act exclusively on the cardiac receptors, while leaving unaffected the other functions of the sympathetic nervous system.

These were powerful ideas, and Black decided that to pursue them he would need the facilities of a major pharmaceutical company. In 1958, he accepted an offer from ICI to work at their brand-new laboratories in Cheshire, and he formed a new team with the objective of designing drugs with the desired effects. They were aided when two of Ahlquist's colleagues discovered that a chemical called DCI (dichloro-isoprenaline) had a partial effect in blocking adrenaline in the heart, and who coined the phrase 'beta-adrenergic blocking drug'. Isoprenaline is itself related to adrenaline, and it activates the production of adrenaline when it binds to receptor sites. Black's novel method was to use the activator or 'agonist' isoprenaline molecule as a template to build an 'antagonist' drug which would bind to the same sites and block the effects of adrenaline, with no other action. At the time, the concept of receptor sites was just beginning to be accepted, so Black's practical approach was also a pioneering test of pharmacological theory.

One seriously complicating factor was that some molecules, known as 'partial agonists', act as both activators and blockers at particular sites. So, a key problem in assessing newly synthesised compounds was how to test their blocking properties when they behaved as partial agonists in the biological tissue being tested. Black's team overcame this by using only *in vitro* tissues which were less susceptible to activation, allowing the blocking action to be revealed. The first 'beta-blocker' drug developed in this way was pronethalol, which was patented and in small-scale trials proved to be effective in treating angina and certain heart arrhythmias. It had also shown some toxicity in tests on mice, but nevertheless it was launched and marketed under the name 'Alderlin' (after ICI's Alderley Park laboratories), primarily to treat conditions that were life-threatening. Black and his team forged on to create even better beta-blockers, and by the time of Alderlin's market launch they had tested some 269 compounds, of which one was clearly superior in effect and low in toxicity. Compound 45520, propranolol, was marketed as 'Inderal', and replaced Alderlin. Inderal became the archetypal beta-blocker and a huge commercial success – the highest-grossing drug ever invented to that point.

In the course of his experiments, Black realised that Ahlquist's dual alpha-beta classification of receptors was too simple to explain the laboratory outcomes. He began to identify a greater number of receptor sub-divisions, which suggested to him that it might be feasible to develop drugs with even more selective blocking capabilities – more selective even than Inderal. His interest moved on to the problem of peptic ulcers, where he saw parallels with angina, in that the agonist histamine was a stimulant for the over-production of gastro-intestinal acid. He could not persuade ICI to start a project, and he was not interested in their further development and promotion of beta-blocker drugs. Edward Paget, an ex-ICI colleague now with the small American drug company Smith, Kline and French (SK&F) asked him to recommend a head of pharmacology for their Welwyn Research Institute (WRI) labs in Hertfordshire, of which Paget was the managing director. Black, already a scientific celebrity and one of ICI's stars, volunteered himself and moved to SKF in 1964.

Given a free hand, Black built a new team, including William A. M. (Bill) Duncan, another Glasgow man, recruited from ICI. They started to test the idea that histamine, like adrenaline, might act on two different beta receptor sub-types. That hypothesis came from observations that existing anti-histamine drugs did not in fact suppress the secretion of gastric acid. Black guessed that this was due to the existence of a second type of histamine 'beta' receptor, that he labelled H2, which was not blocked by current drugs. He resolved to develop an H2 antagonist drug – a histamine beta-blocker.

Feathers were ruffled at the WRI as Black went about building his research team with little regard for seniority or existing laboratory practices. But he had Paget's full support as well as that of the SK&F corporate headquarters in Philadelphia, though HQ were kept unaware of Black's unorthodox approach to drug synthesis. Black forecast confidently that they would develop an H2 beta-blocker by the end of the year. He assumed that the response mechanism of the GI tract to histamine was similar to that of nasal cells, where the stimulus to produce mucus is conveyed in messages only through receptor sites located on the cells which line the sinus passages. That extrapolation of the 'messenger-receptor' hypothesis was as yet just conjecture.

The end of 1964 came and went, without the desired result. Paget was appointed Managing Director of SK&F in the UK, and astutely he appointed Bill Duncan as director of research, to manage the programmes and finances while leaving Black free to drive the laboratory work. That strained the relationship between Black and Duncan for a while; but as time rolled on with no breakthrough, Bill Duncan became crucial in shielding Black's research programme from budget cuts, helped by his cultivation of relationships at SK&F's American headquarters, including with Bryce Douglas, the corporate head of research, an organic chemist with a PhD from Edinburgh University, and a fellow Glaswegian.

Black's optimist forecasts were based on his experience in developing the adrenaline beta-blocker drugs at ICI. That was based on his idea of blocking the stimulating action of a molecule (the agonist) at a receptor site implicated in the disease, with a similar but inactive chemical (the antagonist). The histamine molecule consists of a ringlike structure with a short side chain attached. Black's initial approach was to modify the ring by attaching other chemical groups, which had worked well to produce the adrenaline antagonists. This time, the expected quick success did not happen – no antagonists for histamine were found. However, one compound, called 4-methylhistamine, stimulated acid secretion without producing any other histamine responses. That proved the existence of the hypothesised second type of histamine receptor and pointed the way forward. Black added more chemistry expertise to the team: Graham Durant, Robin Ganellin, John Emmett and Mike Parsons joined to create many more variants of histamine and to test them for their receptor-blocking properties. By 1968, they had synthesised around 200 compounds – but none of them showed any blocking activity.

Meanwhile at SK&F headquarters in Philadelphia, reorganisations were underway as the company's poor performance was of increasing concern. Budget reductions and large-scale redundancies were made in the US research and development programmes and the lack of results from the histamine antagonist project was noted. As part of R&D cuts in the UK, the closure of the H2 antagonist research was proposed. Bill Duncan succeeded in winning the argument that local management was best placed to decide how the UK cuts should be applied, and he bet on his own scientific judgment by closing many projects and actually increasing the funding of the H2 antagonist programme. But if the UK arm of SK&F was to survive, then a result was needed sooner rather than later.

A succession of advances began after Mike Parsons pointed out a deficiency in the team's testing method. They were using an unrealistically low level of histamine to stimulate the secretion of gastric acid in test tissue samples, which meant that promising antagonist molecules could be missed. When the sensitivity of the testing process was improved, a compound called alpha-guanyl histamine was identified as a weak partial agonist. Ironically, it had been synthesised by Graham Durant four years earlier, but its activity had gone undetected in earlier tests. Black had been right after all in 1964, and had even proposed the right compound to synthesise. Using its molecular structure as a clue, the chemists, led by Robin Ganellin, set about engineering and assaying more effective molecules, principally by lengthening the side-chain attached to the histamine ring. Around 700 permutations were synthesised and tested before the creation of the first compound, burimamide, that showed good antagonist action on H2 receptors in animal tissue samples. Its potency was too low for it to be considered as a drug candidate, but nevertheless Black and Duncan decided to undertake single-dose experiments in humans to test if the effect on animal tissues, *in vitro* and *in vivo*, was transferable. The first volunteers were Duncan and Ganellin, and it was confirmed that burimamide acted in humans as it did in anaesthetised laboratory rats, cats and dogs. It reduced histamine-stimulated gastric acid secretion. Burimamide was patented and the experimental findings were published in *Nature* in April, 1972.

The discovery of H2 receptor antagonists, a new class of drug, prompted a burst of research activity resulting in the synthesis of the compound metiamide. Administered orally, it was ten times more potent than burimamide, but was quickly found to have serious side-effects including the reduction of white blood cell counts in laboratory animals and in clinical trials. Prudently and fortunately, the team had foreseen the possibility of problems with metiamide, and created a variant called cimetidine that showed no such side-effects.

In late 1972, with his theories clearly vindicated, James Black shocked his colleagues by announcing his intention to resign from SK&F in order to accept the chair of pharmacology at University College London (UCL), which he did the following year. The onward development and clinical trials of cimetidine continued apace, helped by the early case of one patient who

Illustration 58: James W. Black c.1980

was suffering from metiamide side effects, whose life was saved when he was switched to cimetidine. Yet corporate HQ in Philadelphia was not entirely convinced. They assessed the total market for an anti-ulcer drug at $50 million and declining, but they eventually agreed to commercialise cimetidine as a green-coloured tablet called Tagamet, from the two words 'antagonist' and 'cimetidine'. Tagamet was launched in November, 1976 and was immediately a huge success. To manufacture enough drug to match demand, SK&F constructed a brand-new $10 million chemical plant in Cork, Ireland, consuming most of the company's whole capital investment budget. To enable worldwide sales and distribution, SK&F acquired drug companies in France and Germany, and made a business partnership in Japan. Despite its high cost of around $20 for 100 tablets, Tagamet became the first so-called 'blockbuster' drug, by 1980 the most prescribed medicine in the world, with sales surpassing one billion dollars. James Black and his team gained little or no financial reward for their inventions.

For his services to medical research, Black was knighted in 1981, and he received his Nobel award seven years later for 'discoveries of important principles for drug treatment.' On hearing the news, he reputedly said, *"I wish I had my beta-blockers handy!"* By the time of his Nobel Prize, his wife Hilary had died, aged only 61, and his restless curiosity and scientific ambition had moved him on from UCL, first to direct therapeutic research at the Wellcome Research Laboratories and then to the professorship of analytical pharmacology at King's College London. With funding from Johnson & Johnson, he established the James Black Foundation and led a team that created gastrin inhibitors, effective in preventing some stomach cancers. When he moved back from active research, he renewed his links with what had become the University of Dundee, and served as its Chancellor from 1992 until 2006. He remarried in 1994, to Rona MacKie, Professor of Dermatology at Glasgow University, a Dundonian, and the daughter of J. Norman Davidson, the distinguished biochemist. Black died sixteen years later, at the age of 85, and is buried at Ardclach, near Nairn. Soon after his death, the University of St Andrews created the 'Sir James Black Chair of Medicine' at its Bute Medical School.

After the worldwide commercial and therapeutic success of Tagamet, treatments for stomach ulcers continued to advance, and in one surprising direction. As expected, other successful H2-receptor antagonists were created, notably ranitidine, sold as Zantac by Glaxo, (which eventually merged with SK&F to form Glaxo Smith Kline.) In total, around 500 million patients have been treated by the histamine blocker family of drugs including Tagamet and Zantac, generating more than $30 billion over their lifetimes. The drugs are highly effective in suppressing the over-production of gastric acid, as stimulated by histamine. But what causes the stress reaction and immune-response production of histamine in the first place?

In the early 1980s, two Australian physicians proposed a highly controversial theory. Robin Warren and Barry Marshall discovered – actually re-discovered – that bacteria could exist even in the highly acidic environment of the stomach, and made cultures of what is now called *helicobacter pylori*. They promoted the idea that infection by these bacteria were the cause of the inflammatory response that led to stomach ulcers. Famously, Marshall attempted to prove the theory by drinking a flask of *helicobacter* culture, which indeed resulted in infection and gastritis – inflammation of the lining of his stomach. In 2005, he and Warren shared the Nobel Prize in Physiology or Medicine for their discovery of the bacterium and its role in gastritis and peptic ulcer disease. The presence of *helicobacter pylori* is nowadays recognised as widespread in the human population and infection is regarded as a necessary (though not sufficient) condition for the development of stomach and duodenal ulcers. In response, effective new ulcer treatments have been developed, which combine the use of antibiotics, such as amoxicillin, with a new class of anti-acid drugs called proton-pump inhibitors, the successors to the blockbusting histamine antagonists invented by Sir James Black.

Part Three: Work in progress

28   **Work in progress**

In the process of scientific discovery, one thing leads to another. As the boundaries of our knowledge expand, new questions, more 'known unknowns', are inevitably recognised. It is difficult to envisage a time when scientists will be able to declare that 'everything is done', though such assertions have been made in the past, occasionally and absurdly. On the contrary, the rate of progress is undoubtedly quickening across diverse fields, especially biochemistry and genetics, nanotechnology, cosmology and computer science. The practical benefits are there for all to see, in communications technology, disease diagnosis and control, and the emerging field of AI – artificial intelligence.

Yet recent discoveries have put our existing store of knowledge in perspective. We now know that around 95% of the Universe is composed of an invisible substance, hitherto unknown, dubbed 'dark matter', apparently unrelated to the familiar stuff made of protons, neutrons and electrons, and detectable only by its gravitational influence on stars and galaxies. Accurate observations of distant stellar explosions, type 1a supernovas, imply the surprising conclusion that the expansion of the Universe is accelerating, a discovery that is still to be explained and which led to the 2011 Nobel award in physics. Developments in AI serve to underline the mystery of how animal consciousness arises from the workings of organic neurons. Despite our detailed understanding of DNA and RNA, and their fundamental roles in all life on Earth, the study of their origination from inert components – abiogenesis – remains largely a domain of hypothesis and conjecture.

Unfortunately, alongside our scientific progress, new threats to the well-being of humanity and our environment are emerging, and rapidly. The coronavirus pandemic of 2020-21 eerily mirrored the Spanish Flu epidemic of a hundred years before, and highlighted the ease with which pathogens can be transported around our increasingly populated and interconnected world. The relentless encroachment of human civilisation on animal habitats risks a calamitous mass extinction of species on land and in the sea. Most dangerously of all, studies of Earth's atmosphere and oceans have revealed a mortal threat to our planet's ecosystems, which requires urgent preventative action in the uncomfortable context of imperfect knowledge. As atmospheric levels of CO_2 rise towards 500 parts per million, as tundra and polar ice melts, as sea-levels rise, and as floods and wildfires become more common, remaining scepticism about the reality of human-made climate change must surely be replaced by concerted science-based policy. That may emerge from Glasgow in late 2021, at the COP 26 conference of the United Nations Intergovernmental Panel on Climate Change.

29 The origin of life in earth? Alexander Graham Cairns-Smith

All life on Earth is based on DNA, two chains of simpler molecules containing carbon, hydrogen and nitrogen, called nucleotides. Those molecules are composed of one of only four nucleotide bases: cytosine (C), guanine (G), adenine (A) or thymine (T). As is now well known, every protein in living things is created by a specific combination of those bases, and the double-helix DNA molecule, and its single-stranded equivalent, RNA, have the crucial capability to self-replicate, so that genetic information can be passed between cells and generations.

Similar organic molecules to these basic 'building blocks' of life are also now known to exist in asteroids and even in interstellar space, so the raw materials of life seem to be common. In the 1920s, the Russian biochemist Alexander Oparin, independently with J.B.S. Haldane, proposed that the 'primordial soup' of elements known to exist in the Earth's early atmosphere and oceans could produce simple organic molecules. In testing that idea, the Miller-Urey experiment of 1952 demonstrated the production of amino acids in a flask containing only hydrogen, methane, ammonia and water vapour, with the help of electric discharges to simulate atmospheric lightning bursts. But the leap from the building blocks to a molecule like DNA is a huge one, and how exactly the simple molecules could assemble into self-replicating complexes remains a mystery.

The most intriguing solution was proposed by a molecular biologist at Glasgow University, who developed a hypothesis that remains controversial today. Alexander Graham Cairns-Smith, a lecturer in the University's department of chemistry, began thinking about the problem of life's origins in the 1960s. Born in Kilmarnock in 1931, the son of a lawyer, Alexander Findlay Cairns-Smith and his French-Belgian wife Louise, Graham was educated at Kilmarnock Academy and as a boarder at Fettes College in Edinburgh before gaining his chemistry degree and PhD from that city's University. He was a talented artist, and for the first 20 years of his career he combined science with painting in oils and watercolours, staging several successful one-man exhibitions at the Royal Scottish Academy and the McLellan Galleries. He was appointed to a lecturing position in the University of Glasgow in 1957, where he soon focused his research on the question of the origin of life.

For Cairns-Smith, the Miller-Urey experiment presented more questions than answers. How did amino acids and nucleotides come together in an organised way, to form complex molecules like DNA and RNA? In a paper in the *Journal of Theoretical Biology*, he laid out his radical thought – that life on Earth evolved from the self-replication and natural selection of inanimate entities, specifically, crystals of clay. His reasoning was that clay crystallites display many of the properties required by evolution, and are in some ways rather lifelike. The crystals grow in watery environments which contain similar constituents – silicate 'food'; they can split apart, with the parent crystal giving rise to descendants which inherit their characteristic structures and flaws, conveying information; and those legacies can be altered by the conditions and stresses 'experienced' by the offspring, in a process akin to genetic mutation. Moreover, clay silicates can act as templates for organic molecules, which stick to the clay by surface adsorption. Thus clay earths could have provided the original matrix for the assembly of complex, self-replicating organic molecules. In that first paper, *The Origin of Life and the Nature of the Primitive Gene*, Cairns-Smith wrote, *"A detonator, an egg, and a starter motor have this in common: they are each a special device used to overcome a starting problem. Once the process that they have helped to initiate is under way they can be discarded. The problems of starting are often quite different, and so require different structures, from the problems of further development. If ever a process seemed to need a special starting device, it was organic evolution."*

This hypothesis of 'crystals as genes' was expanded in Cairn-Smith's subsequent book, *Genetic Takeover and the Mineral Origins of Life*, a technical description of how the reproductive process of inanimate crystals could have been high-jacked by organic replicating molecules. His subsequent book, *Seven Clues to the Origin of Life*, laid out the proposition as a Sherlock Holmes detective story. The seven clues, drawn from various branches of science and engineering, can be summarised as follows.

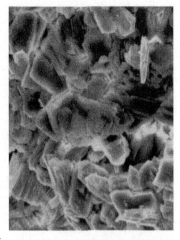

Illustration 59: Crystals of kaolinite clay mineral (x1340 magnification)

1. From biology: the only thing that passes from generation to generation is *information*, and genetic information is not itself a substance, but rather a *form*.

2. From biochemistry: DNA (and RNA) are 'suburban' molecules – complex and difficult to make – far distant from the centre of present biochemical pathways.

3. From the building trade: to build a stone arch requires a scaffolding of some sort. Once built, the scaffold can be removed. Similarly, in evolution, things can be subtracted as well as added, leaving no trace.

4. From the nature of ropes: none of the fibres in a rope needs to stretch from end-to-end, as long as they are sufficiently intertwined. Likewise, in collections of interacting genes, new gene strands can be added, or others taken away, without breaking the continuity of inheritance.

5. From the history of technology: primitive machines are usually designed differently, often in different materials, than their later advanced counterparts.

6. From chemistry: in the right conditions, crystals are self-assembling.

7. From geology: the Earth makes clay continuously, from minerals washed down by the weathering of hard rocks. They could act as primitive 'genes', and as infrastructures or 'catalysts' for biochemical evolution.

Illustration 60: Alexander Graham Cairns-Smith

Seven Clues to the Origin of Life caught the public imagination. It was translated into nine languages and sold more than 40,000 copies. The hypothesis gained traction with the scientific community too. In his captivating book *The Blind Watchmaker*, the evolutionary biologist Richard Dawkins wrote, *"Cairns-Smith's view of the DNA/protein machinery is that it probably came into existence relatively recently, perhaps as recently as three billion years ago. Before that there were many generations of cumulative selection based upon some quite different replicating entities. Once DNA was there, it proved to be so much more efficient as a replicator, and so much more powerful in its effects on its own replication, that the original replication system that spawned it was cast off and forgotten."*

That indeed is the core of the 'clay-as-genes' hypothesis, but it is a difficult supposition to prove. The theory has been subjected to few experimental tests. Nevertheless, the originality and plausibility of Cairns-Smith's work has been widely recognised. He was awarded the Thomas Graham Medal of the Royal Philosophical Society of Glasgow, and elected a Fellow of the Royal Society of Edinburgh in 1994. His last book, *Evolving the Mind*, considered the possible origins of intelligence, including quantum mechanical theories of consciousness. The field of evolutionary biology that he helped to create, the study of the possible origin of life from non-living matter, is now known as 'abiogenesis'.

Graham Cairns-Smith died in 2016, aged 84, survived by his wife, Dorothy Anne, and their two daughters. He is remembered by his friends as a convivial and knowledgeable host (who co-founded Glasgow's Western Wine Club), and by his scientific colleagues as a superb communicator of novel and challenging ideas, which may yet prove to be central in understanding the origin of life on Earth.

30 GCS – the Glasgow Coma Scale: Graham Teasdale and Bryan Jennett

The extent of brain injury, and the associated impairment of consciousness, are initially difficult to diagnose, practically or objectively. Before the mid-1970s, assessments of patients with a head injury or other brain damage were characterised by chaos. Observation of the patient's 'conscious level' was essential, but the gathering and exchange of data were undermined by inconsistent definitions and methods. In 1974, two doctors working in Glasgow recognised the need for a consistent clinical assessment of impaired consciousness, that could be quickly applied by medical practitioners. To address it, they developed a number of evaluating criteria based on three aspects of the patient's presentation: motor responsiveness, verbal performance, and eye opening. They made the assessments easy to evaluate using a simple chart – and a scale to measure conscious response – that is now used worldwide, and has become known as the Glasgow Coma Scale, or GCS.

A better name might be the Glasgow Consciousness Scale, because a high number (the highest being 15) indicates a patient who is fully awake, while the lowest score of 3 implies a deep, and often fatal, coma. The single Glasgow Coma Score is achieved by simply adding up the individual assessments made in each category : 1-6 for motor response, ranging from no limb movement to full obedience to commands; 1-5 for verbal responsiveness, from none, to the ability to correctly give

The Glasgow Coma Scale		
	RESPONSE	SCORE
EYE (4)	Spontaneous	4
	To sound	3
	To pressure	2
	None	1
		( )
SPEECH (5)	Orientated	5
	Confused	4
	Words	3
	Sounds	2
	None	1
		( )
MOTOR (6)	Obey commands	6
	Localising	5
	Normal flexion	4
	Abnormal flexion	3
	Extension	2
	None	1
		( )
Glasgow Coma Score (15)		( )

Illustration 61: The Glasgow Coma Scale assessment criteria and scoring

name, place and date; and 1-4 for eye opening, ranging from no response to stimuli at all, to fully open without interference.

The GCS was conceived by two men, William Bryan Jennett and Graham Teasdale. Jennett was born in London in 1926 to his Scottish mother and Irish father, a civil servant, and he was raised in Twickenham, in west London. After a brief spell working on the family farm in Scotland during the Second World War, he decided on a career in medicine, discovering later that of his mother's Loudon clan of Lanarkshire farming folk, he was the fifth medical doctor. It seems likely that the ancestry included Dr James Loudon who was a friend and correspondent of explorer David Livingstone, and who received Livingstone's body parts back from Africa for positive identification. Jennett won a scholarship to Liverpool Medical School, where he was President of the British Medical Students Association, and where he met his wife, Sheila Pope, who was later to become Professor of Physiology at Glasgow. Captivated by lectures in neurology, Jennett trained in neurosurgery at Oxford, and practised in Cardiff and Manchester, before spending a Rockefeller Fellowship year at the University of California in Los Angeles. He looked to combine medical practice with academic research, and in 1963 he took a combined NHS/university post in Glasgow. A year later he published his benchmark textbook, An Introduction to Neurosurgery. At Glasgow University, he developed a thriving research programme and was appointed to the professorship of neurosurgery in 1968. The regional neurosurgery unit, housed in a collection of converted Nissen huts at Killearn Hospital, was replaced by a purpose-built unit at the Southern General Hospital – the Institute of Neurological Sciences. Due largely to Jennett's inspiring and collaborative style of leadership, the Institute became a magnet for researchers and trainees from all over the world. At one point, seven out of ten professors of neurosurgery in the UK were Glasgow-trained. Jennett and his team published a stream of important papers in the next years, and in 1972, with Fred Plum, Professor of Neurology at New York's Cornell Medical Centre, he highlighted the plight of patients in deep coma who could now survive indefinitely, and named the new syndrome a 'persistent vegetative state', a term which remains in widespread use today.

Graham Teasdale was born in northeast England in 1940, and was a graduate of the University of Durham's medical school. His interest in the assessment of head injury began soon after he qualified, while working for the neurologist, Henry Miller, and with the eminent neurosurgeon George Rowbotham, author of the then standard textbook '*Acute injuries of the head*'. Teasdale went on to work as a surgical trainee at the world's first trauma centre in Birmingham, and joined the Glasgow unit in 1967, as a lecturer in anatomy and a neurosurgeon at the Southern General Hospital, attracted by the team's reputation for clinical and research excellence. In 1971, Teasdale began a close and long-term collaboration with Jennett, first by critically reviewing what was already being done in the clinical assessment of brain injury. As they were to write later, the failures of these assessments were that *"Almost all used a hierarchical system based on a fundamentally unsound assumption about distinct divisions in the… spectrum of severity of consciousness impairment. Moreover, most of these scales were described in ill-defined and obscure terms such as stupor, lethargy, obtundation, obnubilation, automatisms, repetitive movements, typical/atypical decerebration, rigidity, psychomotor excitability, and states such as coma carus or coma dépassé, none of which had the value of clarity in daily clinical practice."* They concluded that there was a need for a clarifying methodology, based on a scale of measurement that could be applied by everyone with a responsibility for head injury care, in all settings. That pointed the way to an assessment scale that avoided complexity and focused on the objective, observable condition of the patient.

The first description of what Teasdale and Jennett came to call the Glasgow Coma Scale was published in *The Lancet* in 1974, in a paper entitled *'Assessment of coma and impaired consciousness – a practical scale'*. It proposed that three basic aspects of patient condition should be independently measured: verbal performance; motor response; and eye opening; and referred to the different scales that had been described by various practitioners previously, but which had failed to gain general acceptance. Interestingly, it had not been originally planned to summarise the assessments in a single number. In late 1973, in a presentation at an Amsterdam conference, Teasdale had said, *"It is no part of our intention to summate the different parts into a score."* That position changed as data was collected on the consistency, reproducibility and reliability of the method. As clinical information accumulated, the finding on each component of the assessment was given a number, to facilitate computer input. The temptation to sum the three numbers together into a single total score, ranging from 3 to 15, proved irresistible, and serendipitous, because it worked. By 1976, data on the practical use of the summed GCS score, initially collected from clinical experience in Scotland and in the Netherlands, showed a good correlation with patient mortality and independent recovery. Nevertheless, the Glasgow team emphasised that in daily clinical care, a patient's condition was best described by using the three responses of the scale separately, and that the exclusive use of the summed score entailed a loss of information.

More international support was forthcoming from the US National Institutes of Health (NIH), prompted by Fred Plum, Jennett's research colleague in America. Plum learned about the advances in Glasgow and the Netherlands in assessing and prognosing head injury, and saw the opportunity to introduce a similar approach to the assessment of coma from other causes, which he termed 'medical comas'. He successfully applied to the NIH and won funding for trans-atlantic studies involving Cornell, San Francisco and Newcastle-upon Tyne in the UK. These were successful in correlating the components of the GCS with the outcomes of medical comas, and the findings were used to construct practical methods

Cuadro # 1. Escala de Coma de Glasgow Modificada para lactantes y niños

Puntuación	>1 año	<1 año
Respuesta apertura ocular	Espontánea	Espontánea
4	A la orden verbal	Al grito
3	Al dolor	Al dolor
2	Ninguna	Ninguna
1		
Respuesta Motriz	Obedece órdenes	Espontánea
6	Localiza el dolor	Localiza el dolor
5	Defensa al dolor	Defensa al dolor
4	Flexión anormal	Flexión anormal
3	Extensión anormal	Extensión anormal
2	Ninguna	Ninguna
1		
Respuesta verbal	Se orienta – conversa	Balbucea
5	Conversa confusa	Llora – consolable
4	Palabras inadecuada	Llora persistente
3	Sonidos raros	Gruñe o se queja
2	Ninguna	Ninguna
1		

Illustration 62: Example of the international adoption of the GCS, in this case applied to children and infants

to predict the probabilities of different coma outcomes, both from medical causes and head injuries. However, predictions of vegetative or severely disabled outcomes proved unreliable, and although Jennett and Michael Bond, later the Professor of Psychological Medicine at Glasgow, devised a 'Glasgow Outcome Scale', the hope that formal prediction would become part of routine clinical practice was unrealised.

The output of 'the Glasgow School' of neurosurgery and neuropathology continued to revolutionise the diagnosis and treatment of head-injured patients, worldwide. In 1978, an editorial in *The Journal of Neurosurgery* advocated that *"the Glasgow coma and outcome scale should be adopted by neurosurgical units throughout the world"*, and the same year, use of the GCS was recommended in the first edition of the *Advanced Trauma Life Support* manual, produced by the American College of Surgeons. In the following years and decades, GCS data became intrinsic to the College's Trauma Data Bank, and the activities of the European Brain Injury Consortium and the Brain Trauma Foundation. Jennett became Dean of Medicine at Glasgow University in 1981, and Teasdale, a charismatic teacher and a prolific research scientist, was chosen as his successor as Professor of Neurosurgery.

Bryan Jennett retired in 1991. Amongst many honours, he was awarded a CBE and an honorary DSc from the University of St Andrews. He died in 2008, leaving behind his wife and research colleague Sheila, their daughter, and their three sons. Jennett had a profile and frankness which had sometimes brought him into the public spotlight. A BBC 'Panorama' documentary titled *Transplants: Are the Donors really Dead?'* was broadcast in 1980 and challenged the criteria used to establish 'brain death' in potential organ-donors. The point of contention was that in the UK, the absence of brainstem function with cessation of breathing were the criteria used, compared to the USA where death of the entire brain was required. In an interview with the programme's lead journalist, Jennett explained that the loss of brainstem function is part of the entire destruction of a brain, not a single part, and the last part to go.

The broadcast created a controversy and prompted angry comments in *The Lancet* and the *British Medical Journal*, whose editor called the premise of programme a 'disgrace' designed to cause 'maximal disquiet'. The programme was accused of having had a detrimental effect in the number of organ donations and Jennett's clarifications were said to be a factor in the recovery of the number of donors in the UK.

Graham Teasdale further developed the world-class team of clinical and laboratory scientists in Glasgow, working on many aspects of acute brain damage from injury and stroke. Forty years after he co-created the GCS, Teasdale led a project, *'The Glasgow Coma Scale at 40 years: standing the test of time'*, in order to understand the current use of the Scale, its successes and its perceived limitations. To address the last of these, new and updated guidance in using the Scale was published as *The Glasgow Structured Approach to Assessment of the GCS*, and made widely available through a dedicated website. In 2018, Teasdale and his colleagues formulated an extension of the Glasgow Coma Scale, emphasising the importance of the reflex contraction of the pupils of the eyes, and calculated by subtracting the number of a patient's non-reactive pupils from the GCS score to widen the range of the possible scoring from 1 to 15. The so-called the GCS-P score was found to have a diagnostic and prognostic value similar to more complicated methods of assessing traumatic brain damage. A GCS-P score of 1 is associated with a high risk of death. Teasdale's team stressed that, *"The combined GCS-P is not intended to replace the role of separate assessment and reporting of each component of the Glasgow Coma Scale and pupil response in the care of individual patients. This remains the most informative way of determining and sharing a 'picture' of the patient's condition and how it may be changing. When the various components of the Glasgow Coma Scale are combined there is some loss of information. This has been accepted as a trade-off in the interests of simplicity and the utility of the total GCS score as a 'shorthand summary.' The GCS-P retains this simplicity while expanding information about the severity of a patient's clinical state and prognosis."* Furthermore, when information on the patient's age was added, 'GCS-PA' prognostic charts were devised, that estimate the probabilities of specific clinical outcomes.

Graham Teasdale received many awards, including Fellowships of the Academy of Medical Sciences and the Royal Society of Edinburgh. As the value of the GCS was increasingly promoted and recognised globally, Teasdale was elected President of the International Neurotrauma Society for four years from 1994, and also served as President of the Royal College of Physicians and Surgeons of Glasgow. In 2005 he became the only Briton to receive the Medal of Honour of the World Federation of Neurosurgical Societies. A year later, he was knighted for his services to neurosurgery. He continues in active research, and is an Honorary Professor in the Institute of Health and Wellbeing at the University of Glasgow.

31 Molecular machines: James Fraser Stoddart

There is a dimensional domain where the boundary becomes blurred between microscopic mechanical structures and molecules. This is where the emerging fields of nanotechnology and supramolecular chemistry meet, turning science fiction into fact, and creating such concepts as nano-scale electrical switches and 'molecular Meccano'. In the last decades of the 20th century and the first years of the 21st, a new field of chemistry has been created – one in which the mechanical bond is the most important feature of molecular compounds. The potential applications are almost endless, ranging from new methods to synthesise and deliver drugs, to high-efficiency electrical batteries and the creation of new materials.

In 1959, the brilliant physicist, Richard Feynman, had asked, how small can you make machinery? In a talk given at Caltech called 'There's plenty of room at the bottom', Feynman said, *"As we go down in size, there are a number of interesting problems that arise. All things do not simply scale down in proportion. There is the problem that materials stick together by the molecular (Van der Waals) attractions...There will be several problems of this nature that we will have to be ready to design for. But I am not afraid to consider the final question as to whether, ultimately - in the great future - we can arrange the atoms the way we want; the very atoms, all the way down! What would happen if we could arrange the atoms one by one the way we want them?"*

The crucial experimental steps towards 'molecular machines' were taken by a team of chemists in France, led by Jean-Pierre Sauvage, in the early 1980s. They succeeded in linking together two ring-shaped molecules with another, to form a short, handcuff-like concatenated chain called a 'catenane', in an assembly that allowed the rings to rotate with respect to each other. The crucial breakthroughs were that the ring molecules were not interlinked by conventional strong chemical bonds, the 'covalent' bonds which share electrons, but mechanically, and the molecular structure was synthesised with a high yield.

That step was followed, in 1991, by a team led by James Fraser Stoddart, who was then at the University of Sheffield, who made what they called a 'molecular shuttle'.

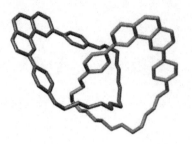

Illustration 63: A schematic of a [2]catenane. The number in brackets indicates the number of interlinked molecular rings

It consisted of a 'rotaxane' – a dumbbell shaped molecule, around a nanometre long, supporting a molecular ring, trapped but free to revolve and move along the 'axle' of the structure, and at room temperature darting back and forth between the ends at around 2000 times per second – a molecular shuttle. To construct the assembly, they chose molecules with appropriate electron affinities, and an initially-open ring molecule which threaded itself onto the axle. The team then closed the ring's opening so that it remained on the axle, prevented from slipping off by the 'stopper' molecules at each end of the dumbbell. They had created the first self-assembling rotaxane that could be produced with high yield. Moreover, Stoddart's group showed that the position of the rings on the axles could be controlled by heat. In the next few years, Stoddart led the development of a number of rotaxane-based molecular machines, including an 'elevator' which can rise to a height of 0.7nm above a surface, and a 'muscle' which can bend a thin cantilever of gold through a distance of around 35nm. By the end of the 1990s, Stoddart was at Northwestern University in Illinois, and with colleagues, demonstrated molecular AND and OR logic gates, formed by a monolayer of rotaxanes sandwiched between metal electrodes, deposited on a silicon substrate.

James Fraser Stoddart was born in Edinburgh during the Second World War. He was the son of Jean and Tom Fraser Stoddart, who was a talented agricultural manager of farms belonging to the city's University. James Fraser was a small baby - his birth weight was so low that he was not expected to live until the next morning. When the young Stoddart was six months old, his father resigned his job at Edinburgh University and took on the tenancy of Edgelaw Farm, only a dozen miles south of the city, but sufficiently remote that the farmhouse lacked electricity then and for the next 18 years. Growing up in the post-war austerity that was the hallmark of Britain in the 1940s and 50s, Stoddart's early life was one of rural simplicity, and he attended the small local village school until he was eight, when his mother decided he should be sent to Melville College, (now Stewart's Melville College), a smart, fee-paying school in the city. At 18, he helped to install copper wiring in the farmhouse, ready for the long-awaited electricity, which arrived on Christmas Eve 1959, and he started four years as an undergraduate at Edinburgh University, studying sciences and mathematics. Excelling in analytical chemistry, as a postgraduate he joined the research group of his tutor Dr Dougie Anderson, and completed a PhD in just two years, for a thesis on the molecular structure of Acacia plant gums. He later wrote, *"the many gum trees in the Sudan, from whence the nodules I studied came, had never managed to produce between all of them through all of time, two gum molecules which were identical in size and constitution. After this period of handling highly heterogeneous mixtures, I longed to grow acquainted with a molecular world where homogeneity ruled the roost, at least for a time."*

At university, Stoddart met Norma Scholan, when she joined the research group as a high-flying chemistry undergraduate. They were married in 1968, not long after Stoddart has taken a postdoctoral fellowship at Queen's University in Kingston, Ontario. While in Canada, Stoddart received breaking news that shaped his career. Charles J. Pedersen, a Norwegian-Japanese-Korean-American chemist at DuPont Laboratories in Delaware, had succeeded in synthesising large, ring-shaped polyether molecules called 'crown ethers', with high yield.

This opened up the possibility to engineer other 'supramolecules' - structures comprising many molecules - designed to accept smaller molecules and ions as 'keys into a lock', and mimicking the actions of enzymes on biological molecules. That

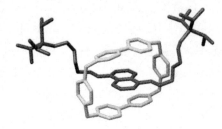

Illustration 64: A representation of a [2]rotaxane

possibility determined the path of Stoddart's future research. For his work on cyclic polyethers, Pedersen would share the Nobel prize for chemistry in 1987.

On his return to the UK for first an ICI Fellowship, then a junior lectureship, both at the University of Sheffield, Stoddart felt restricted and frustrated by chemistry department politics, and planned to return to North America. But after a happy three-year secondment to ICI's Corporate Laboratories in Cheshire, and the joyous arrival of two daughters, he shelved that plan, though he spent a year at the University of California, Los Angeles, (UCLA) in 1978. Back at Sheffield through the 1980s, he formed a research group which engineered molecules they dubbed 'pseudorotaxanes'– templates which could be converted into catenanes or rotaxanes. They were crucial to the process of creating the [2]rotaxane he called the 'molecular shuttle'. Further development of controllable, switchable rotaxanes took place at the University of Birmingham where Stoddart transferred some of his research team upon his appointment as professor of organic chemistry in 1991. His growing reputation prompted the offer of a prestigious appointment at UCLA, but the growth of his Birmingham group, and Norma's convalescence after serious illnesses, led him to decline it.

Meanwhile, another research group was making similar advances in the Netherlands at Groningen University, led by the Dutch organic chemist, Ben Feringa. Like Fraser Stoddart, Feringa was raised on a farm, and as a young researcher became captivated by the power of supramolecular chemistry and *"creating, making molecules and materials that never existed before…"* During the 1990s his group made successive breakthroughs culminating in the construction of molecular switches and unidirectional rotary 'nanomotors', activated by ultraviolet light. By 2006 they had succeeded in demonstrating the use of nanomotors, embedded in a liquid crystal film, to rotate a microscopic rod of glass, dimensions 5 x 28 μm, some 10,000 times larger than the nanoscale molecules.

Fraser Stoddart resigned his professorship at Birmingham in 1997, and accepted the Winstein Chair in organic chemistry at UCLA, partly driven by his determination to obtain world-leading medical treatment for Norma's metastatic cancer. Sadly, she was eventually to succumb to the disease early in 2004.

Despite his wife's ill health, and his unfamiliarity with the funding processes of American universities, Stoddart progressively built a successful team of researchers at UCLA who pioneered the high-yield synthesis of more, complicated mechanically interlocked molecules, (MIMs) including 'Borromean rings' and 'Solomon knots'. He initiated, with Jim Heath, the field of molecular electronics, using monolayers of switchable catenanes and rotaxanes deposited on silicon. As appreciation grew of the new field of molecular Meccano, Stoddart achieved widespread recognition and received, amongst many honours, the University of Edinburgh's Alumnus of the Year award in 2005, a knighthood in the Queen's New Year Honours list of 2006, and the Feynman Prize in Nanotechnology in 2007. That year, Stoddart and Heath demonstrated a 160 kbit molecular Random Access Memory (RAM) device smaller than a white blood cell (around 15 μm).

In 2011, building of the work of the American James M. Tour, Ben Feringa's group demonstrated a four-wheel drive 'nanocar', consisting of a molecular chassis and four nanomotor 'wheels', activated by pulses of electrons fired from the atom-sized tip of a tunnelling scanning microscope (STM). At a temperature of 7 Kelvin, ten pulses of the STM rolled the molecular car 6 nm across a copper surface. These constructions were not frivolous gimmicks. Feringa said, *"At the moment I would not consider the system to have any practical application. However, thinking about future applications, this is a small but significant step forward. Ultimately, nanomachines and devices like sensing and delivery systems need to be powered. For that, molecular motors will be required. Probably future designs will be different from what we show here, but we have to demonstrate the fundamental principles."*

Sir James Fraser Stoddart, Ben Feringa, and Jean-Pierre Sauvage shared the Nobel prize in chemistry in 2016 'for the design and synthesis of molecular machines'. In his Nobel lecture, referring to progress in the construction of 'AMMs' – artificial molecular machines - Stoddart concluded, *"It is too early to speak in an authoritative and informed manner about what will be the killer applications of AMMs. We are at the very early stages of knowing how to build them let alone use them. Let me use the analogy of manned flight, particularly in relation to where aviation had reached in 1927, the year in which Charles Lindbergh crossed the Atlantic Ocean in the Spirit of St Louis…Compare and contrast the situation for aviation in 1927 with where it stands today as a form of mass transport that has, not only opened up country-wide travel, but also brought Continents together on the grandest of scales. As far as MIMs and AMMs are concerned, they await the engagement of the next generation of chemists eager to exploit the nature of the mechanical bond in chemistry, while taking up the task of designing and synthesizing MIMs and putting them to good use."*

Since 2008, Fraser Stoddart has been Emeritus Professor of chemistry at UCLA and professor of chemistry at Northwestern University, where he established the Mechanostereochemistry Group which continues leadership in the emerging fields of drug delivery, energy storage, and molecular machines. In his career to date, he has supervised more than 400 research students, published at least 1000 research papers, which are some of the most cited in the history of chemistry.

32 Supernovas – the making of us all: Tom Boles

The vast majority of the visible matter in the universe consists of the two lightest elements, hydrogen and helium, the constituent gases of stars. Stars convert hydrogen to helium, and some heavier elements, in the process of nuclear fusion which drives their awesome energy output over a lifetime of many millions or billions of years. The lifetime of a star depends on two things: its mass of hydrogen fuel, and the rate at which it consumes that fuel, which determines its luminance. Higher mass means more fuel, but also more gravitational pull, a higher temperature, and a higher luminance. Higher luminosity means the fuel will be exhausted sooner. For typical stars, their lifetime is proportional to mass divided by luminance, and since luminosity scales roughly as the cube of the mass, the net result is that stellar lifetimes scale inversely as the square of their mass – bigger stars die much sooner. Stars of the mass of our sun have lives of around 10 billion years. The smallest stars, of around one-tenth of a solar mass, will survive for 1000 billion years, more than 50 times longer than the present age of the universe. The most massive stars, of about 100 solar masses, survive for only around one million years, and they end their relatively short lives with truly spectacular deaths. Whereas smaller stars tend to expire gently, first swelling, then fading away to become white dwarfs, stars of more than approximately ten solar masses meet a quite different, violent end.

When a large star exhausts its store of hydrogen, the heat pressure generated in the core is no longer sufficient to withstand the inward pull of gravity. The core collapses and starts to fuse helium into carbon. As the helium is exhausted, the core is compressed further and reaches high enough temperatures to fuse carbon into oxygen, then neon, then silicon and sulphur, and finally iron. The ultimate core collapse to nuclear densities takes about 15 seconds and produces a super-energetic explosion ejecting neutrons, neutrinos and the heavy elements far into space at some 30,000 kilometres per second – roughly 10% of the speed of light. The explosion can engulf nearby stars, and the shock wave can induce the formation of new stars from gas clouds. Left behind is

Illustration 65: Supernova SN1997D in galaxy NGC1536, showing brightness comparable to the galactic centre

usually an ultra-dense neutron star, or in extreme cases a black hole - only a few kilometres across but with a mass several times that of our sun. These gigantic explosions – called Type II supernovas - create enough energy and light that they can be seen by the naked eye from earth, even when they occur in other galaxies. It is an astounding fact that the heavy elements which are ejected in supernova explosions are the source of all the material that makes up all the planets throughout the universe, and all the life on earth. Without supernovas, no planets could form, and no life could exist.

Another type of supernova is very important, astronomically. So-called Type Ia supernovas occur when a white dwarf star, a remnant of a dead larger star, and composed of a plasma of carbon and oxygen, attracts enough matter to cause collapse of the core. Type Ia supernovas are thought to occur in binary stars when the gas of a companion star accumulates on its white dwarf partner until the core compression triggers a nuclear reaction and the supernova explosion. The onset of the collapse takes place at a precise mass of 1.44 solar masses. For that prediction, made in 1931, Subramanyan Chandrasekhar shared the

Nobel Prize in Physics in 1983. The thermonuclear trigger point, called the Chandrasekhar Limit, is the same for all white dwarf stars, so each Type Ia supernova is of nearly the same brightness. This provides a 'standard candle' that is highly valued in astronomy as a calibrated distance marker. Once an object is identified by its spectral emissions as a Type Ia supernova, then its apparent brightness from earth can be compared with the known absolute brightness to determine the distance to the object with accuracy.

These massive explosions of dying stars can briefly radiate more energy than our sun will expend in its whole lifetime, and for several days supernovas can outshine entire galaxies. The history of supernova observations is a long one. Several supernovas were observed even before the invention of telescopes - including the observation in 1054 of the stellar explosion that gave rise to what is now the Crab Nebula, and the observation in 1572 of a 'new star' by the Danish astronomer Tycho Brahe, described in his book 'De Stella Nova' - the origin of the term. The term 'supernova' was coined in the 1930s by Walter Baade and Fritz Zwicky at the Mount Wilson Observatory in California. Although a total of more than 10,000 supernovas have been observed throughout the universe, fewer than 10 historical observations have been attributed to supernovas in our own galaxy, most famously the observations in 1054, 1572 (Brahe) and 1604 (Kepler). Some recent work of the rate of supernova explosions estimates that a supernova should occur in our Milky Way galaxy on average every 50 years - but no observation of a supernova in our galaxy has been made for the last 400 years. This is partly due to the fact that light from any supernova that occurs at the other side of our galaxy will be absorbed by galactic dust and so not be observed.

In recent times, the most dedicated and prolific discoverer of supernovas has been a Scottish amateur observer, working from his garden in rural England. Tom Boles was born in Lennoxtown, near Glasgow, in 1944. His early interests in astronomy and optical instruments were developed by working as a telescope designer and

Illustration 66: Tom Boles, supernova hunter

maker at Charles Frank Ltd, a famous Glasgow company renowned for its excellence in the design and sale of optical and photographic equipment. He had several important influencers. *"The late T R Tannahill of Glasgow University was a mentor to me. He helped me sneak into his astronomy lectures when I was 15. He gave me good advice and listened to my half-baked theories about astronomy without laughing. For anyone of my era in the UK, Patrick Moore has got to be the most influential astronomer, with his own work and The Sky at Night, which started the year after I discovered astronomy. I first met Patrick in 1960 when he visited our telescope workshop in Glasgow."* Subsequent work for 'Silicon Glen' computer companies (including NCR and Siemens) served to develop Boles' knowledge and skills in computer technology, which he later exploited in his construction of an automated observatory used for his supernova discoveries.

The observational achievements of Tom Boles are perhaps the most impressive of any amateur astronomer, ever. For twenty years, Boles used his self-constructed observatory to detect and document 155 supernovas, a record for any individual observer that is unlikely to be surpassed. He said, *"I chose supernovae because of my interest in cosmology. Even before the discovery of dark energy, supernovae played a major role in distance determination. A secondary reason – and a practical one – is that I intended to build my own observatory in the UK. The British sky conditions, variable at best, were better suited to searching for supernovae than any other of my interests. I started to look for supernovae in 1996 and now have three telescopes in my observatory in Coddenham, Suffolk. I need, on average, to record 4000 images to discover one supernova. Imaging, processing and checking each image takes about 2 minutes, and I have over half a million images. That is about 17000 man hours."* These days, teams of professional astronomers can scan the entire sky in a period of around 24 hours, using arrays of large optical telescopes with a light-gathering power not attainable by amateurs. By contrast, Boles' methods relied on three relatively modest optical telescopes housed in his garden observatory in Suffolk, and by using clever photography and computer automation, he detected supernova events in selected small sections of the night sky. Knowing that supernovas occur most frequently in spiral-arm galaxies, Boles focused his observations on particular small sections of the night sky which are rich in these galaxies, covering at any one time only an area of around one-ninth of the apparent area of the Moon as seen from Earth, and used 'blink detection' methods to compare current photo images with earlier reference images.

Over time, Boles amassed some half a million star-field images and patrolled around 12,000 galaxies over the course of a year. His first supernova discovery was made in 1997. This Type II supernova was located in the spiral-arm galaxy NGC3451 located around 61 million light-years away. Boles retired from industry in 2001 to concentrate on his astronomical work, and went on to detect between 4 and 12 new supernovas in most years, gaining national and international acclaim for his work. He was President of the British Astronomical Association from 2003 to 2005 and Vice President from 2005 to 2007. He was elected a Fellow of the Royal Astronomical Society and has served as an Examinations Moderator in astronomy with the International Baccalaureate. His many awards for contributions to the advancement of astronomy include the Merlin Medal and the Walter Goodacre Award of the British Astronomical Association. In 2008, the inner main-belt asteroid, discovered by Japanese astronomers, was named 7648 Tomboles. Boles also received the 'Sky at Night' award from the magazine of the same name, and the George Alcock Award from The Astronomer Magazine. Not forgetting his roots, he presented the Inaugural Thomas Tannahill Memorial lecture in 2009, at the request of the Astronomical Society of Glasgow.

Boles' rate of supernova observations averaged around 8 per year peaking at 30 discoveries in 2003. Of Boles' 155 listed discoveries, 51 have been in the Type Ia 'standard candle' category. He was quoted as saying that he was especially proud of the 2003 discovery (2003L) which, at the time of discovery, was the second most powerful supernova at radio-wavelengths ever observed, despite its brightness at optical wavelengths being only modest. This drove a change in thinking about the internal mechanisms which drive supernova events.

Most of Boles' supernova discoveries have been followed up by the world's largest telescopes including the Hubble Space Telescope and the two giant Keck Telescopes in Hawaii. In 2011, the importance of supernova observations was recognised by the award of the Nobel Prize in Physics to a team of astronomers for 'the discovery of the accelerating expansion of the Universe through observations of distant supernovae'. They had discovered, using Type Ia standard candles and 'redshift' spectral observations, that the rate of expansion of the universe is increasing, with potentially profound consequences for cosmology and particle physics. In 2013, the Hubble Space Telescope detected a supernova (SN-UDS10Wil) which is 10 billion light-years from earth - the most distant (and hence oldest) known Type Ia supernova. Truly, the importance of supernovas in the evolution and understanding of our universe cannot be overstated.

33

Diagnosing and controlling diabetes: Ian Shanks

It's a long journey from being a successful electronic engineer to winning worldwide recognition as a pioneer in medical diagnostics. For Ian Alexander Shanks, the path proved to be far more tortuous and stressful than he could ever have imagined. Shanks grew up in Dunbartonshire and attended Dumbarton Academy where he met his future wife, Janice. They married in 1971, a year after Ian had graduated in Electronic and Electrical Engineering from Glasgow University, and they moved, first to Portsmouth and then, in 1973, to Malvern, Worcestershire, where he had secured a job at the Royal Signals and Radar Establishment. At the University of Hull and in collaboration with Cyril Hilsum's group at RSRE, another Scot and Glasgow alumnus, the chemist George William Gray, was formulating a new family of 'nematic' liquid crystals that were stable, for the first time, at room temperature, making them viable for use in commercial Liquid Crystal Displays. Of course, now LCDs are found almost everywhere in smartphones, laptops and televisions. Gray went on to win many awards and a professorship at the University of Hull, where he continued to be at the forefront of liquid crystal developments. Shanks worked on designing practical LCDs, and filed many patents covering innovations in electrode configurations and the production of 3-D images. While working at RSRE, he received his PhD from the Council for National Academic Awards, conferred by Glasgow College of Technology, before moving on in 1982 to work in industry, at Unilever UK Central Resources Ltd. (CRL), in their Colworth Laboratory near Bedford.

At Unilever, Shanks worked mainly in process control, but also initiated research into biosensors, having realised that some aspects of liquid crystal technology had the potential to enable low-cost chemical test devices. Specifically, the tiny cells formed by two thin layers of glass, used to contain the liquid crystals in wristwatch displays, could be re-purposed, taking advantage of capillary action to draw blood, or other liquid samples, into the gap between the layers. Since the glass cells had a well-defined internal volume and avoided interferences from dissolved oxygen and evaporation, it would be possible accurately to measure the relative concentrations of chemicals in the samples. In 1982, working at home in his spare time, he built a prototype using bulldog clips and pieces from his daughter's microscope kit. Thinking about the potential to measure the abnormal blood sugar levels present in diabetic patients, his next step was to coat electrodes on the inner surface of the glass slides with a compound that selectively reacts with glucose and a mediator that allows an electrical current to flow, in proportion to the concentration of glucose in the sample. This current could then be measured to give the glucose concentration in a matter of seconds. This line of thought followed in the footsteps of an American biochemist, Leland C. Clark Jr. who invented the first 'glucometer' in 1956 and who was considered to be 'the father of biosensors'. Shanks' design became known as an Electrochemical Capillary Fill Device (ECFD) and eventually appeared, under licence, in most glucose testing products, enabling diabetics to monitor their condition with a simple finger-prick to produce just a tiny sample of blood.

In 1984, aged 35, Ian Shanks became the youngest Fellow of the Royal Society elected that year, in recognition of his work on LCDs, and he soon moved on from Unilever, to forge an impressive career working across many industry, academic and government roles. He was Chief Scientist at Thorn EMI for eight years from 1986, working on electro-optic displays and light sources, and became a member of the Optoelectronics Committee of the Rank Prize Funds, a consultant to the BBC, and a Visiting Professor at Glasgow University. In 1992,

Shanks was elected a Fellow of the Royal Academy of Engineering. He returned to Unilever Research in 1994, as their Science Adviser , and became a member of the Science Advisory Group for the National Physical Laboratory, proceeding to chair it a few years later. He was elected to the Fellowship of the Royal Society of Edinburgh in the year 2000.

Meanwhile, Unilever had commercialised the ECFD invention by licensing it to third party companies, addressing a competitive but potentially huge market of many billions of dollars, as diabetes continued to become more prevalent in a growing worldwide population. Unilever elected to license the underlying ECFD technology to other firms, relatively cheaply, rather than develop test devices themselves, and as a result they profited only modestly from a digital glucose meter marketplace now worth around $10 billion per year. Over the course of the 1990s, Unilever's licensing deals earned an estimated £24.5 million.

Under UK law, inventions made by an employee, whether or not made in their spare time, are the intellectual property of the employer. However, the Patents Act of 1977 requires companies, where the invention is *"of outstanding benefit to the employer"*, to compensate the inventor with a *"fair share of the benefit which the employer has derived"*. The Act does not define what a 'fair share' might entail and its provisions for assignments and licensing benefits had never before been used.

Ian Shanks retired from Unilever in the year 2003, but continued his work for the National Physical Laboratory, the University of Glasgow and the Rank Prize Funds. In 2006, as the UK and international patents were expiring, Shanks made his first application to receive 'fair share' compensation for his invention of the Electrochemical Capillary Fill Device.

Following a succession of hearings to establish how the Patents Act intended licensing and assignments be treated, his claim was considered by the Comptroller General of Patents, in 2013. The Comptroller's office concluded that Unilever's £24.5 million of benefits from the

Illustration 67: A commercial blood glucose test device

invention did indeed 'stand out', but were 'not outstanding' due to the huge size of the whole Unilever business. If the benefits had been 'outstanding' they judged, then *"a fair share of the benefit for Professor Shanks would be 5%"*. Both parties challenged the ruling, Unilever with regard to the amount of potential fair share, while Shanks maintained that Unilever's benefits were, in fact, 'outstanding', especially given Unilever's decision to license the patents to third parties, on request, as opposed to developing the diabetes testing technology themselves.

Shanks continued to support the teaching, research and development of nanotechnology and optoelectronics, and for his many contributions to science and engineering he was awarded, at the age of 64, an OBE in the Queen's Birthday Honours list of 2012. He was not ready, however, to give up the battle on his diabetic test patents. He made an appeal to the England and Wales High Court (Patents Court), and the case *Shanks v Unilever PLC & Others* was heard over three days by The Hon Mr Justice Arnold in May, 2014. In a lengthy judgment, Justice Arnold noted that it was undesirable that the claim had taken seven years to reach him, but ruled in favour of Unilever on the grounds that that *"the Shanks Patents were not of outstanding benefit to Unilever, and therefore Prof Shanks is not entitled to an award of employee compensation…"*

Undaunted, over the next five years Shanks continued to assert his claim, and appealed again, first to the Court of Appeal and then to the UK Supreme Court, where a new judgment was reached by Lady Hale, Lord Reed, Lord Hodge, Lady Black, and Lord Kitchin in October, 2019. In delivering his conclusions, and referring to the original hearing in the Comptroller's office, Lord Kitchin said, *"The hearing officer's assessment of the benefit of the Shanks patents was flawed. First, he adopted the wrong starting point. CRL's undertaking … was the business of generating inventions and providing those inventions and the patents which protected them to Unilever for use in connection with its business… the hearing officer wrongly adopted an approach which involved assessing the extent and nature of the benefit derived from a patent simply by comparing it to the patent owner's overall turnover or profits… The fair share to which Professor Shanks is entitled is £2m and the appeal is allowed."*

The landmark judgment vindicated what Shanks called his '13-year slog' to obtain fair compensation, and he said the potential impact for other inventors was *"one of the main driving forces that saw me take this on back in 2006…[when it was] 30 years since the Patents Act was introduced, and not a single employee inventor had actually benefited from its provisions."* He also ruefully observed that most of the £2 million award would go to paying his legal costs.

Over his long and inventive career, Ian Shanks submitted more than 70 patent applications, but perhaps none has benefitted the lives of so many people as the glucose-measuring capillary test device. *"It was nice to have been one of the key figures in enabling LCD technology. It is even nicer to have been able to help tens of millions of people around the world in controlling their diabetes."* It is fitting that his achievements were recognised, in 2020, by the Royal Society awarding him the Royal Medal for distinguished contributions in the applied sciences.

34 Looking at life with electrons: Richard Henderson

We take for granted our ability to see with light. But our eyes detect only a tiny portion of the electromagnetic spectrum that stretches from long radio waves to X-rays and gamma-rays. There is another limitation, too. When trying to observe microscopic objects, the resolution that can be achieved is limited by the wavelength of the illuminating light. For the shortest wavelengths in the visible spectrum, that means we are limited to resolving objects around 0.5 micrometres (μm) size, even with the best optical microscopes. That is fine for observing, for example, the nuclei of biological cells (1-15 μm), but useless for the detailed study of much smaller objects, such as an influenza virus (100 nanometres) or a molecule of DNA (typical length 50 nm and diameter 2 nm). For such studies, a range of techniques using shorter and shorter wavelengths have been developed over the years. X-ray crystallography was the method used by Rosalind Franklin to produce the beautiful diffraction patterns that enabled her, Crick, Watson and Wilkins to deduce the regular structure of the DNA helix. As is well known, that led to the award of a Nobel prize to the three men in 1962, Franklin having died four years previously from ovarian cancer, aged just 37.

A still more powerful imaging technique was developed, beginning in the 1930s, using the strange fact that sub-atomic 'particles' are as much wave as particle. In fact, all matter exhibits the properties of both particles and waves, though it is only at the smallest scales that this becomes apparent. The wave-particle duality of electrons endows them with an effective wavelength of the order of 0.1nm (i.e. 1 Ångström), depending on their energy – the higher the electron energy (or momentum), the shorter the wavelength. The possibility to probe microscopic structures by using the diffraction of electrons was recognised by the prolific Hungarian inventor and physicist Leo Szilard, who filed a patent application in Germany for an 'electron microscope' in 1928. He failed to persuade his compatriot, Dennis Gabor (later the inventor of holograms), to act on the idea. That fell to Max Knoll and Ernst Ruska at the Berlin Technische Hochschule, who in 1933 built the first example, using magnetic fields to focus the electrons. Ruska continued to work on electron optics and moved on to work for the Siemens company who produced the first commercial electron microscope in 1939. By then, resolutions of 10nm were being achieved and by the mid-1940s that was improved to around 2nm (20 Å). All the early instruments were Transmission Electron Microscopes (TEMs) where electrons are fired through extremely thin slices of specimens and the resultant diffracted images are focused on the detector, typically a fluorescent screen. In later developments an intensely-focused electron beam spot (around 1 Å wide) is scanned across the sample, and the transmitted electrons are analysed, for example for energy loss, which enables the characteristics of the sample to be assessed at atomic resolution. The first commercial scanning electron microscopes (SEMs) appeared in the mid-1960s and opened up a world of new analytical possibilities for materials scientists.

Biologists were equally intrigued by the potential to analyse and picture the molecules of life. A couple of problems make that more difficult. First, samples in an electron microscope need to be in the high vacuum that is required to maintain a focused electron beam. Living cells are filled with a thick watery solution of cytoplasm, containing salts and proteins, and they react badly to conditions in a vacuum. Secondly, high-energy electrons can burn the sample, which is avoided in inert materials by coating them in a thin layer of gold, but which is difficult to achieve for biological samples.

In 1966, a young graduate from the University of Edinburgh was considering the options for his future scientific career. Richard Henderson was born in Edinburgh, and was raised in the Scottish borders, where his father worked in a bakery in the small village of Newcastleton. His

Illustration 68: Dr Richard Henderson

mother strongly encouraged his studies, and he was educated at the high school in Hawick, (requiring a 45 minute each way journey by steam train) and at Boroughmuir High School in Edinburgh, where his sixth-form physics teacher introduced the class to some concepts in biophysics. Richard's parents received the government 'family allowance' to help him to continue into higher education. Having received special tuition to achieve the O-level in French he needed for university entrance, Henderson studied physics at Edinburgh, supplementing his student grant with income from summer jobs at the local Ferranti factory and the UK Atomic Energy Authority at Aldermaston. He graduated with first-class honours, and started looking for a suitable field for his PhD research. Having considered nuclear and particle physics, he was advised to visit the Medical Research Council Laboratory of Molecular Biology in Cambridge, led by Max Perutz, who had already determined the structure of the haemoglobin protein by using X-ray crystallography. Seeing so many people working enthusiastically in the laboratory on a Saturday, he made up his mind to specialise in biophysics, which also gave him the opportunity, he said later, to do experiments on his own - rather than being a member of a large team of collaborators.

Henderson's chosen subject for his doctoral research was an enzyme called chymotrypsin, which originates in the pancreas and is an important component of the intestinal juices that break down proteins and enable the digestion of food. To figure out how exactly this happens, Henderson joined a group, (led by his PhD supervisor David Blow) that determined the structure of the chymotrypsin molecule using state-of-the-art X-ray analysis techniques at atomic resolution. He followed this with a three-year spell of post-doctoral work at Yale University, accompanied by his wife Penny and their one-year-old daughter, Jennifer. Sadly, in America, they would have another daughter, Elizabeth, who was born with hydrocephalus and died seven months later.

At Yale, Henderson studied the proteins which exist, permanently or transiently, in cell membranes and are vitally important for cell functioning. They are ubiquitous - around a third of human proteins are membrane proteins. Henderson attempted to use X-rays to determine the structure of an important membrane protein – bacteriorhodopsin, found in single-celled organisms and known as 'purple membrane' since it occurs in purplish, two-dimensional crystalline patches in the cell wall. As a 'proton pump' involved in photosynthesis, bacteriorhodopsin absorbs light, and by moving hydrogen ions across the cell membrane, it provides the cell with chemical energy. Henderson tried to make bacteriorhodopsin soluble, in order to crystallise it in three dimensions so that its structure could be determined by X-ray crystallography. He was still trying, without success, when his fellowship at Yale came to an end.

The Hendersons, now with a son Alastair, aged three months, returned to Cambridge in 1973, where Richard resumed work at the MRC Laboratory for Molecular Biology. At the annual laboratory symposium, he heard an impressive talk by a colleague, Nigel Unwin, on the use of electron microscopy to study the protein structures of a plant pathogen called tobacco mosaic virus. This triggered the thought that an electron microscope could be used to visualise the structure of bacteriorhodopsin in its natural two-dimensional crystalline form. After working together for 18 months, the pair succeeded in imaging the protein, at a relatively low resolution of 7Å, but sufficient to see that the molecule consists of seven closely-packed helixes lying roughly perpendicular to the plane of the cell membrane. To protect the biological samples from damage and dehydration in the vacuum, they were coated with glucose solution, and a low electron beam intensity was used, with clever computer analysis applied to the faint electron diffraction patterns and images. Even so, many molecules in the sample were destroyed and only an averaged image of the many molecules in the sample could be obtained. Henderson and Unwin spent many years trying to improve the resolution of the images to the 3Å necessary to understand the detailed atomic structure and chemical mechanisms involved. The attempts were fruitless, partly due to the limitations of electron microscope technology, but also the difficulties of preparing biological specimens to produce crisp images.

Two breakthrough techniques came together to solve the problems. First, it was realised that cooling biological samples to very low temperatures, say around 4 degrees Kelvin, dramatically reduced the radiation burning caused by the electron beams, and also avoided the problem of the liquid water in the samples evaporating in the vacuum of the electron microscope. However, freezing the samples created another difficulty. The ice crystals which formed within and around cells damaged the samples, and interfered with the probing electrons as much as the molecules under study. A light-bulb moment occurred in 1980, when Jacques Dubochet, a biophysicist working at the European Molecular Biology Laboratory (EMBL) in Heidelberg, was called over by one of his colleagues, Alasdair McDowall, to look at something interesting. McDowall and the team had been trying to vitrify water droplets – by rapidly freezing water so that ice crystals do not form. Examining the result through an optical microscope, Dubochet saw a frozen droplet of amorphous material. He said, *"since it didn't have any ice crystals, we figured it couldn't be water. We warmed it slowly to try to see how it evaporated, in order to try to find out what the droplet was made of. At 135 Kelvin – or around minus 138 degrees Celsius – the droplet transformed in a moment into polycrystals that we immediately recognised as ice crystals. So the frozen droplet we had seen before had been exactly what we had been told was impossible to create:*

vitrified water. I remember just at this moment I told Alasdair, 'here we have something essential'." Through rapid 'plunge-freezing' using liquid ethane they had succeeded in creating crystal-free, glass-like frozen water, and enabled the development of a new field called cryo-electron microscopy (cryo-EM). Dubochet reflected later that, *"It was serendipity, luck, and some major failures that led me to the key aha moment."*

Secondly, key developments were made by the German-American biophysicist Joachim Frank, working first at the Max Planck Institute in Munich and then in several laboratories in the USA and UK, including at the University of California, the Cavendish Laboratory of the University of Cambridge, and the Jet Propulsion Laboratory (JPL), at that time the world leader in image processing. Frank became absorbed by the problems of processing electron microscope images produced by disordered molecules, and convinced himself that high-resolution pictures of large proteins could only be obtained by combining and averaging different images. During a two-year spell at the Cavendish, he and a colleague, Owen Saxton, calculated the lowest electron dose needed to produce images that could be combined to yield sufficient sharpness, and formulated an equation relating electron dose, contrast, and resolution. Crucially they showed that, in theory, merging image data even from single molecules would work. Returning to America, Frank pursued the prediction experimentally, using electron microscopy, and developed a software tool to average low-dose electron images and combine them into 3-D. The software, called SPIDER, (System for Processing of Image Data in Electron microscopy and Related fields) became an essential tool for a worldwide community of electron microscopists, and enabled Frank's team to publish the first 3-D images of single ribosomes, the large intracellular molecules which contain RNA and are the construction sites for all proteins. They later developed techniques to take electron micrograph snap-shots of the step-by-step chemical processes and combine the still images into 'movies' of molecular reactions.

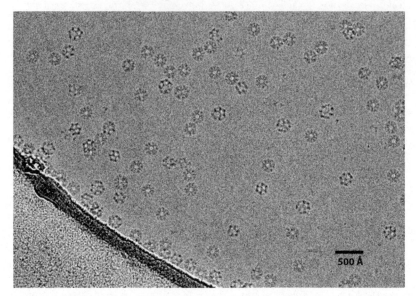

Illustration 69: Cryo-electron micrograph of the icosahedral molecules of an enzyme sub-complex of pyruvate dehydrogenase (PDH). Courtesy of Dr Richard Henderson.

The great power of these methods is that thousands of images of fuzzy electron micrographs can be averaged in three dimensions, to reveal the structure of the molecule, at the atomic level. Illustration 2 shows an image of molecules within the important enzyme complex called pyruvate dehydrogenase (PDH), which sits inside mammalian cells and catalyses the production of glucose and fatty acids the body requires. The molecule consists of 60 sub-units arranged in an icosahedral (20-sided) pattern. Illustration 3 shows a single molecule with an image of a sub-unit superimposed, to scale, and Illustration 4 shows the derived atomic structure of the single sub-unit, measuring around 100Å across. Electron microscopy has advanced to the point that individual atoms can be resolved, and cryo-EM has revealed the atomic structure of many of the molecules of life and death, including the Hepatitis B virus, the Zika virus, the Tau protein implicated in Alzheimer's disease, and rhinovirus C, which causes acute asthma in children. In recognition of their development of cryo-EM "for high-resolution structure determination of biomolecules in solution", the 2017 Nobel Prize for Chemistry was awarded to Jacques Dubochet,

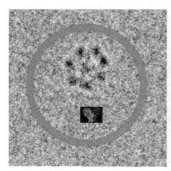 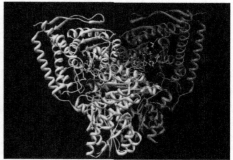

Illustration 70: Cryo-EM image of a 60-unit PDH molecule (left) with image of a single sub-unit inserted to scale, and (right) the atomic structure of a single sub-unit, size around 100Å, derived by averaging thousands of electron micrographs in three dimensions

Joachim Frank, and Richard Henderson. Dubochet gave one of his three replica Nobel medals to Alasdair McDowall, his nomadic Scottish colleague who did the seminal experiment in 'plunge-freezing' to vitrify water, and who went on to a distinguished research career at Caltech and the University of Queensland.

The Nobel committee makes its decisions on the morning of the day of the prize announcements, and when they rang Richard Henderson with news of the award, he was attending a conference and initially refused the call. He remembered that *"I was there happily listening to talks, and then the phone rang at about 10.10…I rarely get phone calls from Sweden, but I'm surrounded by the audience, so I rejected the phone call. And then it rang again, and I thought I had better take it, so I went outside and called back. Eventually after about five minutes I managed to get through…they told me that the chemistry prize was going to be awarded, with Jacques Dubochet and Joachim Frank who of course I know very well, so I think that's quite delightful really."* The Nobel committee chair, Sara Linse, put it this way. *"Soon, there are no more secrets, now, we can see the intricate details of the biomolecules in every corner of our cells and every drop of our body fluids. We can understand how they are built and how they act and how they work together in large communities. We are facing a revolution in biochemistry."*

35 Dolly the sheep: Keith Campbell and Ian Wilmut

On the 5th July 1996, a lamb named Dolly was born at the Roslin Institute, part of the University of Edinburgh, and she soon became the most famous sheep in the world. Admittedly that was a low threshold, but Dolly's fame was justifiable. She was the first mammal of any kind to be cloned by transplanting the nucleus of an adult cell. Her birth, publicly announced seven months later, marked the culmination of many years of

Illustration 71: Dolly with her own first-born lamb, Bonnie. Courtesy of the Roslin Institute, U. of Edinburgh

dedicated and painstaking research by the Roslin team of scientists led by Ian Wilmut.

Cloning – the production of genetically identical copies of an organism - has a long history. Clones have existed in nature since the beginning of life on earth, produced for example by the asexual reproduction of bacteria and some plants, and the occurrence in mammals of identical twins who have almost the same genetic makeup as each other, though they are genetically distinct from either parent. Artificial cloning of organisms dates from work in the early 20th century, especially that of the German embryologist Hans Spemann and his student Hilde Mangold. Working with the embryos of newts, they succeeded in transplanting 'organiser' cells from one embryo to another. After Hilde's terrible death from burns she sustained in a house fire,

Spemann was awarded the Nobel prize for physiology or medicine, in 1935. Incidentally, and perhaps prudently, he distinguished himself by giving a Nazi salute at the award ceremony. Spemann went on to propose that a method of cloning could be through the transfer of the nucleus of an adult ('somatic') body cell to an immature egg cell, an oocyte, whose nucleus had been removed – so-called 'somatic cell nuclear transfer'. The tools available to Spemann at the time were inadequate to enable any experimentation.

In 1952, fourteen years after Spemann's suggestion, two American biologists, Robert Briggs and Thomas King, created the first animal clones – of northern leopard frogs – by transplanting the nuclei of embryonic cells into enucleated egg cells. Further experiments indicated that the same transplantation method, but using the nuclei of more mature cells, did not produce viable cloned embryos. The work was progressed ten years later at the University of Oxford, by the English biologist John Bertrand Gurdon, who successfully cloned a frog using the nuclei of somatic cells from tadpoles of the same species, thus demonstrating that mature cells could indeed produce viable clones – in frogs. In recognition of a long and distinguished scientific career, Gurdon received many prizes and honours, including a knighthood in 1995 and a share in the Nobel prize for physiology or medicine in 2012. Not bad for someone who came last of 250 boys in biology at Eton school, prompting his schoolmaster to report, *"His other work has been equally bad, and several times he has been in trouble, because he will not listen, but will insist on doing his work his own way. I believe he has ideas about becoming a Scientist; on his present showing this is quite ridiculous, if he can't learn simple Biological facts..."*

It remained an open question as to whether similar techniques could be used to produce clones of 'higher animals' including mammals. In 1979, researchers produced the first genetically identical mice by splitting early mouse embryos ('blastomere separation') in the test tube and then implanting them into the wombs of adult mice. More controversially, in 1981, at the University of Geneva, biologists Karl

Illmensee and Peter Hoppe claimed success in producing three mice clones by transplanting embryonic cell nuclei into fertilised, enucleated egg cells. The cloned mice allegedly produced offspring with characteristics of the genes in the donated nucleus, and the work attracted worldwide press attention. However - three members of the laboratory team could not replicate the results, and one of them accused Illmensee of falsifying data. A few months later, Illmensee signed a letter admitting that his results had been manipulated inappropriately. Several subsequent papers by other workers also reported failures to replicate the reported successes of Illmensee and Hoppe. An investigation into Illmensee's work, commissioned by Geneva University, found no definite evidence of fraud, but it was highly critical of his poor record-keeping. He continued as a professor at the university, and then went on to work on genetics and mammalian reproduction at several other research institutions.

A more accepted breakthrough was achieved in 1984 by Steen Willadsen, a Danish scientist working for the British Agricultural Research Council in Cambridge. He successfully transplanted nuclei from early embryonic cells to clone sheep – the first mammals to be undisputedly cloned by nuclear transfer. Two years later, he repeated the success with cattle, establishing the basic method for cloning mammalian embryos by nuclear transplantation. The question now was whether cloning could be achieved by transplanting the nuclei from more plentiful adult, somatic cells, rather than from embryonic cells. This was generally regarded as difficult or impossible, and for a very specific reason. Cell differentiation is the process whereby embryonic cells progressively become more specialised as the embryo develops, so that by the time of birth, each cell contains the same DNA, but with a selected proportion of genes activated, so that each cell has become differentiated to be, for example, a skin cell or a brain cell. The presumption among biologists was that cell differentiation was a one-way process of progressive and permanent change, so that mature cells were assumed to have lost the ability to recover embryo-like 'pluripotency' – the ability to become any cell in the body.

At Edinburgh University, Ian Wilmut's team of biologists were making no such assumption. Wilmut had moved in 1971 to what became the Roslin Institute, after a PhD and post-doctoral fellowship at Cambridge where he studied the cryonic preservation of boar semen, and produced the first calves from frozen embryos - work that would be picked up and developed by Willadsen. At Roslin, Wilmut's initial interest was in understanding the causes of embryo death – an important topic because in mammals, including humans, an estimated 30-70% of embryos die for various obscure reasons. Roslin's management had other ideas. Wilmut said later, *"The institute wanted to bring in molecular biology… and this is becoming a very important thing. And in being able to change genes in animals, you need to work with embryos. And very, very unusually…I was essentially told to stop working on the cause of embryo loss, and to begin working on this area. An instruction which I deeply resented, deeply, deeply resented. Scientists don't like being told what to do at all."* It did not take long for Wilmut to become immersed in the new field, and to recognise the potential of nuclear cell transfer, helped by attendance at a conference in Ireland. *"After a few months of working with the microbiologists for the first time, that is when I began to understand the power of genetics. We're talking about 1983… In a conversation in a bar one evening we were told that somebody working [in Texas A&M University] had achieved a step forward with nuclear transfer and was getting development from cells taken from embryo. And, it sparked across to the fact that in mouse there are ways of culturing those cells in the lab, they're called embryonic stem cells. A specialist population of cells which can give rise to every other tissue. Now, what the person in Texas had done was to take cells from just a day or two earlier than that, so there's sort of a short gap. But, the point that excited me was that if we could bridge that gap, then we would be able to have ways of being able to make genetic changes in animals and make lots of copies of animals."*

A team of molecular biologists slowly coalesced around Wilmut at Roslin, and developed expertise in the methods of nuclear cell transfer throughout the 1980s, initially focused on genetic modification of sheep, to produce milk proteins needed to treat human disease. A commercial company, PPL Therapeutics, was spun out, and the Roslin team was augmented by an Anglo-Scot, Keith Campbell, whose interest (reputedly inspired by the work of Illmensee and of Gurdon) was in cloning mammals. Campbell realised that to achieve successful transfer of cell nuclei, it was important to coordinate events in the egg and donor cells – specifically, the cycles which regulate the processes of DNA replication and cell division. Crucially, he also discovered that the gene functions in the transferred nuclei could be 'reprogrammed' more effectively if the donor cells were put in hibernation before transfer. That could be achieved routinely by starving the donor cells of nutrients, to render them 'quiescent'.

These insights led to the next step, when the team created embryos by transplanting the nuclei of more mature embryonic cells derived from Welsh Mountain sheep, into the enucleated egg cells of Scottish Blackface ewes. Viable embryos were implanted in surrogate Blackface ewes and after 35 days a total of eight fetuses were detected in seven recipient ewes (including a twin pregnancy). Three fetuses were lost at various stages of gestation, but five female Welsh Mountain lambs were carried to term by the Blackface ewes. Two died within a few minutes of birth and a third died after 10 days. The remaining two lambs were normal and healthy. The success was reported eight months later, in a letter to the journal *Nature*. The two Welsh Mountain lambs, named Megan and Morag, were the first mammals to be cloned from embryonic donor cells that had reached the stage of early differentiated specialisation.

Encouraged by this success, the team moved on to the next step, this time using adult donor cells derived from the udder of a six-year-old white Finn Dorset ewe. By a similar procedure than before, the donor cells were quiesced, then injected into enucleated, unfertilised eggs cells from a Scottish Blackface ewe, and stimulated to divide using an electrical pulse. After culture for six or seven days, 29 resulting embryos were implanted into 13 Blackface surrogate mothers. Only one pregnancy went to full term, and in July 1996 after 148 days, a healthy 6.6kg Finn Dorset lamb was born, and named Dolly. Ian Wilmut revealed the thinking behind the name. *"Dolly is derived from a mammary gland cell and we couldn't think of a more impressive pair of glands than Dolly Parton's."* The team's celebrations were muted – Keith Campbell was away on holiday when Dolly was born – and they waited several months to report the breakthrough in *Nature*, stressing that *"The fact that a lamb was derived from an adult cell confirms that differentiation of that cell did not involve the irreversible modification of genetic material required for development to term. The birth of lambs from differentiated fetal and adult cells also reinforces previous speculation that by inducing donor cells to become quiescent it will be possible to obtain normal development from a wide variety of differentiated cells."* The Roslin team had astounded the world and proved the viability of somatic cell nuclear transfer to clone mammals. Their innovations also confirmed the conjectures of Hans Spemann, made 70 years earlier.

Dolly lived a well-protected and pampered existence at the Roslin Institute. She was mated with a Welsh Mountain ram and eventually had a total of six lambs, all normal and healthy, beginning with Bonnie, born in April 1998, followed by twins and then triplets. After Dolly, Keith Campbell and his colleagues again collaborated with Angelika Schnieke and her team at PPL, to create transgenic lambs, by transplanting the nuclei of fetal skin cells from Poll Dorset sheep. The skin cells, or fibroblasts, were genetically modified to contain a human gene. The resulting embryos were again gestated in surrogate Scottish Blackface mothers. The human gene caused two of the offspring ewes, named Polly and Molly, to produce in their milk a protein called human coagulation factor IX, which is deficient in human patients with haemophilia B. The work demonstrated that somatic cell nuclear transfer was an effective way to produce therapeutically useful transgenic animals, (known as 'pharming'), compared to the method of micro-injecting DNA into fertilised egg cells, which was often ineffective and unreliable.

Keith Campbell left the Roslin Institute in 1997 to join PPL Therapeutics as head of embryology. He moved on again two years later, to become professor of animal development at the University of Nottingham, where he continued his research into the basic mechanisms of cell differentiation and reprogramming. Back at Roslin, as Dolly the sheep matured, she developed serious health problems. She became arthritic and contracted a progressive lung cancer called *Jaagsiekte* that is spread between sheep by an ovine retrovirus, and is usually fatal. She was treated with anti-inflammatory drugs but in 2003, she had to be euthanised. She was six and a half years old. Since the normal lifespan of a Finn Dorset sheep is around 11 years, Dolly's early decline led to concerns that cloned animals might in some way age prematurely. Detailed follow-up research, much of it led by Campbell at Nottingham, allayed the concerns and found no detrimental long-term health effects in other cloned sheep, including those cloned from the same cell-line as Dolly.

The hoped-for commercial success of PPL Therapeutics was never realised, and the company was closed, and its assets sold, in 2003. For their advances in the understanding and application of cell differentiation in mammals, Ian Wilmut and Keith Campbell were awarded the 2008 Shaw Prize in life science and medicine, worth one million dollars and sometimes called the 'Nobel of the East.' The prize was shared with the Japanese researcher Shinya Yamanaka, who went on to win the Nobel itself with John Gurdon, in 2012, for his discovery that any mature body cell can be induced to become a pluripotent stem cell. Also in 2008, Wilmut was knighted in the New Year Honours list, and some thought that Campbell should have been too. By then, Wilmut had already decided not to pursue a licence to clone human embryos, and had concluded that somatic cell nuclear transfer was no longer the most effective method for the production of animal clones, given Yamanaka's revolutionary work with induced pluripotent stem (iPS) cells. In an interview with *Scientific American*, Wilmut enthused about the potential to produce therapeutic stem cells to battle human diseases. *"All you have to do is take some skin cells from somebody who apparently has inherited the disease, scatter some 'magic dust' on them and wait for three weeks…and you've got pluripotent [stem] cells."* Needless to say, it is a bit more complicated than that, but the potential for stem cell therapies is undoubted. If iPS pans out, Wilmut predicted, nuclear transfer to produce cell lines may one day become a history lesson.

In 2012, Keith Campbell's life ended at the age of 58 in shocking and tragic circumstances, when he was found dead by hanging, reportedly after an inebriated domestic argument. Ian Wilmut said of him, that he *"played a leading role in making possible the birth of Dolly the cloned sheep. This breakthrough opened up revolutionary new opportunities in regenerative medicine by demonstrating that the future of cells is not rigidly fixed, but can be changed from one tissue type to another… he will be remembered as an enthusiastic participant in discussions lasting late into the night. Always cheerful and friendly – with a strong distaste for bureaucracy – he will be sorely missed."* Sir Ian Wilmut continues with his own work as an Emeritus Professor at the Scottish Centre for Regenerative Medicine, a stem cell research institute of the University of Edinburgh.

His eponymous boson: Peter Higgs

Illustration 72: Peter Higgs at work

When James Clerk Maxwell brilliantly unified the forces of electricity and magnetism, he used the concept of an electromagnetic field that propagated electrical and magnetic forces between bodies, at the speed of light. Light itself was shown to be an electromagnetic field, and Maxwell's insights led to the development of radio transmission and the wirelessly connected world we now inhabit. Maxwell's work was the undoubted pinnacle of 19th century physics, and prompted the idea that physics could be simplified further, if other forces could be unified – and seen to be different facets of an underlying reality. But what exactly is a 'field'? How do electromagnetic forces actually interact across space with material objects?

Albert Einstein won the Nobel prize in 1921, not for his theories of relativity, but for his realisation that electromagnetic fields must be *quantized*. This was demonstrated by the photoelectric effect, where the light-induced ejection of electrons from metal surfaces does not depend only on the intensity of the incoming light, but also on its frequency, which must match specific values. Einstein deduced that light must be not just a wave propagating through space, but is also a collection of wave packets – photons. A full description of the detailed interaction of light with matter was eventually provided by the theory called Quantum Electrodynamics, (QED), best and most graphically described by another Nobel-winning physicist, Richard Feynman. In QED, the photon is the carrier of electromagnetic force – with the exchange of 'virtual' photons between electrons, protons and other charged particles revealed as the fundamental mechanism underpinning the phenomena of electromagnetic attraction and repulsion.

Quantum electrodynamics is one of the most successful theories in all of physics – it correctly predicts the outcomes of particle collisions, and the results of the interactions of light and matter. But we are left wrestling with some deeply unintuitive concepts, beginning with the photon itself – a massless 'particle', which nevertheless has momentum. 'Particle' is a useful shorthand word, but only if it is understood as really meaning 'quantum of energy', an excitation of an underlying field of energy. Two main classes of quantum particles can be defined. The group called 'fermions', named after Enrico Fermi, includes electrons, protons and neutrons. Their distinguishing feature is that only a restricted number of fermions can occupy the same energy levels in a quantum system. The class of elementary particles called 'bosons' is central to our story. Bosons, named for the Indian physicist Satyendra Bose, have two important characteristics which distinguish them from other quantum particles. First, any number of bosons can have the same energy state. Second, all the force-carrying particles within fields, such as the example of the photon in electromagnetic interactions, are also bosons, specifically, vector or 'gauge' bosons - named from the branch of mathematics called gauge theory which found its unexpected practical application in describing the interactions of force-carrying bosons.

From this, other questions arise. Why do some particles have mass while others are massless? What is it that determines the mass of a particle? What is the origin of mass? By the early 1960s, a large number of physicists were pursuing these questions with a view to completing our picture of the sub-atomic world, and progressing the simplifying unification of physical forces begun by Maxwell. In 1961, the first Scottish Universities Summer School in Physics was held at the University of Edinburgh, where a 32-year-old theoretical physicist, Peter Higgs, had been appointed to a lectureship the previous autumn.

Higgs had recently read a paper by Yoichiro Nambu and Giovanni Jona-Lasinio of the University of Chicago, which immediately captured his interest. The paper, published in the *Physical Review*, hypothesised a mechanism whereby nuclear particles (protons and neutrons) in the early birth of the universe could have acquired mass – a mechanism now called 'spontaneous symmetry breaking'. By 'symmetry breaking' physicists mean any event which causes the laws of physics to become specific to a particular physical system, rather than applicable universally. For example, in empty space, and in the absence of a gravitational field, the laws of motion are independent of direction. On the introduction of a gravitational field, the symmetry is broken, and we need to take account of the directions 'up' and 'down'. Nambu and Jona-Lasinio drew on an analogy with the phenomenon of low-temperature superconductivity in solids, to suggest that protons and neutrons acquired mass through symmetry breaking as the early universe cooled. This suggestion interested Higgs and others, and would lead, much later, to Nambu sharing the Nobel prize in physics in 2008.

At the Scottish Universities Summer School, Higgs had other important work to do. As the Steward, he had to buy and look after the wine that would be served at the conference dinners. This was made difficult, thanks to a group of four young physicists who hid some of the cache of wine in a grandfather clock, to lubricate their late-night discussions. The gang of four – the Italian Nicola Cabbibo, the Dutch theoretician Tino Veltman, Derek Robinson of Oxford, and Sheldon Glashow from Harvard – were also intrigued by the question of the origin of mass, and no doubt fuelled by the wine, debated the possibilities for further unification of fundamental physical forces.

After the Summer School, on his return to Harvard, Sheldon Glashow and his mentor Julian Schwinger (a veteran pioneer of QED) continued to work on their mission to achieve the second great step in the history of physics, after Maxwell's, towards a unified theory of forces. They had noticed similarities between electromagnetism and the 'weak' nuclear force (which is a cause of radioactive nuclear decay).

Their hypothesis was that the electromagnetic force merges, at high energies, with the weak force, and in fact were the same 'electroweak' force in the very early stages of the birth of the universe. As the universe rapidly cooled, the forces fell apart into the separate forces we see today, in a process of symmetry breaking. The calculations suggested that the weak force should be mediated – that is, carried – by three new bosons, dubbed Z, W+, and W-. Since the weak nuclear force has an extremely short effective range, these bosons should have mass, as distinct from the massless photons which give the electromagnetic force its long range. To make the mathematics work, Glashow needed to use a fudge to break the symmetry, separate the forces, give mass to the new bosons, and make the theory credible. He needed to find a mechanism of *spontaneous* symmetry breaking – and Glashow was first to coin that term. Back in Edinburgh, Peter Higgs was thinking about Nambu's work, and worrying about one troublesome aspect of it.

Higgs was born in Newcastle-upon-Tyne, and missed some early schooling due to childhood asthma, the impacts of World War II, and his father's peripatetic job as a sound engineer for the BBC, which moved the family around from place to place. After graduating in 1946 with first-class honours in physics from King's College London, he took a Master's degree and then a PhD for his research on *'Some problems in the theory of molecular vibrations'*. As a post-doctoral fellow at the University of Edinburgh, he re-discovered the fondness of his student days for hiking in the Scottish Highlands, and after various further academic appointments in London, he returned to Edinburgh in 1960, as a full lecturer at its Tait Institute of Mathematical Physics. He was a supporter of the Campaign for Nuclear Disarmament, and it was through his CND friends at the Edinburgh University staff club that he met a girl, Jody Williamson, who shared his love of hiking and camping. They were married in 1963. The following spring, one of their hiking trips to the Cairngorms was cut short by bad weather, and Higgs returned to work on his analysis of the Nambu/Jona-Lasinio paper and its implications.

The Nambu and Glashow papers had triggered a large number of physicists to think about how spontaneous symmetry breaking could be the clue to the origin of mass. Jeffrey Goldstone, a British physicist working at MIT, had shown that Nambu's spontaneous symmetry breaking theory predicted the existence of a new triplet of <u>massless</u> bosons, which should be abundant, and easily detected throughout the universe. Since no such particles were seen, Nambu's suggestion must be wrong, and theory of the origin of mass was at an impasse.

During the spring of 1964, a debate played out in the pages of the American journal *Physical Review Letters* as to whether, and how, Goldstone's prediction of the massless, and non-existent, bosons could be avoided, and Nambu's theory rescued. Higgs remembered some crucial work by Julian Schwinger on quantum electrodynamics, which he could draw upon to modify the Goldstone model, by coupling it mathematically to an electromagnetic field. As he later put it, *"Goldstone meets Maxwell."* At the end of July he sent off a short note describing the idea to the journal *Physics Letters,* whose editors were at the European centre for nuclear research (CERN). It was accepted for publication. The following week Higgs submitted a second letter showing how it was done, and it was rejected. He said, much later, in a talk at King's College London, *"It was rejected, and I was rather shocked. I did not see why they would accept a paper that said this is a possible way to evade the Goldstone theorem, and then reject a paper that showed how you actually do it. So, I thought (and this was verified by a colleague of mine, Euan Squires, who came back from time at CERN shortly afterwards) it is no good revising this and sending it to Physics Letters at CERN, the people at CERN do not understand this sort of thing."*

During August, Higgs expanded his paper to point out that his theory had experimentally testable consequences. In the final paragraph of the revised paper, submitted to, and accepted by, the rival journal *Physical Review Letters*, he noted that *"an essential feature of the type of theory which has been described in this note is the prediction of incomplete multiplets of scalar and vector bosons."* In other words, the Higgs model predicted the existence of a new, <u>massive</u> scalar boson – that is, a non-force carrying boson – which should be detectable. The anonymous referee who recommended the acceptance of Higgs' paper by *Physical Review Letters* also drew his attention to a paper published just previously in the same journal, by Francois Englert and Robert Brout at Cornell University, coming to similar conclusions but not mentioning the implication of a new massive scalar boson. Higgs believed that perhaps they thought the implication to be obvious, and he added a reference to their work in his own paper before its publication. The anonymous reviewer was later revealed to be Yoichiro Nambu.

Thus the impasse created by the Goldstone theorem was resolved in 1964, in fact almost simultaneously by three groups: Higgs at Edinburgh; Englert and Brout at Cornell; and Guralnik, Hagen and Kibble in Abdus Salam's group at Imperial College. Collectively, their papers, all published in *Physical Review Letters,* have become known as *'the 1964 PRL symmetry breaking papers'.* Only Higgs was explicit about the prediction of a new massive boson. Over the next couple of years, he developed his theory in more depth, and made presentations to explain it at some of the leading centres of theoretical physics. After writing up the full detail for the *Physical Review*, while on secondment at the University of North Carolina, he gave talks at Princeton and Harvard, stressing, as Nambu had done, the practical implications of spontaneous symmetry breaking as the mechanism that, in the early universe, could have given mass to protons, neutrons and mesons – collectively known as 'hadrons', from the Greek word for 'heavy'. After giving the seminar at Harvard, Higgs was complimented on his work by Sheldon Glashow, one of the bibulous gang of four at the Scottish Summer School, who was still working on electroweak unification. Neither he nor Higgs immediately made the connection between their work, and Higgs later reflected that had he been a member of the discussion group drinking his wine back in Edinburgh, *"I might have thought of applying my ideas about spontaneous symmetry breaking to the electroweak interactions."* In 1967, Steven Weinberg and Abdus Salam's group independently built on Glashow's work to make the connection, and used the Higgs model to show that the as yet undiscovered Z, W+ and W- bosons of the weak nuclear interaction must have mass. They made a rough prediction on the expected masses – around 90 times the mass of a proton. Now it was the turn of experimental physics to test that prediction.

The hunt for the more elementary building blocks of protons and neutrons began in the 1950s, with the construction of accelerators which used high voltages to boost the energy of charged particles and collide them with metal targets, to examine the collision products. Early particle accelerators were linear machines which needed increasingly high voltages and longer lengths to achieve higher particle energies. Later accelerator designs tended to follow the concepts of the American physicists Ernest Lawrence and M. Stanley Livingston, who in 1931 invented an ingenious circular machine they called a 'cyclotron'. An early version that had a diameter of only 11 inches could accelerate protons in a spiral path to an energy of 80,000 electron-volts (80 keV) with an alternating voltage of just 1,800 volts. Lawrence, Livingston and Edwin McMillan went on to develop ever more powerful cyclotrons using synchronised radio-frequency voltages to accelerate circulating particles to higher and higher energies. By the 1950s, helped by wartime and Cold War research funding, these 'synchrotrons' were achieving particle energies of more than a billion electron-volts (1GeV). A synchrotron weighing 10,000 tons, built at the Lawrence Berkeley National Laboratory in California, and called the Bevatron, was in 1955 accelerating protons to energies of 6.2 GeV, and colliding them with static targets after they completed a re-circulating journey of 4 million orbits and 300,000 miles in 1.85 seconds. One result, in 1955, was the discovery of the anti-proton– the first antimatter particle ever detected, and a confirmation of the theoretical predictions of the British physicist, Paul Dirac.

A subsequent decades-long effort went on to probe further, involving many particle physics groups world-wide, using three leading accelerator sites in particular: at Stanford University in California; at Fermilab just outside Chicago; and in the CERN facilities near Geneva on the Swiss-French border. Higher collision energies and increasingly sophisticated particle detectors revealed a plethora of sub-atomic particles that was initially bewildering. Gradually, and by the early 1970s, neutrinos, mesons and quarks were falling into a symmetric picture of elementary particles that made some sense, called the Standard Model - somewhat akin to Mendeleev's Periodic Table of the elements. The bosons – the extremely short-lived particles that carry forces between the others – were the most elusive. In a major coup for the laboratory, in 1979 the Deutsches Elektronen-Synchrotron (DESY) near Hamburg enabled the indirect detection of 'gluons' – confirming both that physicists do have a sense of humour, and that gluons carry the strong nuclear force which holds quarks together, inside protons and neutrons. Glashow, Weinberg and Salam, whose theory predicted the existence of the Z and W bosons of the weak force, won the Nobel Prize for physics in 1979, for 'their contributions to the unification of the weak and electromagnetic interaction between elementary particles', even though evidence for the existence of the weak-force bosons was as yet indirect. That changed in 1983, when they were detected at CERN's Proton-Antiproton Collider. Colliding protons with their counter-circulating antiparticles created much higher energies than firing them at a static target, and if the collision energy is sufficiently high, the mutual annihilation of the particles and antiparticles creates energy which condenses into new particles of equivalent total mass/energy. The CERN collider detected first the W+ and W-, then the Z boson, at close to their predicted masses, around 80 and 91 GeV/c^2 respectively, in a breakthrough which confirmed the Standard Model, although one important piece was missing.

It was Higgs' theory which demonstrated how spontaneous symmetry breaking was the mechanism behind the dissolution of the electroweak force into the separate forces we see today. It also predicted the existence of another boson, of indeterminate mass, that interacted with other massive particles universally. The search for the that boson became a race. The fact that it became a search for the 'Higgs Boson' was said to be a discomfort for Higgs, who maintained that the credit for its prediction should be shared with the other contributors to the theory, and he referred to it himself as 'the scalar boson'. He suggested jokily that it should really be known as the 'Anderson-Brout-Englert-Guralnik-Hagen-Higgs-Kibble and t'Hooft' or ABEGHHKt'H boson.

The search for Higgs' eponymous boson became a competitive endeavour, principally between Fermilab and CERN, seeking the kudos its discovery would bring, as well as justification for the huge financial investments that they had won, with difficulty, from national governments. Fermilab's 'Tevatron' was the first accelerator to collide counter-circulating beams of protons and antiprotons at energies above 1 TeV (10^{12}, a thousand billion electron volts), achieved in 1986. CERN had the 27-kilometer circumference Large Electron-Positron (LEP) collider, constructed underground from 1983 to 1988, then the largest scientific instrument in the world. Many construction issues were overcome, and test runs showed that the alignment of the LEP's particle beams was acutely sensitive. The machine's performance was affected by earthquakes in far-away Turkey, the level of water in Lake Geneva, and the position of the moon.

The LEP's twin objectives were to create W and Z bosons for in-depth study, which it did by the millions, and to look for tell-tale signs of the Higgs boson. It was planned to run the machine until September 2000, when it was due to be decommissioned, and its tunnel reused for the new, higher energy, Large Hadron Collider (LHC), which would revert to using proton-antiproton beams. The LHC construction was scheduled to take five years, and during that time the playing field would be left to the Tevatron team alone. As the switch-off deadline approached, the LEP scientists pushed their machine beyond its design limits in a final attempt to detect the Higgs, concentrating on the mass-energy window between 100 and 250 GeV/c^2, where most theoreticians believed it lay. In June 2000, analysis of collision data from Aleph - one of the LEP's four detectors - showed a possible Higgs particle being briefly created at an energy of around 114 GeV. The signature was encouraging, but other collision events could produce similar products, so the result was uncertain. The CERN scientists implored management to be given more time, and the decommissioning deadline was set back two weeks. During the summer, the Aleph team detected two more similar events, and a second detector called Delphi registered two more possibilities. At a detailed review of all the data in September, the CERN managers agreed another decommissioning delay until November 2nd. Work continued and in the middle of October, another possible Higgs event, at around 115 GeV, with a different but still probable decay pattern, was detected in a third detector. The physics teams asked for another six months, confident that would be enough to remove the uncertainties. That was rejected as unfeasible, since more delay would jeopardise the build of the Large Hadron Collider, break contracts with the construction companies, leave workers standing idle, and undoubtedly lead to lawsuits. The funding for the LHC had been hard-won and it was the future of CERN. Despite the tantalising findings, the Large Electron-Positron collider was de-commissioned on 2nd November 2000. It was a decision which split the physics community, although Peter Higgs was said to agree with it.

At Fermilab, the Tevatron upgrades were complete and the machine was energised in the spring of 2001. Immediately there were problems. It proved hard to keep the proton-antiproton beams correctly aligned, and the number of collisions being produced was far too low. Another time-consuming revamp was needed, and it was not fully completed until 2005. Significant findings were made, building on the discovery of the 'top' quark at Fermilab ten years previously, but no Higgs boson was obvious. The famous cosmologist, Stephen Hawking, had by this time already collected on a $100 bet that the particle did not exist.

The development of the LHC at CERN was painstaking and arduous, beginning with the disaster of a large explosion which nearly destroyed it, nine days after it was first powered-up in September 2008. caused by faulty connections in the liquid-helium-cooled superconducting magnets which steer the particle beams. The helium boiled, and the damage caused by the explosion of high-pressure gas was enormous. Operations were delayed by two years of repair work.

After the reconstruction, the LHC teams searching for the elusive scalar boson were guided by the results from the LEP, which showed that the Higgs must have a mass of more than 114.4 GeV/c^2, and the Tevatron findings, which showed that it probably weighed between 115 and 135 GeV/c^2. In 2012, some 48 years after its existence was predicted, two LHC detector teams found the definitive signature of the decay of a Higgs boson. Its mass lies between 125 and 127 GeV/c^2 and it exists for roughly 10^{-22} seconds, before decaying in a variety of ways, producing for example a Z boson, two 'bottom' quarks, an electron and a positron.

The discovery was greeted with great joy as the conclusive validation of the Standard Model of elementary particles. It was also met with some fairly hysterical press coverage, hailing the finding of the 'God Particle' - an inappropriate nickname intended to convey its importance in endowing other particles with mass, and in completing the jigsaw puzzle of the Standard Model, but annoying scientists and offending many of the religious and non-religious alike. In 2013, the long-awaited confirmation of the Higgs boson's existence was recognised by the award of the Nobel prize in physics, to Peter Higgs and François Englert 'for the theoretical discovery of a mechanism that contributes to our understanding of the origin of mass of subatomic particles, and which recently was confirmed through the discovery of the predicted fundamental particle, by the ATLAS and CMS experiments at CERN's Large Hadron Collider.' Robert Brout would no doubt have shared the prize too, but he had died two years before, and Nobels are not awarded posthumously. Nobel laureates occur, like many fundamental particles, in a maximum of triplets, and the experimentalists who found the Higgs were not included, though Carlo Rubbia and Simon van der Meer of CERN had shared the 1984 Nobel for leading the teams that discovered the W and Z bosons.

The discovery of the Higgs boson completed our understanding of the Standard Model of particle physics. Yet particle physicists and cosmologists are now confronted by more recent discoveries which challenge our understanding of matter. We now recognise that the ordinary matter we know, built from protons, neutrons and electrons, makes up only around 5% of the material stuff in the universe. As of 2021, physicists can as yet only speculate on the composition of the 'dark matter' that makes up the vast bulk of the universe. Yet the history of the consideration of dark matter is a long one. The first calculation of how much 'dark stuff' might be out there was made by another of Scotland's greatest scientists, William Thomson, Lord Kelvin. By treating the stars of our galaxy as particles of gas, acting under the influence of gravity, he established a relationship between the mass of the system and the velocity dispersion of the stars. In 1904 Kelvin concluded, with great prescience, *"Many of our supposed thousand million stars, perhaps a great majority of them, may be dark bodies… many of them may be extinct and dark, and nine-tenths of them though not all dark may be not bright enough to be seen by us at their actual distances."* We now understand dark matter to be dispersed, consisting of unknown particles. Identifying them will certainly result in future Nobel prizes, and a revolution in our understanding of both cosmology, and the physics of 'particles'.

37 Magnetic Resonance Imaging: Jim Hutchison and John Mallard

When hydrogen atoms are immersed in a strong magnetic field, interesting things happen. A hydrogen atom's nucleus consists of a single proton, and protons themselves produce magnetic fields around them, termed their 'magnetic moment'. The magnetic moment of protons was first measured in experiments by the German-American, Otto Stern, in 1933, for which he received the Nobel prize in physics ten years later. His measurements gave an unexpectedly large value – the magnetic moment of protons was almost 2.8 times larger than the theoretical predictions of Paul Dirac, based on an elementary particle of unit electrical charge, with the proton's known mass and 'spin'. The anomalously large magnetic moment of protons remained a puzzle that would not be solved for many years, but it had extremely useful practical consequences. When a group of hydrogen atoms are subjected to an external magnetic field, the previously random orientation of their nuclear protons becomes ordered. Most nuclei align with their magnetic fields aligned parallel, and pointing in the same direction, as the applied field. Some align in the anti-parallel direction. However, their alignment is not purely a passive one. The magnetic axis of each proton precesses, like a spinning top, following a circular path around the direction of the applied field, at a frequency called the Larmor frequency, in honour of the work of the Northern Irish physicist, Joseph Larmor, who studied the effects of magnetic fields on the behaviour of atoms. Very significantly, the frequency of precession is directly proportional to the strength of the externally applied field – the stronger the field, the faster the precession of the nuclei. Hydrogen atoms are not alone in behaving this way – any atomic nucleus, for example carbon-13, which contains an odd number of protons and neutrons, behaves similarly, with its own Larmor frequencies. For hydrogen nuclei, subjected to a magnetic field of strength 1 Tesla (about 20,000 times stronger than the Earth's magnetic field), the Larmor frequency of precession is 42 MHz, in the radiofrequency range.

Studying the effects of magnetic fields on atomic nuclei yielded more Nobel prizes. Isidor Rabi of Columbia University won the Prize in physics, in 1944, for his measurements of nuclear magnetic moments made by passing molecular beams in high vacuum through crossed steady and oscillating magnetic fields. He demonstrated that when the frequency of oscillation matched the Larmor frequency of the nuclei, they absorbed energy which flipped their magnetic orientations. Rabi named the phenomenon 'nuclear magnetic resonance', or NMR. A year after Rabi's Nobel award, separate teams at Stanford University and MIT showed that NMR also occurred in the hydrogen nuclei of liquid water, and solid paraffin, resulting in the award in 1952 of the Nobel in physics for Felix Bloch and Edward Purcell. Those observations paved the way for a whole new field, NMR spectroscopy, for the investigation and analysis of molecular structures. In that technique, the sample to be studied is immersed in a steady magnetic field of variable strength, and subjected to short pulses of a magnetic field oscillating at a suitable radiofrequency. If the frequency matches the Larmor frequency of an element in the sample, the nuclei absorb energy and reorient themselves. When the pulse terminates, the nuclei relax back to their previous states, at characteristic rates, and in doing so they re-emit the energy they absorbed, as electromagnetic radiation which is detected in the spectrometer. The frequency of the emission identifies the nuclei, and its intensity determines the prevalence of that element in the sample.

The anomalously large magnetic moment of the proton was explained in the 1960s, from the realisation that protons (and neutrons) are not truly elementary particles at all, but are composed of three electrically charged quarks, which determine the magnetic properties of nuclei. NMR spectroscopy was taken a stage further in the early 1970s, by Paul Lauterbur at the State University of New York. He proposed that it would be possible to create images of a sample if the steady magnetic field had a gradient in intensity, so that the resonant frequencies of the molecular nuclei varied along its length. Moreover, if magnetic field gradients were applied in all three spatial dimensions, then a sample could be imaged in 3-D, since each part of it would experience a different steady field intensity and exhibit different emission frequencies from its constituent molecules. In 1973, Lauterbur published a paper in the journal *Nature* showing 2D images of two capillary tubes of water attached within a glass tube filled with heavy water (D_2O). The images were obtained by making successive rotations of the tubes through a magnetic field with a single gradient. The paper was initially rejected by *Nature* on account of the fuzziness of the images, despite the fact that they were the first images to show the difference between heavy and ordinary water. Lauterbur appealed successfully for the acceptance of the paper and later remarked, *"You could write the entire history of science in the last 50 years in terms of papers rejected by 'Science' or 'Nature'."* He proposed the name 'zeugmatography' for the new imaging method. That did not catch on. Nuclear Magnetic Resonance Imaging, soon just MRI, became the standard terminology. Lauterbur soon produced more interesting images, including a tiny clam collected from a Long Island beach.

As is usually the case, other scientists were following the same line of thought. In England, at the University of Nottingham, the physicist Peter Mansfield was using his experience in pulsed NMR to explore the use of magnetic field gradients to image solid samples and biological specimens. In Scotland, at the University of Aberdeen, John Mallard was leading a team of medical physicists intent on applying the new MRI techniques to imaging the human body. Mansfield and his Nottingham group introduced new methods of point-by-point and 'slice' scanning of samples in an attempt to reduce the time taken to produce images, and in 1974 they imaged the finger of one of the researchers – which took around 20 minutes to capture. At Aberdeen, Jim Hutchison had made a projected MRI image of a recently-killed mouse, using a permanent magnet and detecting pulsed NMR echoes with electronics designed and built by himself. The results were presented at the 18th Ampere Congress, held in Nottingham in 1975. They excited great interest in the biomedical potential of MRI and the possibility of producing diagnostically useful scanners, efficient enough to image parts, or even all, of the human body, in a way that X-rays could not, given the ability of MRI to detect watery tissues, and discriminate between them. A special meeting of the UK Medical Research Council was convened, and the various teams made bids for funding. Mansfield was keen to progress straight to the development of a whole-body scanner but the head of the Nottingham physics department, Raymond Andrew, disagreed. He won an acrimonious argument with Mansfield to develop instead a scanner of intermediate size, with a sample access diameter of about 10cm. At Aberdeen, a more ambitious strategy was pursued to extend MRI to samples of larger size.

The team at Aberdeen University was led by John Mallard who had become the founding professor of the medical physics department in 1965. Born in Northamptonshire in 1927, he completed his PhD in the magnetic properties of uranium at Nottingham, and worked in the medical applications of physics at the Hammersmith and St Thomas's Hospitals in London. At the Hammersmith, he met Fiona Lawrance, a medical secretary who hailed from Aberdeen, and they married in 1958. While working in London, he discovered that the magnetic response of electrons in tissue samples showed differences between healthy animal tissues and tumours. Having built radioisotope scanners and a gamma-ray camera to detect brain tumours, he was already convinced that scanning technologies were the future of medical diagnosis. In his inaugural professorial lecture at Aberdeen, he forecast the potential of a nascent technique, Positron Emission Tomography (PET) to become a powerful tool in the study of human disease. He recruited a highly talented, international team of scientists and engineers. Jim Hutchison

Illustration 73: John Mallard, Jim Hutchison and some members of the Aberdeen MRI team

was born in Perthshire in 1940, and studied science and mathematics at the University of St Andrews, where his PhD was in electron spin resonance, a subject closely related to NMR. At Aberdeen, Hutchison met another member of Mallard's team, the biologist Meg Foster. They were married in 1972. Bill Edelstein, an American physicist born in New York State in 1944, joined the group after a post-doctoral fellowship at the University of Glasgow, trying to detect gravitational waves. His doctoral studies, at Harvard, were supervised by Robert Pound, one of the co-discoverers of NMR. In Glasgow, he found no gravitational waves, but his attachment to Scotland was confirmed when he found Fiona, his future wife. Just married, they moved north to join the Aberdeen team in 1977.

Mallard persuaded the Medical Research Council to provide a very modest £30,000 to develop a whole-body MRI scanner. Fortunately both Hutchison and Edelstein were fond of finding cheap solutions to daunting problems. To scale up MRI, and image portions of a human torso, a number of engineering problems needed to be solved. First, it was difficult to achieve a high magnetic field strength over larger diameters, of say 50cm. Using lower field strengths resulted in a reduced Larmor frequency of 2 MHz or less for proton imaging, with some loss of sensitivity. Secondly, over a larger expanse, inhomogeneities in the magnetic fields were an issue. Hutchison and Mallard overcame that problem by scanning uniform samples as a reference, and de-convolving the signals from real samples to compensate for magnetic distortions, without requiring detailed knowledge of their nature.

Illustration 74: Jim
Hutchison, c.1980

The next challenge was to produce medically useful images, from relatively weak magnetic fields. Their electromagnet, the first whole-body magnet provided by Oxford Instruments, generated a field of just 0.04T with an unimpressive inhomogeneity of 600 ppm, and was driven by four coils which reached a temperature of 100°C before a water cooling system was hastily rigged up. To achieve the imaging sensitivity and spatial resolution required, the team expanded on the method of using a magnetic field gradient to divide the sample into two dimensional slices, and took it to the next level. By applying a rapid succession of magnetic pulse gradients in each of the three spatial dimensions, they controlled the spin of nuclear precessions both in frequency and in phase. This enabled the division of the sample space into three dimensional 'voxels' whose radiofrequency echo signals were captured and processed as the nuclear spins relaxed to their steady state. Signal processing of the time-varying signals from each voxel of the sample was done by computer-based Fourier transformation to produce the frequency spectra of the echoes, and to construct the images. Jim Hutchison's wife Meg, a big fan of *Star Trek*, named the technique 'spin warp', which was also descriptive of the way the phase distribution of the proton spins was manipulated. In an experiment performed late at night, to ensure access to the department's heavily-used PDP11 computer, the first spin warp image was produced in early 1980, with Hutchison as the subject. The details of the construction of the world's first whole-body MRI scanner were published in the *Journal of Physics* in the spring, and the early spin warp images were published almost simultaneously in a letter to the journal *Physics in Medicine and Biology*. A few weeks later, Frank Smith, a consultant in nuclear medicine at the Aberdeen Royal Infirmary, arranged for some real patients to be scanned. In a second world-first, the scan of a patient with oesophageal cancer clearly showed not just

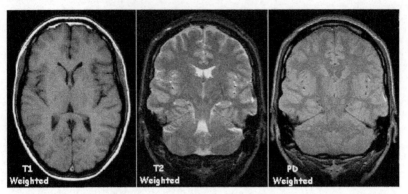

Illustration 75: Examples of MRI scans of a human brain weighted by T1, T2 and proton density measurements.

the tumour but also secondary liver tumours. The scan of another patient with liver cancer showed spleen and spine metastases which had not been previously suspected. In all, the first clinical MRI scanner, the 'Mark 1', made images of more than 900 patients, often with life-saving results.

The spin warp method is the basis of nearly all modern MRI scanners. Their high resolution, and ability to discriminate between types of tissue, derive from a number of factors. Most importantly, both the response of hydrogen nuclei to the radiofrequency impulse, and their subsequent relaxations, are strongly influenced by their chemical environment. If the hydrogen atoms are part of an electron-rich molecule, then they are partially screened from the electromagnetic pulses and the relaxation echoes of the hydrogen nuclei are attenuated. That shows up in the MRI scans as regions of varied hydrogen atom density. And after the excitation pulse, the time taken for the spinning hydrogen nuclei to relax is also dependent on their molecular attachments. There are usually two stages of spin relaxation, each with a different characteristic time of decay. Firstly, the spinning nuclei lose their synchronicity with each other, or 'de-phase', with a time constant that is usually labelled T2. As well, the spinning nuclei lose their energy and alignments that were induced by the radiofrequency pulse, and revert to their steady magnetic alignments, with a time constant labelled

T1. It is by measuring those two relaxation times, as well as measuring proton density, that MRI scanners can achieve precise discrimination between tissues such as muscle, fat, tendons, and cerebral grey matter, resulting in well defined, high contrast images.

In 1982 John Mallard set up a commercial company to exploit the technology developed by the Aberdeen team, but was frustrated by the lack of interest shown by the British financial establishments, and although patents were filed, none of the group profited greatly from their inventiveness. Funding for a second clinical scanner could not be raised in the UK, and eventually the Japanese company Asahi invested in the development of a second machine in return for intellectual property rights. At Nottingham, Peter Mansfield had won his internal battles and secured funding to build a large scanner which he tested on his own abdomen in a scan of 50 minutes duration in 1978. Mansfield fared a little better commercially, through his small company, General Magnetic.

Awards and honours for all the MRI pioneers came in abundance. In 1984, Hutchison, Mallard, Mansfield and Andrew were recognised by the Royal Society's Wellcome Award and Gold Medal, for their development of NMR as a diagnostic tool in medicine. Peter Mansfield was knighted in 1993, and ten years later, Mansfield and Lauterbur shared the Nobel prize in Physiology or Medicine for their fundamental discoveries in magnetic resonance imaging.

The Aberdeen group lost Bill Edelstein when he returned to the USA in 1980, but they continued to develop and refine the clinical application of MRI. The second machine at the Royal Infirmary was used to image more than 9,000 patients, and the Mark I scanner is on public display in the hospital. Jim Hutchison died in 2018, aged 77. His hospital treatment was aided by a type of MRI scanner that he helped to create. John Mallard continued his interest in diagnostic scanning and brought the first positron emission tomography machine to Scotland, installed in what became the John Mallard PET Centre in Aberdeen in 1998. He died, aged 94, in 2021. The leading-edge work in medical physics continues at the University, led by Professor David Lurie. MRI scanning has become perhaps the most valuable diagnostic tool in medicine, worldwide.

38

Detecting gravitational waves: Ronald Drever, James Hough and Sheila Rowan

At the beginning of the 20th century, there was a serious problem in physics. Thanks to the famous equations of James Clerk Maxwell, light was shown to be a wave in a field of electromagnetism; and due to the much earlier work of Sir Isaac Newton, the motion of bodies through gravitational space was well understood. But light travels in a very different way than matter. In free space, light always moves at the same speed, irrespective of the motion of the light source, or the observer. How could this be? Henri Poincaré, Hermann Minkowski, and ultimately Albert Einstein realised the implication. Space and time are inextricably linked, and our measurements of both time and space depend on the relative motions of the observers. In 1908, Minkowski said *"Henceforth space by itself, and time by itself, are doomed to fade away into mere shadows, and only a kind of union of the two will preserve an independent reality."* This was easier said than proved. Initially Einstein dismissed Minkowski's 4-dimensional 'spacetime' interpretation of Special Relativity as *"superfluous learnedness"*, but he quickly accepted it as part of his formulation of General Relativity. Gravitational attraction was shown to be the result of the distortion of spacetime in the presence of matter, which is often summarised by the statement '*matter tells spacetime how to curve, and curved spacetime tells matter how to move*'. Spacetime tells light how to move too. During the solar eclipse of 1919, the measurements of Sir Arthur Eddington showed that light is bent by the warping of spacetime around stars, exactly as predicted by General Relativity. Moreover, the solutions of Einstein's equations predicted that changes in the curvature of spacetime should propagate outward from their source at the speed of light, as 'ripples' in spacetime.

In 1933, Einstein fled from the pogroms in Nazi Germany to Princeton, New Jersey, and began working with his first American assistant, Nathan Rosen, seeking to unify the theories of gravity and quantum physics. He made a surprising announcement to his friend, the physicist Max Born, in a letter of 1936. *"Together with a young collaborator, I arrived at the interesting result that gravitational waves do not exist, though they had been assumed a certainty to the first approximation. This shows that the non-linear general relativistic field equations can tell us more or, rather, limit us more than we have believed up to now."* Einstein, with Rosen, submitted a paper to the pre-eminent academic journal, *Physical Review*, entitled *'Do Gravitational Waves Exist?'* with the conclusion – no, they do not. The submission was sent for peer review, as was standard practice, though a practice that Einstein seemed unaccustomed to. The anonymous reviewer did a thorough job. He pointed out an error in the paper's treatment of mathematical 'singularities' – effectively infinities – in the submission, which when corrected, completely inverted the conclusion. It was the occurrence of these singularities in the solutions of their equations that had persuaded Einstein and Rosen that gravitational waves could not exist. The anonymous reviewer later turned out to be Howard Percy Robertson, an expert cosmologist, of Scottish descent, working also at Princeton. Robertson had observed that the singularities were merely artifacts of Einstein's chosen system of coordinates, and were not so problematic after all. The *Physical Review* returned the paper to the authors, with Robertson's 10-page critique. Einstein was indignant. He wrote back, *"We (Mr. Rosen and I) had sent you our manuscript for publication and had not authorized you to show it to specialists before it is printed. I see no reason to address the—in any case erroneous—comments of your anonymous expert. On the basis of this incident I prefer to publish the paper elsewhere."* In fact, Einstein took Robertson's review comments on board, and corrected the error. The amended and re-titled paper, *'On Gravitational Waves'*, was published the next year in the *Journal of the Franklin Institute*, with a radically altered conclusion. *"It turns out that rigorous solutions do exist and that the problem reduces to the usual cylindrical waves in Euclidean space."* The equations predicted the reality of gravitational waves after all. But Einstein never again submitted a paper to the *Physical Review*.

Theoretical predictions are the food of heaven for experimental physicists, and the search for gravitational waves was on. The effect to be detected was a tiny change in the length of space – or the direction of the Earth's gravitational field – caused by the passing spacetime ripples. The problem is that the predicted effect due even to huge (and therefore distant) astronomical events is truly miniscule, of the order of 10^{-21} – a fractional change in length of a thousandth of a billionth of a billionth, about the size of a single atom relative to the distance from the Earth to the Sun, and moreover, at a ridiculously wide range of possible frequencies between 10^4 Hz – 10,000 vibrations per second - and 10^{-4} Hz, a slow vibration completed in 3 hours. For decades after Einstein's paper, the experimental detection of gravitational waves seemed hopelessly beyond technical capabilities. Attempts began in the late 1950s, and by the late 60s, the favoured detection method used piezoelectric strain gauges attached to one-ton aluminium bars, about two metres long, designed to 'ring' resonantly when perturbed by passing gravity waves of the right frequency. The bars were suspended on anti-vibration mounts within vacuum tanks, to minimise extraneous disturbances. In 1969, Joseph Weber of the University of Wisconsin claimed to have detected correlated gravity wave signals at the rate of one per day using two such systems located 1,000 km apart, at the Argonne National Laboratory in Illinois and at the University of Maryland. The claims were met with some scepticism, and similar detectors at other laboratories, including at the University of Glasgow, failed to replicate Weber's results.

The Glasgow team was set up in 1970 by Ronald Drever, who was born just outside the city in 1931, and was already a distinguished member of the University faculty. As a young boy, he hated school, but showed a knack for science and engineering, and built a television set out of spare parts left over from the Second World War. Drever's research background was in the detection of sub-atomic particles rather than in gravitational waves or General Relativity, and he had performed a landmark experiment to measure the motion of the nuclei of lithium atoms with respect to the galactic plane, which established the uniformity of space with unprecedented precision. The measurements were performed in his parents' back-garden, to avoid the electromagnetic disturbances at the Glasgow University labs, and was called *"the most precise null experiment ever performed"*. Drever soon became engrossed in the search for the gravity waves, those elusive ripples in spacetime. He was joined by Jim Hough, a young Glasgow physicist aged 25, and initially they built aluminium bar detectors similar to Weber's, but with improved sensitivity. They achieved no confirmed results, though they made one detection of a possible gravitational wave event in 1972, as reported in the journal *Nature*. It could not be confirmed because, incredibly, all the other gravity wave detectors around the world were off-line, including both of Weber's at MIT, two more in the USA, one in West Germany and two in Italy. Soon Drever and Hough agreed that a better approach to building sensitive detectors was to use laser interferometry, as proposed a few years earlier by a number of scientists, including the cosmologist Kip Thorne of the California Institute of Technology (Caltech), Rainer Weiss of MIT and Weber himself. Interferometers can detect minute changes of a fraction of a wavelength in the light paths of a laser beam split into two perpendicular arms, each beam reflected by mirrors on the heavy 'test masses' and recombined to detect their movement. The sensitivity of detection can be improved in several ways: by maximising the length of the arms of the interferometer, increasing the power of the source laser, and reducing all sources of 'noise' such as mechanical vibrations; thermal noise in the optical signal detectors; and jitter in the frequency of the laser source. Drever and James Hough built a laser

Illustration 76: Ronald Drever at the University of Glasgow in 2007

interferometer, and in 1979 Drever, on sabbatical at Harvard University, learned about a method invented by R.V. Pound to control the frequency of microwaves by using a resonant microwave cavity. With Hough, he adapted the method to stabilise the frequency of lasers, using optical resonators, a technique now known as Pound-Drever-Hall (PDH) cavity stabilisation.

Around the same time, Drever was recruited by Kip Thorne and his Caltech colleagues to work in California, to initiate an experimental group in gravitational wave detection, leaving James Hough in charge of the Glasgow group. Caltech with Drever, and MIT with Weiss, were for a while in competition to build the most sensitive prototype laser interferometers. Under pressure from the U.S. National Science Foundation (NSF), they were forced to cooperate, and in 1984 an ambitious plan was hatched - to build a large-scale interferometer with mirrors spaced kilometres apart - the Laser Interferometer Gravitational-Wave Observatory (LIGO). The project was directed jointly by Drever, Weiss and Thorne, but after several years of slow progress, and the rejection of several funding proposals, a change was needed. Weiss said later, *"we had different visions and were unable to make decisions. In 1987, the project moved forward under a single director, Rochus Vogt, who helped us to write a definitive proposal that attracted the funds to design and construct the initial detector. The project — the largest ever funded by the US National Science Foundation — consisted of two L-shaped detectors, each with arms 4 kilometres long, in Washington state and Louisiana...Drever was a strong contributor to the conceptualization of LIGO. But he struggled to move from the freedom of table-top science to the rigorous schedule and firm decision-making necessary to pin down a large-scale project. In such projects, thorough engineering practice and careful analysis take priority over intuition and pictorial reasoning..."*

The successful proposal was to build, at each of the two sites, so-called 'initial interferometers', based on proven technology and a sensitivity that <u>might</u> be enough to detect gravity waves. These would be followed by 'advanced interferometers' using more leading-edge techniques. LIGO director Vogt established strict control, but funding remained problematic, and by 1992, Drever and Vogt fell out. Drever formally left the LIGO project, and established a separate laboratory at Caltech to develop new advanced detector technology. Three years later, with construction of the sites almost complete, a new director, Barry Barish, was appointed and split the LIGO organisation into two parts. First, the 'LIGO Laboratory' at Caltech, MIT, Hanford in Washington State and Livingston in Louisiana, was charged with experimental operations and advanced interferometer R&D. Second, the LIGO Scientific Collaboration (LSC), was to coordinate research and data analysis, and expand LIGO to include scientists elsewhere, internationally.

In Glasgow, James Hough, now the Professor of Experimental Physics, was continuing to lead the gravitational waves group, which was developing stabilised, low-noise lasers, and novel mirror-suspension systems using 'wires' made of fused-silica glass. Hough submitted a proposal to the UK Science and Engineering Research Council (SERC) to build an interferometer with 1km-long arms, to be sited in Scotland, near St Andrews. The SERC reviewers suggested

Illustration 77: Professor Sir James Hough

that instead, Hough should cooperate with the gravitational wave group at the Max Planck Institute in Munich, led by Heinz Billing, to propose something more ambitious that could be funded jointly by the UK and

West Germany. Discussions were derailed by the appearance of a 'Black Swan' event – the unexpected fall of the Berlin Wall in 1989, and the subsequent reunification of Germany. Billing's group partly disbanded, and the leader left to work in other fields. Hough however managed to keep his Glasgow team together, and he focused it on developing a second generation of detection systems that would certainly have the sensitivity required to detect gravity waves – if they actually existed.

As something like political normality slowly returned to Germany, the proposal for the joint project was revived. It was agreed to build an interferometric detector called GEO near Hannover, with 600m-long arms in high vacuum, doubled in optical length by using a two laser passes through each. Construction began in 1995 and many of the advanced features derived from the innovations of Hough's team, including the work of his young PhD student, Sheila Rowan. Her developments included the pendulum mirror suspensions of silica glass fibres, under vacuum, to reduce vibrational noise; and a frequency-stabilisation system for a solid-state laser made of Neodymium-Yttrium Aluminium Garnet (Nd-YAG), which was chosen to replace the Argon-ion gas lasers used in early gravity-wave detectors. The outcome was that the GEO600 construction had a sensitivity similar to that of the 'initial interferometers' in the LIGO project. Unfortunately, though as was feared, that sensitivity was inadequate. Though both GEO600 and the initial LIGO detectors worked at their designed sensitivities, and despite joint detection operations between the groups from 2005, year after year of careful measurements to detect a gravitational wave signal revealed – nothing.

LIGO was shut down in 2010 for a major upgrade that took five years and cost more than 500 million dollars, led by the US NSF. 'Enhanced LIGO' incorporated many of the technical advances pioneered by the GEO600 project, improving its sensitivity by a factor of 4, and the gravitational wave detector of another European project, Virgo, was also upgraded at its site near Pisa, Italy, as part of the LIGO Scientific Collaboration. Almost unbelievably, the new advanced interferometers were capable of detecting mirror displacements of 10^{-19} m - 10,000 times smaller than the diameter of a proton – the smallest measurement ever attempted by science. Enhanced LIGO began operation in September 2015, and amazingly, within a few days, made the world's first detection of gravitational waves – the culmination of more than six decades of scientific endeavour and precision engineering development. The event detected was attributed to the collision and merger of two black holes almost 1.3 billion light-years distant. The signals detected lasted less than a quarter of a second, and arrived 7ms apart at the detectors in Hanford and Livingston. The fractional change in the distance between the mirrors, spaced 4km apart at each site, was of the order 10^{-21} – in other words, a detected mirror displacement of around a billionth of a billionth of a metre. This astounding scientific and engineering achievement, an event prosaically labelled GW150914, was perhaps the ultimate validation of Einstein's General Relativity. The first detection of gravitational waves was hailed by scientists and popular news releases worldwide. Since then, LIGO has detected eight more events, most made jointly with the Virgo detector, including the October 2017 detection of neutron stars spiralling together, the first time a cosmic event was observed with both light and gravity waves.

Illustration 78: Professor Sheila Rowan

In 2017, Rainer Weiss, Kip Thorne and Barry Barish shared the Nobel Prize in physics 'for decisive contributions to the LIGO detector and the observation of gravitational waves', an endeavour which as Thorne stressed, had involved more than a thousand scientists and engineers, over many decades. Ron Drever had been diagnosed with dementia in 2008, and had retired home to Scotland, where he was still able to celebrate the news of LIGO's first gravity wave detections. He died in March 2017, a few months before the Nobel award, which is never given posthumously. Jim

Hough was elected a Fellow of the Royal Society in 2003, and has been awarded many honours from other distinguished institutions, including the Institute of Physics and the Royal Society of Edinburgh. He was created an Officer of the Order of the British Empire (OBE) in 2013, and was knighted in 2019. He is Emeritus Professor in the Kelvin Chair of Natural Philosophy at the University of Glasgow. Sheila Rowan has succeeded Hough as Professor of Experimental Physics and director of Glasgow's Institute for Gravitational Research. She was appointed an MBE in 2011, and became a Fellow of the Royal Society in 2018. Since 2017, she has been the Chief Scientific Adviser to the Scottish government.

39

Cat man: David MacMillan

Illustration 79: Professor David MacMillan

When David MacMillan received an early morning text message from someone in Stockholm, telling him that he had been awarded the 2021 Nobel Prize in chemistry, he saw that his name had been wrongly spelled. He concluded that the text was a prank from one of his mischievous laboratory co-workers, and went back to sleep. When Ben List, the co-recipient of the Prize, phoned to tell him what was happening, MacMillan bet him 1,000 dollars that it was a hoax, and went back to sleep again. By the time he was convinced of the truth, MacMillan was $1,000 poorer but he was a very happy man.

David MacMillan was born in 1968 in Bellshill, near the former steel-making centre of Motherwell, about ten miles from Glasgow. He was the youngest of three children of May and Billy MacMillan. His father was a steel-worker, his grand-father was a coal miner, and David attended the local state schools, New Stevenston Primary and Bellshill Academy. He enjoyed school, but by his own admission he was not obviously someone who would become a research scientist. His brother Iain was the first in the family to attend university, and studied physics. David's parents decided he had to follow in his brother's footsteps, and in 1986 David began his studies at the University of Glasgow. He later recalled, *"Basically I was this working class kid. I went off to uni and it was just really overwhelming for me. I remember getting there and the physics lecture was the first thing in the morning in this lecture theatre that was absolutely freezing and there was no heating. So in the dead of winter in Scotland you'd be in this freezing lecture theatre, and when it would rain – which in Scotland it rains – the roof would leak and you'd actually get water falling on you which, for me, was just a really tough time. I went to uni to emulate my brother and it was just clearly not working.*

"But what for me was kind of interesting, was an hour later you would cross the road and I was taking chemistry as my secondary subject. It was this beautiful, warm lecture theatre. It was this great place to be. And I started to realise I loved this thing called organic chemistry. And the more and more I read about it, the more and more I really enjoyed it and appreciated it."

In 1990, MacMillan graduated from Glasgow in chemistry and moved to the United States to pursue a doctorate at the University of California, in Irvine. As an outstanding research scientist, in 2021, MacMillan became the fifth Scots-born Nobel laureate in chemistry, after William Ramsey in 1904, Alexander Todd (1957), James Fraser Stoddart (2016) and Richard Henderson in 2017.

The Nobel award to MacMillan and List cited 'the development of asymmetric organocatalysis' which is a mouthful that requires some careful deconstruction. Catalysis is perhaps the most familiar term, encountered by many a high school chemistry student. The term was coined in 1835 by the Swedish chemist Jacob Berzelius, though the phenomenon was discovered a generation earlier by the remarkable chemist Elizabeth Fulhame, based in Edinburgh. 'Catalyst' derives from the Greek, 'kataluein', meaning to 'untie' or 'loosen'. You may own a catalytic device embedded in the exhaust system of your diesel or petrol car. Basically, catalysts facilitate and accelerate chemical reactions, without becoming a part of the reaction products themselves. In motor vehicles, catalysts including platinum, rhodium and palladium metals are used to neutralise the toxicity of pollutants such as carbon monoxide, nitrogen oxides (NOx) as well as unburned hydrocarbons, to produce carbon dioxide, nitrogen and water vapour. Catalytic converters of that type work because the pollutant molecules stick to the lattice presented by the hot metal surfaces in a process called adsorption, and then can be more easily split apart into their constituent atoms. This enables the desired chemical reactions to progress at a suitably fast rate.

Historically, most known catalysts were one of two types. Firstly certain 'noble' metals, such as those already mentioned. Secondly, 'enzymes', which are proteins that act as catalysts in certain biochemical reactions. Some specific enzymes are used commercially, for example in 'biological' washing powders, accelerating the break-up of fat or starch stains on clothes. Enzymes are important in the digestive systems of many organisms, including humans, where they play a crucial role in breaking down larger protein molecules into their component parts. 'Enzyme' comes from the Greek meaning 'in yeast' or 'leavened', and the discovery of the first enzymes was prompted by the study of fermentation, specifically the process of converting sugar into alcohol by yeast. That conversion, which is of course the basis of beer- and wine-making, was studied by many scientists including Louis Pasteur, and was believed to be due to the action of live yeast cells 'digesting' the sugar, excreting ethanol and carbon dioxide. Around the beginning of the 20th century, the German biochemist Eduard Buchner conducted a series of experiments which showed that no live yeast cells were needed to produce the fermentation, and that it was due instead to an enzyme contained in yeast cell extracts. He named the enzyme 'zymase', and in 1907 he was awarded the Nobel Prize in chemistry for 'his discovery of cell-free fermentation'. Work in enzymology continued, and in 1946 the American biochemists James Sumner, John Northrop and Wendell Stanley shared the Nobel Prize in chemistry for showing that pure proteins could be enzymes. Northrop and Stanley had developed methods for the preparation of digestive enzymes in a purified form, while Sumner had demonstrated that enzymes could be crystallised. Since then, catalysts of both types have become increasingly important, indeed critical, to chemical engineering and the world economy. These days, 90% of industrial-scale chemical reactions use catalysts, including the crucial Haber-Bosch process that converts nitrogen in the air into ammonia for agricultural fertilisers. David MacMillan has estimated that

50% of the nitrogen in our bodies comes from synthetic ammonia produced by that single catalytic reaction, and that 35% of the world's gross domestic product (GDP) depends on catalysis.

In 1996, MacMillan finished his PhD studies at the University of California in Irvine, and moved to Harvard University as a post-doctoral researcher in the group of Professor Dave Evans, one of the world's foremost experts in the field of asymmetric metal catalysis. What does 'asymmetric' mean in this context? Many molecules exist as mirror images of each other. Indeed, that applies to most organic (carbon-containing) molecules that are crucial to biological processes, including proteins, carbohydrates, and DNA. All the building blocks of life are made up of one mirror image of the molecules, and not the other one. Despite being chemically identical, the mirror images of these molecules can behave very differently. In pharmaceutical drugs, one mirror image may have a therapeutic effect while the other is toxic. The mirror images, called enantiomers, look different, react differently, and can even have distinct smells. And importantly for the production of drugs and other useful chemicals, catalysts often act on one mirror image but not the other. That is asymmetric catalysis.

At Harvard, MacMillan studied reactions using those metals that can act as asymmetric catalysts, including ruthenium, cobalt and titanium. But metals like these can be difficult to handle. They may oxidise easily on exposure to air or moisture, are often expensive, and can even be poisonous to life. While spending many hours every day handling these difficult substances at arm's length using a 'glove box', MacMillan began to think laterally – truly 'out-of-the-box' thinking! Asymmetric metal catalysts actually consist of two parts – the metal centre, but also an organic part that confers the preference for one mirror image molecule rather than the other. MacMillan wondered if it was possible just to use the organic part, and dispense altogether with the costly, awkward metal component. Organic materials are often plentiful, safe, inexpensive, easy to handle and sustainable. Could it work?

In 1998, MacMillan completed his post-doc research and secured a job as an assistant professor back at the University of California, this time in Berkeley. On his way there, he was given some useful advice by Professor Erick Carreira at Caltech, who told him to assume, given that Berkeley has some of the smartest students in the world, that any problem he chose to address would eventually be solved. Therefore, choose to work on those problems whose solutions will have the greatest impact. That advice clinched MacMillan's intention to work on his exciting idea – to develop a new type of catalyst built from cheap, readily available organic molecules – organocatalysis.

To turn the idea into reality, MacMillan turned for help to his newly formed group of Berkeley research students, always remembering that to be truly useful, a catalyst had to be 'enantio-selective', that is, to act preferentially on one mirror image of a molecule, and not the other. The group started working to find organic catalysts for important chemical reactions, including the Diels-Alder reaction which is central in the synthesis of many organic substances based on rings of carbon atoms, such as cholesterol and the steroid hormone, cortisol. The initial breakthrough was achieved by a first-year research student in early 1999. Kateri Ahrendt demonstrated a Diels-Alder reaction catalysed by a purely organic catalyst that produced a 48% excess of one mirror image molecule over the other. Though that was a highly significant result in itself, MacMillan decided to stay silent while the team worked on discovering an organic catalyst that was even more enantioselective – 90% or more. That was achieved six months later, using a catalyst produced by reacting two readily available substances: phenylalanine, an essential amino acid found in food and used in many artificial sweeteners; and acetone, commonly used as paint stripper.

That breakthrough result was published in April of the year 2000 in the Journal of the American Chemical Society as *New Strategies for Organic Catalysis: The First Highly Enantioselective Organocatalytic Diels-Alder Reaction*. The paper introduced the term 'organocatalysis' to the wider community of research chemists. It was followed by a stream of evermore impressive results from MacMillan's group, who developed second-generation organic catalysts which were shown to accelerate, selectively, a wide range of important chemical reactions.

Of course, given the potential importance of organocatalysis, MacMillan's team was not alone in striving to develop catalysts based on organic molecules. Most notably, in the 1990s the German chemist Benjamin List was working in a group not far away at the Scripps Research Institute in southern California, which was trying to develop new enzymes that could catalyse more of the chemical reactions needed by humanity. List thought about how enzymes actually work. Enzymes are usually huge molecules built from hundreds of amino acids, and many also contain metal atoms that help to drive the chemical reactions. But many enzymes catalyse reactions without the help of metals, instead driving reactions using a few, or even just one, of the amino acids in the enzyme. List wondered if the amino acids needed to be part of an enzyme to catalyse a chemical reaction, or could they do it in stand-alone form? He remembered some work in the 1970s which used a simple amino acid called 'proline' as a catalyst, but assumed that it had not been very effective. He tested whether proline could catalyse the formation of carbon-carbon bonds between atoms from different molecules, in a so-called 'aldol' reaction. It worked straight away, thanks to the nitrogen atom in the proline molecule, which makes it a ready donor and acceptor of electrons needed for the reaction to proceed. List realised the enormous potential of that result, which he published in February 2000.

David MacMillan and Benjamin List had independently created an entirely new concept of catalysis. Since then, they and others have designed a veritable constellation of stable, efficient and cheap organocatalysts, which are used to drive a huge variety of chemical reactions. Many pharmaceutical drugs previously contained both mirror images of a molecule, sometimes with catastrophic results. Using asymmetric organocatalysis, pharmaceutical companies can streamline the production of large quantities of selected mirror-image molecules relatively simply. Two examples are paroxetine, used to treat anxiety, PTSD and depression, and oseltamivir (Tamiflu), an antiviral medication used to treat respiratory infections.

The award of the 2021 Nobel Prize in chemistry to both MacMillan and List recognised their pioneering research in founding a new and highly applicable field of chemistry. MacMillan's Princeton colleague, chair of department and fellow Scot, Professor Tom Muir, said after learning of the announcement, *"This award is so well-deserved. I think many of us knew this was a real possibility, but it's so wonderful to see this happen for Dave and for the department. And for Scottish chemistry. It's a fantastic day."* MacMillan has said that his Scottish upbringing helped him to win the Nobel. *"Growing up in Scotland, you learn how to talk and you learn how to tell a joke and you can get to a punchline. You can convey ideas quickly from growing up in Scotland - you're good at it.*

"So we were able to convey to people that this was actually a pretty interesting and valuable concept that people could use in science, and it certainly helped my career and certainly helped the science move forward, but it wouldn't have happened if I was not Scottish." In honour of his parents, MacMillan founded The May and Billy MacMillan Foundation to fund programs that provide educational opportunities for financially disadvantaged students in Scotland. He gave the Foundation his share of the Nobel Prize money — the equivalent of about $500,000 — as well as proceeds from all talks and appearances throughout the following year.

In June 2022, MacMillan was knighted by Queen Elizabeth II in her Platinum Jubilee Honours List, for his 'exceptional and sustained contribution to chemistry and science'. He was quoted as saying, *"It was difficult to keep it a secret when I found out in mid-May because I could only tell a very few people, but it was tremendously emotional for me. I was able to tell my family and they were ecstatic and excited and taken aback. Everyone, especially my sister and brother, kept talking about what it would have meant for my mum and dad, who would have been so honoured and excited by the whole thing… One friend of mine, who is just the funniest guy you'll ever meet, found out about this a few days ago. He had a suit of armour shipped from India to my home in Princeton. So, I now have a real suit of armour sitting in my garage waiting to be opened.*

40 Last of the summer snow: Adam Watson and Iain Cameron

In December 2015, at the Mauna Loa Observatory in Hawaii, the measured concentration of atmospheric carbon dioxide exceeded 400 parts per million. The last time the Earth's atmosphere contained that much CO_2 was some 4 million years ago, when average global surface temperatures were around 3C higher than now. From

Illustration 80: Dr Adam Watson on Glas Maol, Gleann Beag

samples of air bubbles in ancient ice cores, we know that for the past 800,000 years, CO_2 concentration has cycled within the range 170 to 300 ppm. The breakout above 300 ppm started in the 1920s, driven by a huge increase in CO_2 emissions due to human activity – mainly the consumption of fossil fuels, the burning of which releases CO_2 trapped underground since the aptly-named Carboniferous Period 300 million years ago. In less than 100 years, our annual CO_2 emissions have jumped from 4 billion to nearly 40 billion tons. Those who doubt the cause of sudden global climate change should study those numbers.

The action of atmospheric CO_2, water vapour and methane in warming the planet is well understood, as the 'greenhouse effect'. Shorter solar radiation wavelengths pass through the atmosphere easily, warm the ground, which reflects longer infrared wavelengths that are absorbed and trapped by the blanket of greenhouse gases in the lower atmosphere. The effects of a 3C rise in average surface temperature on climate are difficult to predict, and such a temperature increase may sound small. But by 2021 we already have had an approximate 1.2C rise from average pre-industrial temperatures, and are now seeing unexpectedly fast melting of polar ice, combined with droughts in tropical and sub-tropical areas and increased incidence of wildfires around the world. There is a risk that melting permafrost in the tundra of Canada and Siberia will release large quantities of methane – four times more potent than CO_2 as a greenhouse gas - and create a dangerous runaway effect.

In Scotland, the effects of a warming climate were observed continuously for decades by one remarkable scientist, long before climate science became fashionable and imperative. As a young boy, Adam Watson developed a fascination for snow. He remembered how *"I could see these pale veils coming out of the sky, and as it got near the ground I saw they were actually snowflakes."* Prodigiously bright at school, he was inspired by the writings and friendship of the naturalist, photographer, folklorist and piper, Seton Gordon. By the age of 14, Adam was keeping a 'snow diary', monitoring weather events around his home in Turriff, Aberdeenshire. Despite a teenage attack of emphysema that kept him in hospital for several months, he was soon walking the hills again, confounding his doctor's predictions. Watson's interest in ornithology led to local surveys of rooks and herons, and he made increasingly adventurous trips, climbing and skiing into the Scottish mountain ranges. He graduated with first-class honours in zoology from the University of Aberdeen in 1952, and used his PhD research to study the annual cycle of the rock ptarmigan, the archetypical grouse of the high Cairngorms. A year later, he won a Carnegie Arctic Scholarship to McGill University in Montreal, and then worked as a zoologist in the Baird Expedition to Baffin Island for the Arctic Institute of North America. Back home again, he joined the Institute for Terrestrial Ecology in Banchory, edited *The Scottish Naturalist* for eight years, and in 1967 he was awarded a second doctorate for his published research on the populations and behaviour of northern animals. His intimate knowledge of the terrain of the mountains led to his appointment as Chief Expert Witness in a fatal accident enquiry into the deaths, in a blizzard, of five children and one of their instructors in the 'Cairngorm Plateau disaster' of December 1971.

From Seton Gordon, Watson inherited many interests, including the monitoring of the deep snow patches which lie in the northeast-facing corries of the high Scottish mountains, the nearest things to glaciers in present-day Scotland, and persistent all through the summer – in the past. The observatory on the summit of Ben Nevis reported persistent snow on the mountain's northeast cliffs for most years from 1883 to 1904. Adam Watson's own detailed field observations from 1938 to 2011 were summarised in *'A snow book, northern Scotland'*. For 64 years, he recorded the proportion of snow cover at the start of June on the Ben Macdui plateau of the Cairngorms, excluding ephemeral summer snowfalls that can briefly give 100% cover. As residents and visitors know all too well, Scotland's weather is highly variable, and over the decades Watson found summer snow cover extremes of 2% and 98%, with no particular trend in the cover until 1986. Since then, he recorded a clear trend of diminishing summer snow cover on the plateau. An irregular decline in the persistence of snow patches in the high corries was observed too, in Watson's surveys of northeast Scottish mountains from 1974 to 1989. Over those years, the number of snow-beds surviving till October fluctuated widely, between 2 and 79. Only 2 snow patches endured every year over the whole period. The study, published in the journal *Artic and Alpine Research*, concluded that, *"we aimed to compare changes in snow patches between years with changes in regional climate in the same years. This is a considerable improvement on the use of glaciers as indicators of climate change…where a big drawback is the long, variable time-lag between climate change and glacier response. The more rapid response and easier measurement of snow patches is particularly important when climate is very variable over short periods. Moreover, snow patches can themselves provide a good index of increasing variability in climate (as in our data). Summer snow patches, therefore, are a useful single index, integrating the effects of many aspects of short- and medium-term climate change."*

In the summer of 1996, no snow patches persisted anywhere in Scotland, the first year without surviving patches since 1959. The most durable snow patches in the Cairngorms are those in Garbh Choire Mòr on Braeriach, the third highest mountain in the British Isles. The two snow-beds in this

Illustration 81: Garbh Choire Mòr on Braeriach showing Scotland's most durable snow patch

corrie, probably the most-studied in the world, are nicknamed the Sphinx and the Pinnacles. They have melted completely in only six summers over the last two centuries, but with increasing frequency, in 1933, 1959, 1996, 2003, 2006 and 2017. In 2018, the Sphinx succumbed to full melting for an unprecedented second year in a row. In 2019, as reported by the part-time researchers Iain Cameron and Blair Fyffe, the Pinnacles snow patch had expired by mid-October, and although the Sphinx patch survived through to winter, it was the smallest it had ever been without entirely disappearing.

Iain Cameron is foremost among the researchers who follow the life-cycles of Scottish snow patches, in the footsteps of Adam Watson – who died at the age of 88 in 2019, a much-honoured Fellow of the Royal Meteorological Society (RMetS), the Institute of Biology, and the Royal Society of Edinburgh. Cameron inherited Watson's interest when becoming intrigued by the spring snow on Ben Lomond, visible from his childhood vantage point in his parent's house in Port Glasgow. Though self-trained and employed as a health and safety specialist for a construction firm, Cameron makes fortnightly summer trips into the mountains in his own leisure time, to monitor and report on snow patches. With colleagues, he writes the twice-yearly reports in the RMetS journal *Weather* on the continuing diminution of the number and extent of summer snow patches in the Scottish hills.

The steady drips of the thawing summer snow in Scotland's mountain corries mark time on the unabating advance of global warming. The former weather forecaster turned forester, Matthew Hay, has written, *"As The Sphinx thaws, it does so alongside our planet's sea ice, and the permafrost of the Arctic tundra. These frozen worlds are more than just habitats: they are our safeguards. If they disappear, they will likely send the planet spiralling inexorably towards its next stable-state, a world that is 4 or 5°C warmer than present. The suffering this would cause, to both human and non-human life on Earth, would be unimaginable.*

So it is incumbent on all of us to take an interest in The Sphinx, and its frozen allies around the globe. These far-flung pieces of snow and ice may feel more distant and removed from our daily lives than ever, but what they tell us about the world we are living in, and the way we live our lives, has never been more relevant."

The poignant disappearance of Scotland's summer snow may be the least of our problems. Concerted, decisive international action is required to ameliorate and manage the effects of climate change. There is widening recognition of the seriousness of our situation, and the 2015 Paris Agreement on climate change targeted reductions in CO_2 emissions of 40% by 2030, compared to 1990, and carbon neutrality by the end of the 21st century. As of 2021, annual average atmospheric CO_2 levels were nearly 420 parts per million, rising at a rate of 2.5 ppm per year. It is not obvious that the world has the collective foresight, will or political unity to implement meaningful countermeasures. The United Nations Climate Change Conference (COP 26), held in Glasgow in November 2021, brought together around 20,000 experts, delegates and heads of state to agree some coordinated actions. The climate change clock is ticking.

41 Sources and further reading

The principal research sources that informed the stories in the book are listed chapter-by-chapter below, together with suggestions for further reading in the subjects. I have deliberately avoided the use of footnotes and specific detailed references in the main text, in order to keep the stories flowing and as accessible as possible for the general reader, but the references roughly correspond to the order in which they were used to construct the chapters. In most cases, the sources are available online at the link addresses listed, courtesy of digital libraries such as the Internet Archive, JSTOR, Project Gutenberg, and many other websites and blogs. They are a mix of popular articles and books, with more technical papers drawn from learned journals, for those more interested in the specialist details of the science. It should I hope, be obvious which is which.

1. The Scottish Diaspora

1. Angela McCarthy, 'The Scottish Diaspora since 1815', in the Oxford Handbook of Modern Scottish History, ed. T.M. Devine and Jenny Wormald, pub. Oxford U. Press (2012). Accessed at https://www.oxfordhandbooks.com/view/10.1093/oxfordhb/97801995 63692.001.0001/oxfordhb-9780199563692-e-28

2. Tom Steele, 'Scotland's Story' pp 214-246, pub. Wm. Collins (1984)

3. W.W. Knox, 'Health in Scotland 1840-1940' in 'A History of the Scottish People'. Accessed at https://www.scran.ac.uk/scotland/pdf/SP2_3Health.pdf

4. T.M. Devine, 'To the Ends of the Earth: Scotland's Global Diaspora', pub. Penguin (2011)

5. 'The Scottish diaspora: How the Scots spread across the globe', The Scotsman, 25th January (2016). Accessed at

https://www.scotsman.com/whats-on/arts-and-entertainment/scottish-diaspora-how-scots-spread-across-globe-1484633

2. All the tea in China

1. Robert Fortune, 'Three years' wanderings in the northern provinces of China', pub. John Murray (1847). Accessed at https://www.gutenberg.org/ebooks/54720

2. Robert Fortune, 'A Journey to the Tea Countries of China', pub. John Murray (1852). Accessed at https://archive.org/details/ajourneytoteaco00fortgoog/

3. Robert Fortune, 'Two Visits to the Tea Countries of China', vol. 1, pub. John Murray (1853). Accessed at https://www.biodiversitylibrary.org/item/181321#page/8/mode/1up

4. G.S. Boulger and Elizabeth Baigent, 'Fortune, Robert (1812-1880)', Oxford Dictionary of National Biography (2010). Accessed at https://doi.org/10.1093/ref:odnb/9953

5. Roy Moxham, 'A brief history of tea', pub. Constable & Robinson Ltd (2009)

6. British Parliamentary debate, 'The Opium Trade-Observations', Hansard vol. 252 4th June (1880). Accessed at https://hansard.parliament.uk/Commons/1880-06-04/debates/b53a59e8-4235-47f9-beec-31da92fdfbf4/TheOpiumTrade%E2%80%94Observations

7. WiC, 'Tea total: How the Scots stole China's beverage heritage', (2010). Accessed at https://www.weekinchina.com/2010/04/tea-total/

8. C.A. Bruce, ' An account of the manufacture of the black teas now practised at Suddeya in Upper Assam by the Chinamen sent thither for that purpose', pub. Bengal Military Orphan Press (1838). Accessed at https://babel.hathitrust.org/cgi/pt?id=hvd.32044106385073&view=1up&seq=7

9. 'Mr Bruce's Report on Assam Tea', Chambers' Edinburgh Journal, 25th Jan. (1840). Accessed at https://web.archive.org/web/20061220204732/http://liyn-an.com/tea_room/bruce/

10. Sarah Rose, 'For all the tea in China: Espionage, empire and the secret formula for the world's favourite drink', pub. Arrow Books (2010)

11. Jonathon D. Spence, 'God's Chinese Son: The Taiping Heavenly Kingdom of Hong Xiquan', pub. Norton & Co. Inc. (1996). Accessed at https://archive.org/details/godschinesesonta0000spen

12. David R. Hershey, 'Doctor Ward's Accidental Terrarium', The American Biology Teacher, vol. 58, 5, pp 276-281 (1996). Accessed at https://doi.org/10.2307/4450151

13. Picture credit: Illustration 1. John Forbes Royle c. 1851. Public domain. {{PD-US-expired}}. Accessed at https://commons.wikimedia.org/wiki/File:Royle_1851.jpg

14. Picture credit: Illustration 2. An example of a Wardian Case. Public domain. {{PD-US-expired}}. Accessed at https://commons.wikimedia.org/wiki/File:Ward%27scher_Kasten.jpg

15. Picture credit: Illustration 3. Dr Hugh Falconer, Director of the Calcutta Botanic Garden. Public Domain. {{PD-US-expired}}. Accessed at https://commons.wikimedia.org/wiki/File:Hugh_Falconer.jpeg

16. Picture credit: Illustration 4. Robert Fortune (1812-1880) Public domain. {{PD-US-expired}}. Accessed at https://commons.wikimedia.org/wiki/File:RobertFortune.gif

3. The telephone and the Big Bang

1. Robert V. Bruce, 'Bell: Alexander Graham Bell and the Conquest of Solitude', pub. Cornell University Press (1973)

2. Michael E. Gorman, 'Alexander Graham Bell's Path to the Telephone'. Accessed at http://www2.iath.virginia.edu/albell/

3. David Hochfelder, 'Alexander Graham Bell', Encyclopaedia Britannica'. Accessed at https://www.britannica.com/biography/Alexander-Graham-Bell (2020)

4. R.W. Burns, 'Bell, Alexander Graham', Oxford Dictionary of National Biography (2011). Accessed at https://doi.org/10.1093/ref:odnb/30680

5. Harold S. Osborne, 'Biographical memoir of Alexander Graham Bell 1847-1922', National Academy of Sciences of the USA (1943). Accessed at http://www.nasonline.org/publications/biographical-memoirs/memoir-pdfs/bell-alexander-graham.pdf

6. I. Berberis et al, 'The history of tuberculosis: from the first historical records to the isolation of Koch's bacillus', J. Prev. Med. Hyg. 58, 1, pp E9-E12 (2017). Accessed at https://www.ncbi.nlm.nih.gov/pmc/articles/PMC5432783/

7. Matthew Baillie, ' The Morbid Anatomy of Some of the Most Important Parts of the Human Body', pp 36-39. Pub. Albany (1795). Accessed at https://collections.nlm.nih.gov/bookviewer?PID=nlm:nlmuid-2542005R-bk#page/52/mode/2up

8. Tom Everrett, 'Writing sound with a human ear: reconstructing Bell and Blake's 1874 ear phonautograph' Science Museum Group Journal, 12, (2019). Accessed at http://journal.sciencemuseum.ac.uk/browse/issue-12/writing-sound-with-a-human-ear/

9. David Macdonald, 'How Bell invented the telephone', Macleans's, 15th Sept (1953). Accessed at https://archive.macleans.ca/article/1953/9/15/how-bell-invented-the-telephone

10. Neal McEwen, 'The Telegraph Office' (2004). Accessed at http://www.telegraph-office.com/tel_off.html

11. Alexander Graham Bell, 'Improvement in Transmitters and Receivers for Electric Telegraphs', US Patent 161739 (1875). Accessed at https://patents.google.com/patent/US161739A

12. Alexander Graham Bell, 'Improvement in telegraphy', US Patent 174465 (1876). Accessed at https://patents.google.com/patent/US174465A

13. Wikipedia, 'Elisha Gray and Alexander Bell telephone controversy' Accessed 2020

14. Alexander Graham Bell, 'Multiple telegraph' Statement of Inventions (1876). Accessed at https://www.loc.gov/item/magbell.26910105/

15. Jon Gertner, 'How Bell Labs invented the world we live in today', Time magazine, March 21st (2012). Accessed at https://business.time.com/2012/03/21/how-bell-labs-invented-the-world-we-live-in-today/

16. Picture credit: Illustration 5. Alexander Graham Bell, standing, photograph by Timoleon Marie Lobrichon (public domain). Accessed at https://commons.wikimedia.org/wiki/File:Alexander_Graham_Bell,_three-quarter_length_portrait,_standing,_facing_left_-_3c04275r.jpg

17. Picture credit: Illustration 6. Bell System advertisement c.1918 Accessed at https://commons.wikimedia.org/wiki/File:Bell_System_Flu_Quarantine.png (public domain).

4. Adventurous doctress

6. Mary Seacole, 'Wonderful Adventures of Mrs Seacole in Many Lands', pub. Blackwood (1857). Accessed at https://digital.library.upenn.edu/women/seacole/adventures/adventures.html

7. Jane Robinson, 'Mary Seacole: The charismatic black nurse who became a heroine of the Crimea' pub. Robinson (2005)

8. Jack L. Summers and Rene Chartrand, 'History and Uniform of the 60th (Royal American) Regiment of Foot, 1755-1760'. Accessed at https://www.militaryheritage.com/60thregt.htm (2021)

9. Stephen Mullen, 'Scots in the West Indies in the colonial period: a view from the Archives', Scottish Archives, vol 22, (2016). Accessed at https://www.scottishrecordsassociation.org/2304.Scottish%20Archives%20-22.2%20Mullen.web.2018-01-29.pdf

10. Alan Palmer, 'Seacole (née Grant), Mary Jane (1805-1881)', Oxford Dictionary of National Biography (2006). Accessed at https://doi.org/10.1093/ref:odnb/41194

11. Victorian London - People - Mary Seacole. Accessed at https://www.victorianlondon.org/people/seacole.htm (2021)

12. Mary Seacole Trust, 'Read Mary's Story'. Accessed at https://www.maryseacoletrust.org.uk/learn-about-mary/ (2021)

13. Helen Rappaport, 'Mary Seacole: Creole Doctress, Nurse and Healer'. Accessed at https://helenrappaport.com/footnotes/mary-seacole-creole-doctress-nurse/ (2021)

14. Elizabeth Anionwu, 'Scotching three myths about Mary Seacole', British J. of Healthcare Assistants, 7, 10, pp 508-511 (2013). Accessed at https://www.uwl.ac.uk/sites/default/files/Academic-schools/College-of-Nursing-Midwifery-and-Healthcare/Web/PDF/Elizabeth%20Anionwu%20Papers/BJHA_2013_07_10_508%20Anionwu%20Seacolemyths.pdf

15. Picture credit: Illustration 7. Mary Seacole photograph by Maull & Co., London c.1873. Accessed at https://commons.wikimedia.org/wiki/File:Seacole_photo.jpg (public domain)

16. Picture credit: Illustration 8. Statue of Mary Seacole by Martin Jennings at St Thomas' Hospital, London. Photo by Sumit Surai (cropped). Accessed

at https://commons.wikimedia.org/wiki/File:Mary_Seacole_Statue.jpg
under CC Attribution -Share Alike 4.0 International licence

5. The Real Deal

1. 'Mackay', Scottish National Dictionary (1856). Accessed at
   https://dsl.ac.uk/entry/snd/snds4002

2. Michael Quinion, 'Real McCoy, the', World Wide Words (2011). Accessed
   at http://www.worldwidewords.org/qa/qa-mcc1.htm

3. The Phrase Finder, 'The Real McCoy'. Accessed at
   https://www.phrases.org.uk/meanings/real-mccoy.html (2021)

4. Wayback Machine, 'The not-so-real McCoy' (2011). Accessed at
   https://web.archive.org/web/20110517111621/http://www33.brinkster.
   com/iiiii/mccoy/

5. Mary Bellis, 'Biography of Elijah McCoy American inventor.' (2019).
   Accessed at https://www.thoughtco.com/elijah-mccoy-profile-1992158/

6. Wendy Towle, 'The Real McCoy - the life of an African-American
   inventor', pub. Scholastic (1993). Accessed at
   https://archive.org/details/realmccoylifeofa00towl/mode/2up

7. Scottish Engineering Hall of Fame, 'Elijah McCoy'. Accessed at
   http://www.engineeringhalloffame.org/profile-mccoy.html (2021)

8. Elijah McCoy, 'Improvement in Lubricators for Steam Engines', US
   Patent No. 129,843. Accessed at
   https://patents.google.com/patent/US129843A/en

9. Elijah McCoy, 'Lubricator', US Patent No 1,192,083 (1916). Accessed at
   https://patentimages.storage.googleapis.com/7f/38/48/5f7132367353ef
   /US1192083.pdf

10. Picture credit: Illustration 9. Elijah McCoy c.1900s. Unknown author,
    public domain. Accessed
    https://commons.wikimedia.org/wiki/File:EJMcCoy.jpg

11. Picture credit: Illustration 10. Dwight Burdette, photo of commemorative
    historical marker of Elijah McCoy in Ypsilanti, Michigan (cropped).
    Accessed
    https://commons.wikimedia.org/wiki/File:Elijah_McCoy_Commemorati
    ve_Historical_Marker_Ypsilanti_Michigan.jpg under CC Attribution 3.0
    Unported licence.

6. Pneumatic tyres

1. B.W. Best, 'Dunlop, John Boyd (1840-1921), Oxford Dictionary of National Biography (2004). Accessed at https://doi.org/10.1093/ref:odnb/32935

2. Jim Cooke, 'John Boyd Dunlop 1840-1921, Inventor', Dublin Historical Record, vol. 49, 1, pp 16-31 (1996). Accessed at www.jstor.org/stable/30101131

3. G.C. Boase and R. Harrington, 'Thomson, Robert William (1822-1873)', Oxford Dictionary of National Biography (2004). Accessed at https://doi.org/10.1093/ref:odnb/27323

4. Ben Johnson, 'Robert William Thomson', Historic UK. Accessed at https://www.historic-uk.com/HistoryUK/HistoryofScotland/Robert-William-Thomson/ (2021).

5. Martin Adeney, 'Du Cros, (William) Harvey', Oxford Dictionary of National Biography (2008). Accessed at https://doi.org/10.1093/ref:odnb/46891

6. Arthur Du Cros, 'Wheels of Fortune, a salute to pioneers' pub. Chapman & Hall (1938). Accessed at https://archive.org/stream/in.ernet.dli.2015.184704/2015.184704.Wheels-Of-Fortune_djvu.txt

7. John Boyd Dunlop, 'Wheel-tire for cycles', US patent 435,995 (1890). Accessed at https://patentimages.storage.googleapis.com/fd/b7/1c/8fee4e0db3-Da9d/US435995.pdf

8. Robert William Thomson, 'An Improvement in Carriage Wheels, which is also applicable to other Rolling Bodies', GB patent 10,990 (1845). Accessed at https://onlinebicyclemuseum.co.uk/pneumatic-tyre-patents/

9. BBC History, 'Kirkpatrick Macmillan (1812-1878)' (2014). Accessed at https://www.bbc.co.uk/history/historic_figures/macmillan_kirkpatrick.shtml

10. 'Tyre patents', Grace's Guide to British Industrial History. Accessed at https://www.gracesguide.co.uk/Tyre_Patents (2021).

11. Oxford Academic, 'Edlin & Co. v The Pneumatic Tyre and Booth's Cycle Agency, Limited', High Court of Justice Reports of Patent, Design and Trademark Cases vol X, 22, pp 311- 316 (1893). Accessed at https://academic.oup.com/rpc/article/10/22/311/1591868

12. Tom McGovern, 'Dominance to Decline: A case study of the demise of Dunlop' (2006). Accessed at https://web.archive.org/web/20140126000223

13. Picture credit: Illustration 11. John Boyd Dunlop, c. 1900? Accessed at https://commons.wikimedia.org/wiki/File:John_Boyd_Dunlop.jpg. Public domain. {{PD-US-expired}}

14. Picture credit: Illustration 12. Robert William Thomson, engraving by R&E Taylor from a photograph by Mr Peterson of Copenhagen. Accessed at https://commons.wikimedia.org/wiki/File:Robert_William_Thomson.png. Public domain {{PD-US-expired}}

15. Picture credit: Illustration 13. John Boyd Dunlop c.1915. Accessed at https://commons.wikimedia.org/wiki/File:John_Boyd_Dunlop_(c1915).jpg. Public domain.

7. Star-spangled skies

1. Harvard Library, 'Journal of Williamina Paton Fleming, 1900, Mar 1- Apr 18'. Accessed at https://curiosity.lib.harvard.edu/women-working-1800-1930/catalog/45-990095497780203941

2. Lindsay Smith, 'Williamina Paton Fleming', Project Continua March 14: Vol 1. (2015). Accessed at http://www.projectcontinua.org/williamina-paton-fleming/

3. 'Williamina Fleming', Accessed at https://biography.yourdictionary.com/williamina-fleming (2021)

4. Anne Gordon, 'Williamina Fleming: "Women's Work" at the Harvard Observatory', CUNY Academic Works, (1978). Accessed at https://academicworks.cuny.edu/cgi/viewcontent.cgi?article=1413&context=wsq

5. Sue Nelson, 'Williamina Fleming, Star of Scotland', The Finding Ada Virtual STEM conference, Accessed at https://findingada.com/shop/a-passion-for-science-stories-of-discovery-and-invention/williamina-fleming-star-of-scotland/ (2021)

6. Galactic Gazette, 'The first computer: Williamina Fleming and the Horsehead Nebula' (2017). Accessed at https://web.archive.org/web/20190929142207/http://altbibl.io/gazette/the-first-computer-williamina-fleming-and-the-horsehead-nebula/

7. Edward C. Pickering, 'The Meridian Photometer', Monthly Notices of the Roy. Astron. Soc. 42, 8, pp 365-366 (1882). Accessed at https://academic.oup.com/mnras/article/42/8/365/951134

8. Edward C. Pickering, 'The Henry Draper Memorial', Nature, 36, pp 31-34 (1887). Accessed at https://www.nature.com/articles/036031b0

9. George F. Barker, 'Memoir of Henry Draper 1837-1882', Read before the National Academy (1888). Accessed at http://www.nasonline.org/publications/biographical-memoirs/memoir-pdfs/draper-henry.pdf

10. Natasha Geiling, ' The women who mapped the Universe and still couldn't get any respect', Smithsonian Magazine, (2013). Accessed at https://www.smithsonianmag.com/history/the-women-who-mapped-the-universe-and-still-couldnt-get-any-respect-9287444/

11. Michelle Starr, ' The Harvard Computers who changed astronomy (pictures)'. Cnet (2016). Accessed at https://www.cnet.com/pictures/the-harvard-computers-who-changed-astronomy/

12. Women Working 1800-1930, 'Williamina Paton Stevens Fleming (1857-1911)', Harvard Open Collections Program. Accessed at https://web.archive.org/web/20180402041723/http://ocp.hul.harvard.edu/ww/fleming.html (2021)

13. Gabriele Kass-Simon, Patricia Farnes, Deborah Nash, 'Women of science: righting the record' pp 86- 116. pub. Indiana Univ. Press (1993). Accessed at https://archive.org/details/womenofsciencer000kass/page/86/mode/2up

14. Edward C. Pickering, 'The Draper Catalogue of Stellar Spectra', Annals of the Astronomical Observatory of Harvard College, vol. 27, pub. John Wilson & Son (1890). Accessed at http://articles.adsabs.harvard.edu/pdf/1890AnHar..27....1P

15. M. Fleming, 'Stars having peculiar spectra: Eleven new variable stars', Astrophysical J. vol. 1, (Jan-May) pp 411-415 (1895). Accessed at https://babel.hathitrust.org/cgi/pt?id=uc1.c040948667&view=2up&seq=465

16. M. Fleming, 'Stars having peculiar spectra: Eight new variable stars in Cetus, Vela, Centaurus, Lupus, Scorpio, Aquila and Pegasus', Astrophysical J. vol. 2 (Jun-Dec) pp 354- 359 (1895). Accessed at

https://babel.hathitrust.org/cgi/pt?id=uc1.c038658017&view=2up&seq=395

17. Williamina Fleming, 'A Field for Women's Work in Astronomy', Address to the Congress of Astronomy and Astrophysics, Chicago (1893). Accessed at https://speakingwhilefemale.co/science-fleming/

18. Annie J. Cannon, 'Williamina Paton Fleming', obituary, Science, vol. 33, 861, pp 987-988 (1911). Accessed at https://zenodo.org/record/1448062#.YBaq8-j7SUl

19. Henri M.J. Boffin et al, 'An interacting binary system powers precessing outflows of an evolved star', Science, vol. 338, 6108, pp 773-775 (9 Nov 2012). Accessed at https://science.sciencemag.org/content/338/6108/773.long

20. Picture credit: Illustration 14. Ken Crawford, The Horsehead Nebula, also known as Barnard 33, in the constellation Orion. Accessed at https://commons.wikimedia.org/wiki/File:Barnard_33.jpg under CC Attribution SA 3.0 Unported licence

21. Picture credit: Illustration 15. The planetary nebula Fleming 1 seen with European Southern Observatory's Very Large Telescope. Accessed at https://commons.wikimedia.org/wiki/File:The_planetary_nebula_Fleming_1_seen_with_ESO%E2%80%99s_Very_Large_Telescope.tiff under CC- Attribution 4.0 International Licence.

22. Picture credit: Illustration 16. Williamina Paton Stevens Fleming c 1890s. Courtesy Curator of Astronomical Photographs at Harvard University. Accessed at https://commons.wikimedia.org/wiki/File:Williamina_Paton_Stevens_Fleming_circa_1890s.jpg. Public domain.

8. The fact of fingerprints

1. Alex Paton, 'Faulds, Henry (1843-1930), Oxford Dictionary of National Biography, (2008). Accessed at https://doi.org/10.1093/ref:odnb/48854

2. Alex Paton, 'Fingerprint Faulds: the rehabilitation of Henry Faulds (1843-1930)', J. Med. Biography vol. 9, pp 132-136 (2001). Accessed at https://journals.sagepub.com/doi/10.1177/096777200100900302

3. Henry Faulds, 'On the skin-furrows of the hand', Nature, vol. 22, Oct. 28th, p 605, (1880). Accessed at https://www.nature.com/articles/022605a0.pdf

4. W.J. Herschel, 'Skin Furrows of the Hand', Nature, vol. 23, Nov. 25th, p76, (1880). Accessed at https://www.nature.com/articles/023076b0.pdf

5. 'Hand Marks Under the Microscope', lecture report, American J. of Microscopy, vol. 2, 7, p 89 (July 1877). Accessed at https://babel.hathitrust.org/cgi/pt?id=mdp.39015081146964&view=2up&seq=98&size=125

6. Francis Galton, 'Personal identification and description', Nature, pp 201-202, June 28th (1888). Accessed at https://www.nature.com/articles/038201a0.pdf

7. Francis Galton, 'Fingerprints', pub. Macmillan & Co (1892). Accessed at https://galton.org/books/finger-prints/galton-1892-fingerprints-1up-lowres.pdf

8. University of Strathclyde, 'Henry Faulds – Originator of fingerprint identification'. Accessed at https://www.strath.ac.uk/alumni/connectandnetwork/notablealumni/alumniinhistory/henryfaulds/ (2021)

9. Ibid., 'Fingerprinting in detection' (2013). Accessed at http://www.strath.ac.uk/media/ps/comms/itallstartedhere/Faulds.pdf

10. Henry Faulds, 'On the identification of Habitual Criminals by Finger-Prints', Nature, Oct. 4th, p 548, (1894). Accessed at https://www.nature.com/articles/050548a0.pdf

11. Henry Faulds, ' Guide to fingerprint identification', pub. Wood, Mitchell & Co (1905). 'Dactylography, or the Study of Fingerprints', pub. Halifax, Milner & Co (1912). 'A Manual of Practical Dactylography' pub. Police Review (1923). All accessed at https://galton.org/fingerprints/books/index.htm

12. Sir William J. Herschel, 'The origin of fingerprinting', pub. Oxford U. Press (1916). Accessed at https://galton.org/fingerprints/books/herschel/herschel-1916-origins-1up.pdf

13. Henry Faulds, and reply by C. Ainsworth Mitchell, 'Science and the investigation of crime', J. Roy. Soc. Arts, vol. 69, 3573, pp 420-421 (May 13th 1921). Accessed at https://www.jstor.org/stable/41355494?read-now=1&refreqid=excelsior%3A3b4b9cdad0ccdd820883ba74eff039a4&seq=1#page_scan_tab_contents

14. 'The history of fingerprints' Accessed at https://onin.com/fp/fphistory.html (2021)

15. Steven J. Faulds, 'Papers relating to Dr Henry Faulds', Archives Hub. Accessed at https://archive.is/20121223032056/http://archiveshub.ac.uk/data/gb25 0rcpsg13 (2021)

16. Ed German, 'A report on the dedication of the Faulds Memorial in Beith, Scotland', The Weekly Detail (2004). Accessed at http://www.clpex.com/Articles/TheDetail/100-199/TheDetail173.htm

17. 'The Henry Faulds Memorial in Japan'. Accessed at http://www.oninonin.com/fp/faulds_memorial.html

18. Henry Faulds, 'Nine Years in Nipon – Sketches of Japanese life and manners', pub. Alexander Gardner (1885). E-book accessed at https://books.google.co.uk/books?hl=en&lr=&id=ZU7cmrd4RhYC&oi =fnd&pg=PA9&ots=4TjafPQphu&sig=CSiTJk_meG54VaymI1Jdeji_D U8&redir_esc=y#v=onepage&q&f=false

19. Colin Beavan, ' Fingerprints: The origins of crime detection and the murder case that launched forensic science', pub. Hyperion (2002)

20. Gavan Tredoux, 'Henry Faulds: the invention of a fingerprinter', (2003). Accessed at https://galton.org/fingerprints/faulds.htm#faulds1894

21. Anil K. Jain et al., 'On the similarity of identical twin fingerprints', Pattern Recognition, vol. 35, pp 2653-2663 (2002).

22. E.R. Henry, 'Classification and Uses of Finger Prints', (8th Edition) pub. HMSO (1937). Accessed at https://babel.hathitrust.org/cgi/pt?id=uc1.$b382207&view=2up&seq=1

23. F.G(alton), 'Fingerprint identification', (review of Faulds book of 1905). Nature, vol. 72, 1877, supp. iv, Oct 19th (1905). Accessed at https://galton.org/cgi-bin/searchImages/galton/search/essays/pages/galton-1905-faulds-review-nature_1.htm

24. T.H(opkins), 'Proof by fingers', Law Times, vol. 119 pp 561-562, Oct. 28th (1905). Accessed at https://heinonline.org/HOL/Index?index=journals/lawtms&collection= journals

25. Richard Clark, 'The UK's first murder case solved by a fingerprint'. Accessed at http://www.capitalpunishmentuk.org/strattons.html (2021)

26. Henry Faulds, 'The permanence of finger-print patterns', Nature, vol. 98, pp 388-389 (1917). Accessed at https://www.nature.com/articles/098388c0.pdf

27. Picture credit: Illustration 17. Henry Faulds, unknown author, c.1890s. Public domain. Accessed at https://commons.wikimedia.org/wiki/File:Henry_Faulds2.jpg

17. Picture credit: Illustration 18. Distinguishing features as illustrated in 'Guide to fingerprint identification' (Faulds, 1905). Courtesy Wellcome Library, public domain.

9. Moving mountains

1. James Hutton, 'Theory of the Earth', Trans. Roy. Soc. Edinburgh, vol. 1, 2, pp 209 – 304 (1788). Accessed at https://www.biodiversitylibrary.org/item/19839#page/325/mode/1up and also at https://web.archive.org/web/20030729055405/http://www.uwmc.uwc.edu/geography/Hutton/Hutton.htm

2. Sir Charles Lyell, 'Principles of Geology', (9th ed.) pub. D. Appleton & Co. (1854). Accessed at https://www.gutenberg.org/files/33224/33224-h/33224-h.htm

3. Mary R.S. Creese, 'Maria Ogilvie Gordon (1864-1939)', Earth Sciences History vol. 15, 1, pp 68–75 (1996). Accessed at https://www.jstor.org/stable/24138562?seq=1#metadata_info_tab_contents

4. M. Wachtler and C.V. Burek, 'Maria Matilda Ogilvy Gordon (1864-1939): a Scottish researcher in the Alps, from Burek & Higgs (eds.) The Role of Women in the History of Geology, Geol. Soc. special publications vol. 281, pp 305-317 (2007). Accessed at https://sp.lyellcollection.org/content/specpubgsl/281/1/305.full.pdf

5. 'A lady geologist', The Review of Reviews, vol. 8, pp 287-288, (1893) Accessed at https://babel.hathitrust.org/cgi/pt?id=hvd.32044092829118&view=2up&seq=315&size=125

6. Mary R.S. Creese, 'Gordon (née Ogilvie) Dame Maria Matilda (1864-1939), Oxford Dictionary of National Biography (2004). Accessed at https://doi.org/10.1093/ref:odnb/46415

7. Maria M. Ogilvie, 'Contributions to the geology of the Wengen and St. Cassian strata in southern Tyrol', Qtrly J. Geol. Soc. London, vol. 49, pp 1-78, (1893). Accessed at https://jgs.lyellcollection.org/content/jgsleg/49/1-4/1.2.full.pdf

8. C. Lapworth, 'Presidential Address to the Geological Section', Reports of the British Association, vol. pp 695-707 (1892). Accessed at https://www.jstor.org/stable/pdf/24138562.pdf?refreqid=excelsior%3A d943951f5aaaf4e6f897156002a3226a

9. Maria M. Ogilvie and Gordon, 'The Torsion-Structure of the Dolomites', Quarterly Journal of the Geological Society, vol. 55, pp 560-634, (1899). Accessed at https://jgs.lyellcollection.org/content/55/1-4/560

10. M. Ogilvie Gordon, 'Guide for Geological Tours in the South Tyrolean Dolomites', pub. L. Waldmann, Erläut Exkurs. Deutsche Geol. Ges. Wien (1928).

11. Picture credit: Illustration 19. M. Wachtler, ' Maria Matilda Ogilvie Gordon' (1900). Public domain.

10. Surgery and suffrage: the Scottish Women's Hospitals for Foreign Service

1. Leah Leneman, 'Inglis, Elsie Maud', Oxford Dictionary of National Biography (2004). Accessed at https://doi.org/10.1093/ref:odnb/34101

2. J.M. Somerville, 'Dr Sophia Jex-Blake and the Edinburgh School of Medicine for Women, 1886-1898', J. R. Coll. Physicians Edinb vol. 35, pp 261-267 (2005). Accessed at http://www.rcpe.ac.uk/sites/default/files/somerville_jex_blake.pdf

3. The Women's Suffrage Movement in Scotland, 1867-1928. Accessed at https://womenssuffragescotland.wordpress.com/ (2021)

4. I. Miller, 'A Prostitution of the Profession?: The Ethical Dilemma of Suffragette Force-Feeding, 1909-14', in 'A History of Force-Feeding : Hunger Strikes, Prisons and Medical Ethics, 1909-1974' pub. Palgrave Macmillan (2016). Accessed at https://www.ncbi.nlm.nih.gov/books/NBK385295/

5. Agnes Savill, C. Mansell Moullin, and Sir Victor Horsley, 'Preliminary Report on the Forcible Feeding of Suffrage Prisoners', Br. Med. J., vol. 2, 2696, pp 505-508 Aug 31st (1912). Accessed at https://dx.doi.org/10.1136%2Fbmj.2.2696.505

6. June Purvis, 'Cat and mouse: force feeding the suffragettes', BBC History Magazine, (Nov, 2018). Accessed at https://www.historyextra.com/period/edwardian/cat-mouse-force-feeding-suffragettes-hunger-strike/

7. M.F. Weiner, 'The Scottish Women's Hospital at Royaumont, France 1914-1919', J. R. Coll. Physicians Edinb. vol. 44 pp 328-336 (2014). Accessed at http://www.rcpe.ac.uk/sites/default/files/weiner.pdf

8. E. Morrison and C. Parry, 'The Scottish Women's Hospitals for Foreign Service – the Girton and Newnham Unit, 1915-1918', J. R. Coll. Physicians Edinb. vol. 44 pp 337-343 (2014). Accessed at https://www.rcpe.ac.uk/sites/default/files/morrison_0.pdf

9. Eva Shaw McLaren (ed.), 'A History of the Scottish women's hospitals', pub. Hodder & Stoughton (1919). Accessed (in microform) at https://archive.org/details/cihm_65037/page/n7/mode/2up

10. Obituary, Dr Alice M. Hutchison, Br. Med. J., vol. 2, 4844, p1052, Nov. 7th (1953). Accessed at https://www.ncbi.nlm.nih.gov/pmc/articles/PMC2029985/?page=3

11. Kirsty Topping, 'House with Suffragette story to tell', (Grace Cadell's Mosspark House) The Courier and Advertiser, Perthshire Ed., 21st Jan. (2013). Accessed at https://www.pressreader.com/uk/the-courier-advertiser-perth-and-perthshire-edition/20130121/281539403321150

12. Picture credit: Illustration 20. Grace Ross Cadell, by John Campbell Harper (c.1891). Accessed at https://commons.wikimedia.org/wiki/File:Grace_Cadell.jpg Public domain {{PD-US-expired}}

13. Picture credit: Illustration 21. Agnes Forbes Blackadder Savill, (1894), courtesy of the Decker family. Accessed at https://commons.wikimedia.org/wiki/File:Agnes_Forbes_Blackadder.jpg under CC Attribution Share-Alike 3.0 Unported Licence.

14. Picture credit: Illustration 22. Elsie Inglis, by Lady Francis Balfour (1918). Accessed at https://commons.wikimedia.org/wiki/File:Elsie_Inglis.jpg under CC Attribution 4.0 International Licence

15. Picture credit: Illustration 23. Frances Ivens, courtesy Wellcome Images. Accessed at https://commons.wikimedia.org/wiki/File:Portrait_of_Frances_Ivens._Wellcome_L0004410_(cropped).jpg under CCR Attribution 4.0 International Licence

16. Picture credit: Illustration 24. Louise McIlroy, during WWI, author unknown. Accessed at https://commons.wikimedia.org/wiki/File:Louise_McIlroy_during_WWI.jpg. Public domain {{PD-US-expired}}

17. Picture credit: Illustration 25. Alice Hutchison in Russian cap and coat, during her internment (1917). Accessed at https://commons.wikimedia.org/wiki/File:Dr._Alice_Hutchison.png. Public domain {{PD-US-expired}}

11. Pandemic ! Fighting the Spanish Flu

1. Joan Mottram, 'Niven, James', Oxford Dictionary of National Biography, (2010). Accessed at https://doi.org/10.1093/ref:odnb/57128 Char

2. W.P.Povey, 'James Niven' in 'Some Manchester doctors: a biographical collection…' ed W.J.Elwood and A.F. Tuxford pp 98-100 pub. Manchester University Press (1984)

3. Matt Hartless, 'James Niven: the doctor who saved Manchester from worst effects of Spanish Flu epidemic', The Northern Quota (Oct. 2018). Accessed at https://thenorthernquota.org/features/james-niven-doctor-who-saved-manchester-worst-effects-spanish-flu-pandemic

4. Kansas Historical Society, 'Flu epidemic of 1918', (2020). Accessed at https://www.kshs.org/kansapedia/flu-epidemic-of-1918/17805

5. Peter C. Wever and Leo van Bergen, 'Death from 1918 pandemic influenza during the First World War: a perspective from personal and anecdotal evidence', Influenza and Other Respir Viruses, 8, 5, pp 538-546 (2014). Accessed at https://dx.doi.org/10.1111%2Firv.12267

6. 1918 pandemic (H1N1 virus), Centers for Disease Control and Prevention. Accessed at https://www.cdc.gov/flu/pandemic-resources/1918-pandemic-h1n1.html (2020)

7. History.com 'Spanish Flu', Accessed at https://www.history.com/topics/world-war-i/1918-flu-pandemic (2020)

8. Fred R. Hartesveldt, 'The Doctors And The Flu: The British Medical Profession's Response To The Influenza Pandemic Of 1918-19', Intl. Soc. Sci. Rev. 85,1/2, pp 28-39 (2010). Accessed at https://www.jstor.org/stable/41887429

9. James Niven, 'Report on the Epidemic of Influenza in Manchester, 1918-19', Accessed at http://influenza.sph.unimelb.edu.au/data/S0001/chapters/app_4.pdf

10. 'The influenza: Dr Niven's warning', Manchester Guardian, 2nd Nov. 1918. Accessed at https://www.theguardian.com/society/1918/nov/02/health.lifeandhealth

11. Helen Pidd, 'First 'Geek-in-Chief': shy Scot who paved way for Prof Chris Whitty', The Guardian, 27th Mar 2020. Accessed at https://www.theguardian.com/society/2020/mar/27/first-geek-in-chief-shy-scot-dr-james-niven-paved-way-prof-chris-whitty

12. Ashlie Blakey, 'How Manchester beat the Spanish Flu pandemic that put a prime minister in hospital', Manchester Evening News, 13th Apr 2020. Accessed at https://www.manchestereveningnews.co.uk/news/greater-manchester-news/how-manchester-beat-spanish-flu-18067909

13. Niall Johnson, 'Aspects of the historical geography of the 1918-19 influenza pandemic in Britain', PhD thesis, U. of Cambridge, (2001). Accessed at https://doi.org/10.17863/CAM.27727

14. Matthew Smallman-Raynor et al, 'The Spatial Anatomy of an Epidemic: Influenza in London and the County Boroughs of England and Wales, 1918-1919', Trans. Inst. of British Geographers, 27, 4, pp. 452-470 (2002). Accessed at https://www.jstor.org/stable/3804472?seq=5#metadata_info_tab_contents

15. Douglas Jordan, 'The deadliest flu: The complete story of the discovery and reconstruction of the 1918 pandemic virus', Centers for Disease Control. Accessed at https://www.cdc.gov/flu/pandemic-resources/reconstruction-1918-virus.html (2020)

16. Jeffrey K. Taubenberger and David M. Morens, '1918 influenza: the mother of all pandemics', Emerg. Infect. Dis. 12, 1, pp 15-22 (2006). Accessed at https://www.ncbi.nlm.nih.gov/pmc/articles/PMC3291398/

17. M. Martini et al., 'The Spanish Influenza Pandemic: a lesson from history 100 years after 1918', J. Prev Med Hyg. 60, 1, E64-E67 (2019). Accessed at https://www.ncbi.nlm.nih.gov/pmc/articles/PMC6477554/

18. Spanish Flu -The Forgotten Fallen (BBC dramatisation). Accessed at https://www.youtube.com/watch?v=MtdtikULIoM (2021)

19. Picture credit: Illustration 26. Emergency hospital at Camp Funston, Kansas, during the epidemic. Accessed at https://commons.wikimedia.org/wiki/File:Emergency_hospital_during_Influenza_epidemic,_Camp_Funston,_Kansas_-_NCP_1603.jpg (public domain)

20. Picture credit: Illustration 27. Dr James Niven, medical officer of Manchester, 1894 to 1922. From: Obituary notice, Lancet, 1925. Accessed

at https://en.wikipedia.org/wiki/File:James_Niven.jpg under Creative Commons licence Attribution 4.0 International (CC BY 4.0)

12. The disputed discovery of insulin

1. A.K. Das and Siddarth Shah, 'History of Diabetes: from Ants to Analogs', J. Assoc. Phys. Of India, vol. 59, Special Issue, April (2011). Accessed at https://www.japi.org/u2d4d484/history-of-diabetes-from-ants-to-analogs

2. Ananya Mandal, 'History of diabetes', Medical Life Sciences News, Jun 4th (2019). Accessed at https://www.news-medical.net/health/History-of-Diabetes.aspx

3. Edwin A.M. Gale, 'The Rise of Childhood Type 1 Diabetes in the 20th Century', Diabetes, vol. 51 pp 3353-3361 (2002). Accessed at https://diabetes.diabetesjournals.org/content/51/12/3353

4. Margaret DeLacy, 'Dobson, Matthew (1732-1784)', Oxford Dictionary of National Biography (2015). Accessed at https://doi.org/10.1093/ref:odnb/55275

5. Norman Moore and Claire E.J. Herrick, 'Rollo, John (d. 1809)', Oxford Dictionary of National Biography (2004). Accessed at https://doi.org/10.1093/ref:odnb/24028

6. John Rollo, 'An Account of Two Cases of the Diabetes Mellitus', Ann. Med. (Edinb.) vol. 2, pp 85-105 (1797). Accessed at https://www.ncbi.nlm.nih.gov/pmc/articles/PMC5112440/pdf/annmed edinb75118-0092.pdf

7. John Rollo, 'A Short Account of the Royal Artillery Hospital at Woolwich', pub. J. Mawman (1801). Accessed at https://books.google.co.uk/books?id=jZIwAAAAYAAJ&printsec

8. R. Luft. 'Oskar Minkowski: Discovery of the pancreatic origin of diabetes, 1889', Diabetologia, vol. 32, pp 399-401 (1989). Accessed at https://link.springer.com/content/pdf/10.1007/BF00271257.pdf

9. John Rennie and Thomas Fraser, 'The Islets of Langerhans in relation to diabetes', Biochem. J. vol. 2, (1-2), pp 7-19 (1907). Accessed at https://doi.org/10.1042/bj0020007

10. Sir Edward A. Shäfer, 'Nature of the pancreatic autacoid', pp 128-130 in 'The Endocrine Organs', pub. Longmans, Green & Co. (1916). Accessed at https://doi.org/10.5962/bhl.title.1131

11. Elizabeth P. Sparrow and Stanley Finger, 'Edward Albert Shäfer (Sharpey-Shafer) and his Contributions to Neuroscience', J. Hist. Neurosciences, vol. 10, 1, pp 41-57 (2001). Accessed at

12. J.J.R. Macleod, 'Physiology and Biochemistry in Modern Medicine', 3rd ed. Pub. C.V. Mosby Co. (1920). Accessed at https://archive.org/details/physiobiochemist00maclrich

13. Moses Barron, 'The Relation of the Islets of Langerhans to Diabetes', Surgery, Gynecology and Obstetrics, pp 437-448 Nov. (1920). Reprint accessed at https://insulin.library.utoronto.ca/islandora/object/insulin%3AT10001

14. Joseph H. Pratt, 'A Reappraisal of Researches Leading to the Discovery of Insulin', J. Hist. Medicine and Allied Sciences, vol. 9, 3 pp 281-289. (1954). Accessed at https://doi.org/10.1093/jhmas/IX.3.281

15. F.G. Banting et al., 'The effect produced on diabetes by extracts of pancreas', Trans. Assoc. Am. Physicians, vol. 37, pp 337-347 (1922). Accessed at https://insulin.library.utoronto.ca/islandora/object/insulin%3AT10010

16. F.G. Banting, C.H. Best, J.B. Collip, 'Extract obtainable from the mmalian pancreas… and a metod of preparing it', US Patent 1,469,994 (1923). Accessed at https://insulin.library.utoronto.ca/islandora/object/insulin%3AQ10017

17. Michael Bliss, 'J.J.R.Macleod and the discovery of insulin', Qtrly. J. Experimental Physiology, vol. 74 pp 87-96 (1989). Accessed at https://physoc.onlinelibrary.wiley.com/doi/pdf/10.1113/expphysiol.1989.sp003266

18. Michael Bliss, 'The Discovery of Insulin: The Twenty-fifth Anniversary Edition', pub. U. of Toronto Press (1982). Accessed at https://www.jstor.org/stable/10.3138/j.ctt1wn0sjc

19. Michael Bliss, 'The History of Insulin', Diabetes Care, vol. 16, supp 3, pp 4-7 (1993). Accessed at https://doi.org/10.2337/diacare.16.3.4

20. Michael Bliss, ' The eclipse and rehabilitation of JJR Macleod, Scotland's insulin laureate', J. R. Coll. Physicians Edinb. vol. 46, 4, pp 366-73 (2013). Accessed at http://dx.doi.org/10.4997/JRCPE.2013.401

21. Louis Rosenfeld, 'Insulin: Discovery and Controversy', Clinical Chemistry, vol. 48, 12, pp 2270-2288 (2002). Accessed at https://doi.org/10.1093/clinchem/48.12.2270

22. C. Stylianou and C. Kelnar, 'The introduction of successful treatment of diabetes mellitus with insulin', JLL Bulletin: Commentaries of the history of treatment evaluation (2008). Accessed at https://www.jameslindlibrary.org/articles/the-introduction-of-successful-treatment-of-diabetes-mellitus-with-insulin/

23. Alberto de Leiva-Hidalgo et al., 'From pancreatic extracts to artificial pancreas: History, science and controversies about the discovery of the pancreatic antidiabetic hormone', Avances en Diabetología, vol. 27, 1, pp 15-26 (2011). Accessed at https://doi.org/10.1016/S1134-3230(11)70004-7

24. Royal College of Physicians of Edinburgh, ' Time to Recognise Scottish Doctor's Role in the Discovery of Insulin' (2013). Accessed at https://www.rcpe.ac.uk/time-recognise-scottish-doctors-role-discovery-insulin

25. A.H. 'John James Rickard Macleod, 1876-1935', Obituary in Experimental Physiology, vol. 25, 2, pp105-108 (1935). Accessed at https://doi.org/10.1113%2Fexpphysiol.1935.sp000668

26. Ignazio Vecchio et al., 'The Discovery of Insulin: An Important Milestone in the History of Medicine', Frontiers in Endocrinology, vol. 9, 613, pp 1-8 (2018). Accessed at https://www.ncbi.nlm.nih.gov/pmc/articles/PMC6205949/

27. Picture credit, Illustration 28. J. J.R. Macleod, c.1928. Unknown author. Public domain. Accessed at https://commons.wikimedia.org/wiki/File:J.J.R._Macleod_ca._1928.png

28. Picture credit, Illustration 29: C.H. Best and F.G. Banting c. 1924. Courtesy Thomas Fisher Rare Book Library, U. of Toronto under CC Attribution 2.0 Generic Licence. Accessed at https://commons.wikimedia.org/wiki/File:Photograph_of_C.H._Best_and_F.G._Banting_ca._1924_(12309018974).jpg

29. Picture credit, Illustration 30: J.B. Collip at McGill U. c.1930 by Barbara Collip-Wyatt. Courtesy U. of Toronto. Accessed at https://commons.wikimedia.org/wiki/File:J._B._Collip_in_his_office_at_McGill_University_ca._1930.png

13. First men on the Moon

1. Reginald Turnill, 'The Moonlandings – An eyewitness account', pub. Cambridge Univ. Press (2003)

2. 'Adam Abraham Armstrong III' Accessed at
https://www.geni.com/people/Adam-Armstrong-III/ (2021)

3. James R. Hansen, 'First Man - The life of Neil A. Armstrong' pub. Simon
& Schuster (2005)

4. Kelly Sands (ed.), 'Biography of Neil Armstrong', (2019). Accessed at
https://www.nasa.gov/centers/glenn/about/bios/neilabio.html

5. Alan Bean, 'My life as an astronaut', (as told to Beverly Fraknoi) pub.
Pocket Books (1988). Accessed at
https://archive.org/details/mylifeasastronau00bean/mode/2up

6. 'John (MacBayne) Bean bef. 1634-1718' Accessed at
https://www.wikitree.com/wiki/MacBayne-2

7. 'Passengers of the ship "John and Sara": Scots prisoners of war, 1651'.
Accessed at https://www.geni.com/projects/Passengers-of-the-ship-
John-and-Sara-Scots-Prisoners-of-War-1651/12051

8. John F. Kennedy, speech to the United States Congress, May 25th (1961).
Accessed at https://www.space.com/11772-president-kennedy-historic-
speech-moon-space.html

9. Sarah Loff (ed.) NASA, 'Apollo 11 Mission Overview' (2019). Accessed at
https://www.nasa.gov/mission_pages/apollo/missions/apollo11.html

10. NASA Mission Evaluation Team, 'Apollo 12 Mission Report', (1970).
Accessed at https://www.hq.nasa.gov/alsj/a12/A12_MissionReport.pdf

11. Paul Shillito, "How did the Apollo flight computers get men to the moon
and back?" in Computers, Moon, Videos (2017). Accessed at
http://curious-droid.com/214/apollo-flight-computers-get-men-moon-
back/

12. Crystal Chesters, 'Moon landing 50 years on: why astronaut Neil
Armstrong calls Scotland home', The Scotsman, July 19th (2019).
Accessed at https://www.scotsman.com/regions/dumfries-and-
borders/moon-landing-50-years-why-astronaut-neil-armstrong-calls-
scotland-home-543968

13. Ian Harvey, ' Neil Armstrong's last name posed a problem…' The
Vintage News (2019). Accessed at
https://www.thevintagenews.com/2019/04/15/armstrong/

14. Ken MacTaggart, 'Obituary - Alan Bean, American-Scottish astronaut
who took tartan to the moon', The Herald, May 30th (2018). Accessed at
https://www.heraldscotland.com/opinion/16258325.obituary---alan-
bean-american-scottish-astronaut-took-tartan-moon/

15. Picture credit: Illustration 31. 'Earthrise', photographed by Bill Anders while in lunar orbit in Apollo 8. Courtesy of NASA – Johnson Space Center. Accessed at https://commons.wikimedia.org/wiki/File:NASA-Apollo8-Dec24-Earthrise.jpg (public domain, PD-USGov).

16. Picture credit: Illustration 32. Neil Armstrong photographed by Buzz Aldrin after completion of the lunar EVA on the Apollo 11 mission. Accessed at https://commons.wikimedia.org/wiki/File:Neil_Armstrong_2.jpg (public domain, PD-USGov).

17. Picture credit: Illustration 33. Alan L. Bean, 22 Sept. 1969. Courtesy of NASA-Johnson Space Center. Accessed at https://commons.wikimedia.org/wiki/File:Alan_Bean_NASA_portrait_(S69-38859).jpg (public domain, PD-USGov).

14. Twentieth century triumphs

18. George Cameron Peden, 'A New Scotland? The Economy', in The Oxford Handbook of Modern Scottish History, ed. T.M. Devine and Jenny Wormald, pub. Oxford U. Press (2012). Accessed at https://www.researchgate.net/publication/324112662_A_New_Scotland_The_Economy

19. Nobel Organisation, 'Alfred Nobel's life and work'. Accessed at https://www.nobelprize.org/alfred-nobel/alfred-nobels-life-and-work/ (2021)

15. Noble gases and the Nobel prize

1. The Royal Society of Chemistry, 'Periodic Table'. Accessed at https://www.rsc.org/periodic-table/element/ (2021)

2. Sir William A. Tilden, 'Sir William Ramsay KCB, FRS - Memorials of his life and work', pub. Macmillan & Co. (1918). Accessed at https://babel.hathitrust.org/cgi/pt?id=uc1.31822007567639&view=1up&seq=1

3. Alwyn G. Davies, 'Sir William Ramsay and the noble gases', Science Progress, 95, 1, pp 23-49 (2012). Accessed at https://journals.sagepub.com/doi/pdf/10.3184/003685012X13307058213813

4. K.D. Watson, 'Ramsay, Sir William (1852-1916)', Oxford Dictionary of National Biography (2004). Accessed at https://doi.org/10.1093/ref:odnb/35663

5. D. Thorburn Burns, 'Robert Rattray Tatlock (1837-1934) Public Analyst for Glasgow', J. of the Assoc. of Public Analysts, 39, pp 38-43 (2011). Accessed at http://www.apajournal.org.uk/2011_0038-0043.pdf

6. William Ramsay, 'The gases of the atmosphere - the history of their discovery', pub. Macmillan & Co. (1896). Accessed at http://www.gutenberg.org/ebooks/52778

7. Jaime Wisniak,, 'William Ramsay', Educación Quimica, 19, 4, pp 303-310 (2008). Accessed at https://www.researchgate.net/publication/236619953_William_Ramsay

8. Lord Rayleigh and Professor William Ramsay, 'Argon, a new Constituent of the Atmosphere', Phil. Trans. Roy. Soc. 186A, pp 187-241 (1895). Accessed at https://royalsocietypublishing.org/doi/pdf/10.1098/rsta.1895.0006

9. Louis Cailletet, 'The liquefaction of oxygen', Science, 6, 128, pp 51-52 (1885). Accessed at https://zenodo.org/record/1448347#.YBFd_ej7SUk

10. Robert J. Soulen Jr., 'James Dewar, His Flask and Other Achievements', Physics Today, 49, 3, pp 32-37 (1996). Accessed at https://physicstoday.scitation.org/doi/pdf/10.1063/1.881490

11. C.E.H. Bawn, 'Morris William Travers 1872-1961', Biographical memoirs of the Fellows of the Royal Society, 9, pp 82-87 (1963). Accessed at https://royalsocietypublishing.org/doi/pdf/10.1098/rsbm.1963.0016

12. William Ramsay and Morris W. Travers, 'On a new constituent of atmospheric air', [krypton], Proc. Roy. Soc. 63, 405 (1898). Accessed at https://royalsocietypublishing.org/doi/pdf/10.1098/rspl.1898.0051

13. William Ramsay and Morris W. Travers, 'On the companions of Argon', [mainly neon], Proc. Roy. Soc. 63, pp437-440 (1898). Accessed at https://royalsocietypublishing.org/doi/pdf/10.1098/rspl.1898.0057

14. Sir William Ramsay, Nobel lecture, Nobel Prize.org (1904). Accessed at https://www.nobelprize.org/prizes/chemistry/1904/ramsay/ lecture/

15. Picture credit: Illustration 34. William Ramsay, in his laboratory. Accessed at https://commons.wikimedia.org/wiki/File:William_Ramsay_working.jpg (public domain) {{PD-US-expired}}

16. Picture credit: Illustration 35. Grasso Luigi, Noble gases from the periodic table (2019) Accessed at https://commons.wikimedia.org/wiki/File:Noble-gas_spe.png under CC-BY-SA-4.0 licence

16. Head in the clouds

1. Malcom S. Longair, Wilson, Charles Thomson Rees', Oxford Dictionary of National Biography, (2006). Accessed at https://doi.org/10.1093/ref:odnb/36950

2. Significant Scots, 'Professor Charles Thomson Rees Wilson'. Accessed at https://electricscotland.com/history/other/wilson_charles.htm (2021)

3. Nobel Lectures, 'C.T.R. Wilson - Biographical', NobelPrize.org (1927). Accessed at https://www.nobelprize.org/prizes/physics/1927/wilson/biographical/

4. Cambridge Physics, 'The cloud chamber'. Accessed at http://www.cambridgephysics.org/cloudchamber/cloudchamber_index.htm (2021)

5. John Aitken, 'Dust, Fogs and Clouds', Nature, vol. 23, pp 384-385 (1881). Accessed at https://www.nature.com/articles/023384a0.pdf

6. J.J. Thomson and J.A. McClelland, 'On the Leakage of Electricity through Dielectrics traversed by Rontgen Rays', Proc. Cambridge Phil. Soc. Vol. 9, pp 126-140 (1896). Accessed at https://www.biodiversitylibrary.org/page/30529581#page/146/mode/1up

7. C.T.R. Wilson, 'The Effect of Röntgen Rays on Cloudy Condensation', communicated by J.J. Thomson, Proc. Roy. Society, vol. 59, pp 338-339, Mar. 19th (1896). Accessed at https://doi.org/10.1098/rspl.1895.0101

8. J.J. Thomson, 'On the Cathode Rays', Proc. Cambridge Phil. Soc., vol. 9, pp 243-244, Feb. 8th (1897). Accessed at https://archive.org/details/proceedingsofcam9189598camb/page/242/mode/2up

9. J.J. Thomson, 'Carriers of negative electricity', Nobel lecture, Dec. 11th (1906). Accessed at https://www.nobelprize.org/uploads/2018/06/thomson-lecture.pdf

10. J.J. Thomson, 'On the Masses of the Ions in Gases at Low Pressures', Phil. Mag. vol. 48, 295, pp 547-567 (1899). Accessed at https://www.chemteam.info/Chem-History/Thomson-1899.html

11. C.T.R. Wilson, 'On a Method of making Visible the Paths of Ionising Particles through a Gas', Roy. Soc. Proc. A, vol. 85, pp 285 – 288 (1911) Accessed at https://royalsocietypublishing.org/doi/pdf/10.1098/rspa.1911.0041

12. Charles T.R. Wilson, 'On the cloud method of making visible ions and the tracks of ionizing particles', Nobel lecture, Dec. 12th (1927). Accessed at https://www.nobelprize.org/uploads/2018/06/wilson-lecture.pdf

13. N.N. Das Gupta and S.K. Ghosh, 'A Report on the Wilson Cloud Chamber and Its Applications in Physics', Rev. Mod. Phys. Vol. 18, 1, pp 225-284, (1946). Accessed at http://hep.ucsb.edu/people/hnn/cloud/articles/rmp1949.pdf

14. Clinton Chaloner, 'The most wonderful experiment in the world: a history of the cloud chamber', British J. for History of Science, vol. 30, 3, pp 357-374 (1997). Accessed at https://www.jstor.org/stable/4027867

15. C.T.R. Wilson, 'Ben Nevis Sixty Years Ago', Weather, vol. 9, 10, pp 309-311 (1954). Accessed at https://doi.org/10.1002/j.1477-8696.1954.tb01693.x

16. Karen L. Aplin, 'CTR Wilson – Honouring a Great Scottish Physicist', Weather, vol. 68, 4, p 96 (2013). Accessed at https://doi.org/10.1002/wea.2095

17. Steven Brocklehurst, 'Charles Thomson Rees Wilson: The man who made clouds', BBC News (2012). Accessed at https://www.bbc.co.uk/news/uk-scotland-20608377

18. Picture credit: Illustration 36. Charles Thomas Rees Wilson c.1927. Source http://nobelprize.org/nobel_prizes/physics/laureates/1927/wilson-bio.html. Public domain.

19. Picture credit: Illustration 37. Cloud chamber photograph of the first positron ever observed, in 1932. The thick horizontal line is a lead plate. The positron entered the cloud chamber in the lower left, was slowed down by the lead plane, and curved to the upper left. The curvature of the path is caused by an applied magnetic field that acts perpendicular to the image plane. The higher energy of the entering positron resulted in lower curvature of its path. Acknowledgement Quibik, accessed at: https://commons.wikimedia.org/wiki/File:PositronDiscovery.jpg. Public domain.

20. Picture credit: Illustration 38. Carol Spears: NASA Physicist studying Alpha Rays in a continuous cloud chamber. Here, alpha particles from a polonium source emit in a flower-like pattern at the cloud chamber's centre. Accessed at https://commons.wikimedia.org/wiki/File:Physicist_Studying_Alpha_Rays_GPN-2000-000381.jpg Courtesy NASA, public domain.

17. Range and vision

1. Michael Moss and Iain Russell, 'Range and Vision - the first hundred years of Barr & Stroud', pub. Mainstream Publishing (1988)

2. Iain Russell, 'Technical transfer in the British optical instruments industry 1888-1914: The case of Barr & Stroud', in Scottish Industrial History vol 21, pp 15-33 (2000) pub. Business Archives Council of Scotland. Accessed at https://busarchscot.org.uk/wp-content/uploads/2019/11/Scottish-Industrial-History-Vol-21-and-index-1960-2000-compressed.pdf

3. Peter Ifland, ' Finding Distance – The Barr & Stroud Rangefinders', J. of Navigation, vol. 56, 315-321 (2003). Accessed at https://www.cambridge.org/core/journals/journal-of-navigation/issue/5E62D42E241589206FBE7613C20DF6B6

4. Stephen Sambrook, U. of Glasgow PhD thesis, 'The optical munitions industry in Great Britain 1888 - 1923' (2005). Accessed at http://theses.gla.ac.uk/3451/1/2005SambrookPhD.pdf

5. 'Archibald Barr 1855-1931', Biographical memoirs of Fellows of the Royal Society, Accessed at https://royalsocietypublishing.org/doi/pdf/10.1098/rsbm.1932.0008

6. The University of Glasgow Story, 'Archibald Barr'. Accessed at https://universitystory.gla.ac.uk/biography/?id=WH2060&type=P

7. Grace's Guide to British Industrial History, 'Archibald Barr', Accessed at https://www.gracesguide.co.uk/Archibald_Barr

8. Ibid., 'William Stroud'. Accessed at https://www.gracesguide.co.uk/William_Stroud (2021).

9. Ibid., 'Barr and Stroud'. Accessed at https://gracesguide.co.uk/Barr_and_Stroud (2021)

10. U. of Glasgow, 'Inventing the range-finder and other optical instruments'. Accessed at https://www.worldchanging.glasgow.ac.uk/article/?id=21

11. U. of Glasgow Archive Services, 'Records of Barr & Stroud Ltd. optical instrument engineers, Glasgow, Scotland', Accessed at https://archiveshub.jisc.ac.uk/search/archives/c6835648-5da1-3a9e-b180-b89317cd09a3

12. Professors Barr and Stroud, 'Telemeters and range-finders for naval and other purposes', Proc. Inst. Mech. Eng. vol. 50, 1, pp 33-78 (1896). Accessed at https://journals.sagepub.com/doi/pdf/10.1243/PIME_PROC_1896_050_009_02

13. The Dreadnought Project, 'Barr and Stroud Rangefinders', Accessed at http://dreadnoughtproject.org/tfs/index.php/Barr_and_Stroud_Rangefinders (2021).

14. Scotland's War, 'Barr & Stroud'. Accessed at http://www.scotlandswar.co.uk/barr_stroud.html (2021)

15. David Parry, 'The history of the British submarine periscope', RN Subs. Accessed at http://rnsubs.co.uk/articles/development/scope.html (2021)

16. Gordon Petrie and Michael Nolan, 'Development of the Barr & Stroud ZD range of topographical stereoscopes for mapping applications', The Photogrammetric Record, vol. 31, 156, pp 428 – 455 (2016). Accessed at https://onlinelibrary.wiley.com/doi/epdf/10.1111/phor.12161

17. K.B. Atkinson, ' Creators of odd volumes: Detached thoughts on the work of Wollaston, Wheatstone and Barr', The Photogrammetric Record, vol. 9, 51, pp 343 – 359 (1978). Accessed at https://onlinelibrary.wiley.com/doi/epdf/10.1111/j.1477-9730.1978.tb00428.x?saml_referrer

18. William Stroud (obituary), The Engineer, June 3rd, p 625 (1938). Accessed at https://www.gracesguide.co.uk/Special:MemberUsers?file=5/54/Er19380603.pdf

19. James B. Henderson, 'The Stroud system of teaching dynamics', Math. Gaz. vol. 12. 170, pp 99-105 (1924). Accessed at https://www.jstor.org/stable/3604647

20. G.N. Copley, 'William Stroud and the Quantity Calculus', Nature, vol. 188, p 254 (1960). Accessed at https://www.nature.com/articles/188254a0

21. Picture credit: Illustration 39. Andy Dingley (scanner). Barr & Stroud rangefinder/heightfinder with four operators c. 1920s. Accessed at

https://commons.wikimedia.org/wiki/File:Rangefinder_(Warships_To-day,_1936).jpg. Public domain.

22. Picture credit: Illustration 40. Retail advertisement for Barr & Stroud binoculars, c. 1935. Accessed at https://www.gracesguide.co.uk/Barr_and_Stroud

23. Picture credit: Illustration 41. Hpeterswald, A Barr & Stroud attack periscope type CH74 aboard an Oberon Class submarine (1957-1999). Accessed at https://commons.wikimedia.org/wiki/File:Attack_Periscope_Type_CH74_-_RAN_Oberon_Class_Submarine_1957-99.jpg under CC Attribution-SA 3.0 Unported licence.

18. Televisionary

1. 'R.W. Burns, 'John Logie Baird, television pioneer', pub. Inst. Electrical Engineers, (2000). Accessed at https://archive.org/details/johnlogiebairdte0000burn/mode/2up

2. J.L. Baird and Malcolm Baird (ed.), 'Television and Me – The memoirs of John Logie Baird', pub. Mercat Press (2004) and updated edition pub. Birlinn (2020)

3. Antony Kamm and Malcolm Baird, 'John Logie Baird, a Life', pub. National Museum of Scotland (2002)

4. Margaret Baird, 'Television Baird', pub. Haum (1973). Accessed at https://worldradiohistory.com/BOOKSHELF-ARH/History/Television-Baird-1973-Margaret-Baird.pdf

5. R.W. Burns, 'Baird, John Logie (1888-1946)', Oxford Dictionary of National Biography (2017). Accessed at https://doi.org/10.1093/ref:odnb/30540

6. 'The case of the Hannay diamonds', New Scientist, 21st Feb. 1980. Accessed at https://books.google.co.uk/books?id=fzzLC1-qqrwC&pg=PA591

7. A.A. Campbell-Swinton, 'Distant Electric Vision', Nature, vol. 78, p 151, (1908). Accessed at https://doi.org/10.1038/078151a0

8. J.L. Baird and W.E. Day, 'A system of transmitting views portraits and scenes by telegraphy or wireless telegraphy', British patent application GB222604 26th July (1923). Accessed at https://worldwide.espacenet.com/patent/search/family/010124945/publication/GB222604A?q=GB222604

9. J.L. Baird, 'Improvements in or relating to television systems and apparatus', British patent application GB270222 Oct 21st (1925). Accessed at https://worldwide.espacenet.com/patent/search/family/009822947/publication/GB270222A?q=GB270222

10. J.L. Baird, 'Apparatus for providing a visible image of an object which is in darkness', British patent application GB288882 (Oct 15th 1926)

11. F. Gray, J.W. Horton, R.C. Mathes, 'The Production and Utilization of Television Signals', Bell System Tech. J. vol. 6, 4, pp 560-603, (1927). Accessed at https://doi.org/10.1002/j.1538-7305.1927.tb00209.x

12. A.A. Campbell-Swinton, 'Electric television', Nature, vol. 118, 2973, p 590, Oct 23rd (1926). Accessed at https://doi.org/10.1038/118590a0

13. Ray Herbert, 'Seeing by wireless', Early television (1990). Accessed at http://www.earlytelevision.org/pdf/seeing_by_wireless.pdf

14. Brandon D. Inglis and Gary D. Couples, 'John Logie Baird and the Secret in the Box: The Undiscovered Story Behind the World's First Public Demonstration of Television', Proc. IEEE, vol. 108, 8, pp 1371-1382 (2020). Accessed at https://doi.org/10.1109%2FJPROC.2020.2996793

15. Donald F. MacLean, 'The Achievement of Television: The Quality and Features of John Logie Baird's System in 1926', Intl. J. for the History of Science and Technology, vol. 84, 2, pp 227-247 (2014). Accessed at https://doi.org/10.1179/1758120614Z.00000000048

16. Iain Logie Baird, 'Televising the Derby (1931): the world's first televised sporting event', Baird Television (2021). Accessed at https://www.bairdtelevision.com/televising-the-derby-1931.html

17. J. L. Baird, 'Television in 1932', in BBC Annual Report (1933). Accessed at https://www.bairdtelevision.com/television-in-1932-bbc-annual-report-1933.html

18. Malcolm Baird, 'Alice, Who art Thou? An old mystery', at Baird Television (2019). Accessed at https://www.bairdtelevision.com/alice-who-art-thou-an-old-mystery.html

19. Tom McArthur and Peter Waddell, 'Vision Warrior – The hidden achievement of John Logie Baird', pub. The Orkney Press (1990)

20. Douglas Brown, 'The electronic imaging of Baird television', PhD thesis, U. of Strathclyde (2000). Accessed at https://ethos.bl.uk/OrderDetails.do?did=3&uin=uk.bl.ethos.423860

21. Picture credit: Illustration 42. John Logie Baird 1917. Library of Congress, George Grantham Bain collection, modified by Opencooper. Accessed at

https://commons.wikimedia.org/wiki/File:John_Logie_Baird_in_1917.jp g (public domain).

22. Picture credit Illustration 43. A Baird televisor c.1930. Courtesy National Museum of Science and Technology, Milan. Accessed at https://commons.wikimedia.org/wiki/File:Televisore_meccanico,_a_disc o_di_Nipkow_-_Museo_scienza_tecnologia_Milano_02201.jpg under CC Attribution Share-Alike licence 4.0

19. The race for radar

1. Martin Hollmann, 'Christian Hülsmeyer, the inventor', Radar World (2007). Accessed at http://www.radarworld.org/huelsmeyer.html

2. 'Watt, Sir Robert Alexander Watson- (1892-1973)', Oxford Dictionary of National Biography (2017). Accessed at https://doi.org/10.1093/ref:odnb/31811

3. Oliver Dalton and Lionel Kreps, 'A History of the Analog Cathode Ray Oscilloscope' Accessed at https://vintagetek.org/wp-content/uploads/2018/02/A-History-of-the-Analog-Oscilloscope-by-Kreps-and-Dalton.pdf (2021).

4. R.A. Watson-Watt and E.V. Appleton, 'On the Nature of Atmospherics', Proc R. Soc. Lond. A vol 103,720, pp 84-102 (1923). Accessed at https://www.jstor.org/stable/94099

5. R.A. Watson Watt and J.F. Herd, ' An instantaneous direct-reading radiogoniometer', J. Inst. Electrical Engineers, vol.64, 353, pp 611-617 (1926). Accessed at https://doi.org/10.1049/jiee-1.1926.0051

6. R.A. Watson Watt, 'The directional recording of atmospherics', J. Inst. Electrical Engineers, vol. 64, 353, pp 596-610 (1926). Accessed at https://doi.org/10.1049/jiee-1.1926.0050

7. E.V. Appleton, R.A. Watson Watt, J.F. Herd, 'On the nature of atmospherics – III', , Proc R. Soc. Lond. A vol. 111, 759, pp 654-677 (1926). Accessed at https://doi.org/10.1098/rspa.1926.0086

8. J.L. Baird, 'Improvements in or relating to Apparatus for Transmitting Views or Images to a Distance', British Patent Application GB292186 (1926). Accessed at https://worldwide.espacenet.com/patent/search/family/010337304/pub lication/GB292185A?q=GB292185

9. Malcolm Baird, Douglas Brown and Peter Waddell, 'Television, Radar and J.L. Baird', Baird Television (2005). Accessed at https://www.bairdtelevision.com/radar.html

10. A.H. Taylor, L.C. Young, and L.A. Hyland, 'System for detecting objects by radio', US Patent 1,981,884 (1933). Accessed at https://patents.google.com/patent/US1981884A/en

11. Robert Watson-Watt, 'The evolution of radiolocation', J. Inst. Electrical Engineers Part IIIa, vol. 93, 1, pp 11-19 (1946). Accessed at https://doi.org/10.1049/ji-3a-1.1946.0002

12. Dick Barrett, 'Radar personalities' (2000). Accessed at https://www.radarpages.co.uk/people/watson-watt/watson-watt.htm

13. J.A. Ratcliffe, 'Robert Alexander Watson-Watt', Biographical memoirs of Fellows of the Royal Society (1975). Accessed at https://doi.org/10.1098/rsbm.1975.0018

14. 'History of radar', Wikipedia. Accessed at https://en.wikipedia.org/wiki/History_of_radar (2021)

15. Yves Blanchard, Gaspare Galati, Piet van Genderen, 'The cavity magnetron: Not just a British invention', IEEE Antennas and Propagation Magazine, vol. 55, 5, pp 244- 254 (2013). Accessed at https://ieeexplore.ieee.org/document/6735528

16. John Dingwall, 'How a trove of letters reveal the secret (and very tangled) life of the Scot who downed the Luftwaffe', Sunday Post, Oct 1st (2019). Accessed at https://www.sundaypost.com/fp/pity-sir-robert-watson-wattstrange-target-of-this-radar-plotand-thus-with-others-i-can-mentionthe-victim-of-his-own-invention-his-magical-all-seeing-eyeenabled-cloud-bound-planes-to-flybut-no/

17. Made in Perth, 'Margaret Watson-Watt' (2020). Accessed at https://madeinperth.org/margaret-watson-watt/

18. Sir Robert Watson-Watt, 'Man's means to his end', pub. Heinemann (1962).

19. Picture credit: Illustration 44. Chain Home tower at Gt. Baddow, Chelmsford. Public domain, courtesy Stuart166axe. Accessed at https://commons.wikimedia.org/wiki/File:Chain_home.jpg

20. Picture credit: Illustration 45. Sir Robert Watson-Watt c.1944. Public domain courtesy Gordon W. Powley. Accessed at https://commons.wikimedia.org/wiki/File:Robert_Watson-Watt.JPG{{PD-US-expired}}

20. Penicillin, the first antibiotic

1. Lieut. A. Fleming, 'Physiological and antiseptic action of Flavine (with some observations on the testing of antiseptics)', The Lancet, vol. 190, 4905, pp 341-345 (1917). Accessed at https://doi.org/10.1016/S0140-6736(01)52126-1

2. Leonard Colebrook, 'Alexander Fleming, 1881-1955' Biographical memoirs of Fellows of the Royal Society, vol. 2, pp 117-127, (1956). Accessed at https://doi.org/10.1098/rsbm.1956.0008

3. B. Lee Ligon, 'Sir Alexander Fleming: Scottish Researcher Who Discovered Penicillin', Seminars in Pediatric Infectious Diseases, vol. 15, 1, pp 58-64 (2004). Accessed at https://doi.org/10.1053/j.spid.2004.02.002

4. B. Lee Ligon, 'Penicillin: Its Discovery and Early Development', Seminars in Pediatric Infectious Diseases, vol. 15, 1, pp 52-57 (2004). Accessed at https://doi.org/10.1053/j.spid.2004.02.001

5. Michael Worboys, 'Fleming, Sir Alexander (1881-1955)', Oxford Dictionary of National Biography (2017). Accessed at https://doi.org/10.1093/ref:odnb/33163

6. Kevin Brown, 'Alexander Fleming, Scottish bacteriologist'. Britannica (2021). Accessed at https://www.britannica.com/biography/Alexander-Fleming

7. Nobel Organisation, 'Sir Alexander Fleming Biographical', (1945). Accessed at https://www.nobelprize.org/prizes/medicine/1945/fleming/biographical/

8. Alexander Fleming, 'On a remarkable bacteriolytic element found in tissues and secretions', Proc. Roy. Soc. B, vol. 93, 653, pp 306-317, (1922). Accessed at https://doi.org/10.1098/rspb.1922.0023

9. Alexander Fleming and V.D. Allison, 'Observations on a Bacteriolytic Substance ("Lysozyme") Found in Secretions and Tissues', Brit. J. Experimental Pathology, vol. 3, 5, pp 252-260 (1922). Accessed at https://www.ncbi.nlm.nih.gov/pmc/articles/PMC2047739/

10. Alexander Fleming, 'On the antibacterial action of cultures of a penicillium, with special reference to their use in the isolation of B. influenzae', Brit. J. Experimental Pathology, vol. 10, 3, pp 226-236 (1929). Accessed at https://www.ncbi.nlm.nih.gov/pmc/articles/PMC2048009/

11. E. Chain, H.W. Florey et al., 'Penicillin as a chemotherapeutic agent', The Lancet, vol. 236, 6104, pp 226-228, Aug 24th (1940). Accessed at https://doi.org/10.1016/S0140-6736(01)08728-1

12. Sir Alexander Fleming, 'Penicillin', Nobel lecture, Dec. 11th (1945). Accessed at https://www.nobelprize.org/prizes/medicine/1945/fleming/lecture/

13. Sir Howard Florey, 'Penicillin', Nobel lecture, Dec. 11th (1945). Accessed at https://www.nobelprize.org/prizes/medicine/1945/florey/lecture/

14. Picture credit: Illustration 46. Alexander Fleming, courtesy of Calibuon at English Wikibooks. Public domain. https://commons.wikimedia.org/wiki/File:Alexander_Fleming.jpg under

15. Picture credit: Illustration 47. Sample of penicillium mould presented by Alexander Fleming to Douglas Macleod, 1935. Accessed at https://commons.wikimedia.org/wiki/File:Sample_of_penicillin_mould_presented_by_Alexander_Fleming_to_Douglas_Macleod,_1935_(967223 9344).jpg under CC Attribution Share-Alike 2.0 Generic licence.

16. Picture credit: Illustration 48. Alexander Fleming at SPA during the 2nd National Congress of Antibiotics, Milan, 1950 (cropped). Accessed at https://commons.wikimedia.org/wiki/File:Fleming_esce_dalla_SPA.png. Public domain.

21. Scientific refugees

1. G.H. Beale, 'Charlotte Auerbach', Biographical Memoirs of the Royal Society, vol. 41, pp 20-42 (1995). Accessed at https://doi.org/10.1098/rsbm.1995.0002

2. C. Auerbach and J.M. Robson, 'Chemical production of mutation', Nature, vol. 157, p 302, (1946). Accessed at https://www.nature.com/articles/157302a0

3. Brain J. Kilbey 'In memoriam Charlotte Auerbach, FRS (1899-1994), Mutation Research, vol. 327 pp 1-4 (1995). Accessed at https://doi.org/10.1016/0027-5107(94)00187-A

4. Picture credit: Illustration 49. Charlotte Auerbach photographed by Prof. Yataro Tazima on 25th September 1953. Courtesy of Royal Society of London.

5. R. Alan North and John Hughes, 'Hans Walter Kosterlitz' Biographical Memoirs of the Royal Society vol. 59, pp 171-192 (2013). Accessed at https://doi.org/10.1098/rsbm.2012.0037

6. R. Alan North, 'Dr Hans Kosterlitz', INRC. Accessed at https://www.inrconference.org/in-memoriam/2019/1/7/dr-hans-kosterlitz (2021)

7. Hans W. Kosterlitz, 'The best laid schemes o' mice and men gang aft agley', Ann. Rev. Pharmacol. Toxicol. vol. 19, pp 1-12, (1979). Accessed at
https://www.annualreviews.org/doi/pdf/10.1146/annurev.pa.19.040179.000245

8. J. Hughes, 'Isolation of an endogenous compound from the brain with pharmacological properties similar to morphine', Brain Res. vol. 88, 2, pp 295-308 (1975). Accessed at https://doi.org/10.1016/0006-8993(75)90391-1

9. Hans W. Kosterlitz and John Hughes, 'Some thoughts on the significance of enkephalin, the endogenous ligand', Life Sciences, vol. 17, 1, pp 91-96 (1975). Accessed at https://doi.org/10.1016/0024-3205(75)90243-X

10. J. Hughes et al., 'Identification of two related pentapeptides from the brain with potent opiate agonist activity', Nature vol. 258, pp 577-579 (1975). Accessed at https://www.nature.com/articles/258577a0

11. John Hughes, 'Hans Kosterlitz' (obituary), Nature vol. 384,p 418 (1996). Accessed at https://www.nature.com/articles/384418a0

12. Towards Dolly, 'Research and Refugees – Edinburgh genetics during the 1940s' (2014). Accessed at
https://libraryblogs.is.ed.ac.uk/towardsdolly/tag/f-a-e-crew/

13. G.B. Stefano et al., 'Endogenous morphine', Trends Neurosci. Vo. 23, 9, pp436-442 (2000). Accessed at https://doi.org/10.1016/S0166-2236(00)01611-8

14. Picture credit: Illustration 50. Hans Kosterlitz. Courtesy International Narcotics Research Conference.

22. Nourishing science and peace

1. Lord Boyd Orr, 'Science and Peace', Nobel lecture (1949). Accessed at https://www.nobelprize.org/prizes/peace/1949/orr/lecture/

2. Nobel organisation, 'Lord Boyd Orr – Biographical' (1949). Accessed at https://www.nobelprize.org/prizes/peace/1949/orr/biographical/

3. Lord Boyd Orr, 'As I Recall – The 1880's to the 1960's', pub. Macgibbon and Kee (1966). Accessed at http://www.fao.org/fileadmin/templates/library/docs/As_I_Recall.pdf

4. K.L. Blaxter, 'Orr, John Boyd, Baron Boyd Orr (1880-1971)', Oxford Dictionary of National Biography (2008). Accessed at https://doi.org/10.1093/ref:odnb/31519

5. Sir John Orr, 'Food Health and Income. Report on a Survey of Adequacy of Diet in Relation to Income', pub. Macmillan & Co (1936). Accessed at https://www.sochealth.co.uk/national-health-service/public-health-and-wellbeing/food-policy/food-health-and-income/

6. Pete Ritchie, 'What would Boyd Orr Do?', Nourish Scotland, Issue 6, pp 3-5, Jan. (2017). Accessed at https://www.nourishscotland.org/wp-content/uploads/2017/01/Nourish-Magazine-Issue-6-Boyd-Orr.pdf

7. Herbert Davenport Kay, 'John Boyd Orr, Baron Boyd Orr of Brechin Mearns, 1880-1971', Biographical Memoirs of Fellows of the Royal Society (1972). Accessed at https://doi.org/10.1098/rsbm.1972.0004

8. D.P. Cuthbertson, 'Lord Boyd Orr', (Obituary), Br. J. Nutr. vol. 27, 1, pp 1-5 (1972). Accessed at https://doi.org/10.1079/BJN19720063

9. Picture credit: Illustration 51. John Boyd Orr, Nobel Peace Prize, 1949. Unknown author. Courtesy Nobel Organisation. Public domain {{PD-Sweden-photo}}. Accessed at https://commons.wikimedia.org/wiki/File:John_Boyd_Orr_nobel.jpg

23. DNA and the chemistry of life

1. James Watson, 'DNA – The Secret of Life', pub. Arrow Books (2004)

2. Alexander Todd, 'A Time to Remember – the autobiography of a chemist' pub. Cambridge University Press (1983)

3. W.H. Brock, 'Todd, Alexander Robertus, Baron Todd (1907-1997). Oxford Dictionary of National Biography (2004). Accessed at https://doi.org/10.1093/ref:odnb/64697

4. Fred Griffith, 'The significance of pneumococcal types', J. of Hygiene, vol. 27, 2, pp 113-159 (1928). Accessed at https://doi.org/10.1017/S0022172400031879

5. The Oswald T. Avery Collection, 'Shifting Focus: Early Work on Bacterial Transformation 1928-1940'. Accessed at https://profiles.nlm.nih.gov/spotlight/cc/feature/shifting (2021).

6. Oswald T. Avery, Colin M. MacLeod, Maclyn McCarty, 'Studies on the chemical nature of the substance inducing transformation of pneumococcal types', J. Exp. Med. vol. 79, 2, pp 137-158 (1944). Accessed at https://dx.doi.org/10.1084/jem.79.2.137

7. Walsh McDermott, 'Colin Munro MacLeod', National Academy of Sciences (1983). Accessed at http://www.nasonline.org/publications/biographical-memoirs/memoir-pdfs/macleod-colin.pdf

8. A.R. Todd, 'Chemical structure of the nucleic acids', Proc. Natl. Acad. Sci. USA vol. 40, 8, pp 748-755 (1954). Accessed at https://www.pnas.org/content/40/8/748

9. Alexander Robertus Todd, 'Scientific policy in Britain', Science, vol. 149, 3680, pp 156-162 (1965). Accessed at https://www.jstor.org/stable/1716286

10. Daniel M. Brown and Sir Hans Kornberg, 'Alexander Robertus Todd, OM, Baron Todd of Trumpington' Biographical Memoirs of Fellows of the Royal Society (2000). Accessed at https://royalsocietypublishing.org/doi/10.1098/rsbm.1999.0099

11. Picture credit: Illustration 52. Alexander Todd in 1957. Accessed at https://commons.wikimedia.org/wiki/File:Alexander_Todd_Nobel.jpg. Public domain, courtesy of Nobel Organisation.

24. Evidence-based medicine

1. A.L. Cochrane with Max Blythe, 'One Man's Medicine: An autobiography of Professor Archie Cochrane', pub. British Medical Journal (1989)

2. Antonio Stavrou et al., 'Archibald Cochrane (1909-1988): the father of evidence-based medicine', Interact. Cardiovasc. Thorac. Surg. vol. 18, 1, pp 121-124 (2014). Accessed at https://www.ncbi.nlm.nih.gov/pmc/articles/PMC3867052/

3. Sandy Macleod, 'Cochrane's problem: psychoanalysis and anejaculation', Australas. Psychiatry, vol. 15, 2, pp 144-147 (2007). Accessed at https://journals.sagepub.com/doi/10.1080/10398560701200117

4. A.L. Cochrane, 'Sickness in Salonika: my first, worst and most successful clinical trial', Br. Med. J. vol. 289, 6480, pp 1726-1727 (1984). Accessed at https://dx.doi.org/10.1136/bmj.289.6460.1726

5. A.L. Cochrane et al., 'Observers' errors in taking medical histories' The Lancet, vol. 257, 6662, pp 1007-1009 (1951). Accessed at https://doi.org/10.1016/S0140-6736(51)92518-4

6. Annotations, 'The Rhondda Fach Scheme', The Lancet, vol. 256, 6624, p 261(1950). Accessed at https://www.sciencedirect.com/science/article/pii/S0140673650911251

7. A.L. Cochrane et al., 'Pulmonary tuberculosis in the Rhondda Fach', Br. Med. J., 4789, pp 842-853 (1952). Accessed at https://dx.doi.org/10.1136/bmj.2.4789.843

8. L.K. Atuhaire, M.J. Campbell, A.L. Cochrane et al., 'Mortality of men in the Rhondda Fach 1950-1980', Br. J. Ind. Med. vol. 42, 11, pp 741-745 (1985). Accessed at https://dx.doi.org/10.1136/oem.42.11.741

9. L.K. Atuhaire, M.J. Campbell, A.L. Cochrane et al., 'Specific causes of death in miners and ex-miners of the Rhondda Fach 1950-1980', Br. J. Ind. Med. vol. 43, pp 497-499 (1986). Accessed at https://dx.doi.org/10.1136/oem.43.7.497

10. A.L. Cochrane and W.W. Holland, 'Validation of screening procedures', Br. Med. Bulletin, vol. 27,1, pp 3-8 (1971). Accessed at https://doi.org/10.1093/oxfordjournals.bmb.a070810

11. Tim Harford, 'Trial, error and the God complex', TED talk (2011). Accessed at https://www.ted.com/talks/tim_harford_trial_error_and_the_god_complex

12. H.G. Mather et al., 'Acute Myocardial Infarction: Home and Hospital Treatment', Br. Med. J. vol. 3, pp 334-338 (1971). Accessed at https://dx.doi.org/10.1136/bmj.3.5770.334

13. P.C. Elwood, A.L. Cochrane et al., 'A Randomised Controlled Trial of Acetyl Salicyclic Acid in the Secondary Prevention of Mortality from Myocardial Infarction', Br. Med. J. 5905, pp 436-440 (1974). Accessed at https://dx.doi.org/10.1136/bmj.1.5905.436

14. A.L. Cochrane, 'Effectiveness and Efficiency: random reflections on health services', pub. Nuffield Provincial Hospitals Trust (1972). Accessed at https://www.nuffieldtrust.org.uk/research/effectiveness-and-efficiency-random-reflections-on-health-services

15. R.A. Robbins, 'Profiles in medical courage: Evidence-Based Medicine and Archie Cochrane', Southwest J. of Pulmonary & Critical Care, vol. 5, 9, pp 65-73 (2012). Accessed at https://www.swjpcc.com/general-

medicine/2012/8/2/profiles-in-medical-courage-evidence-based-medicine-and-arch.html?SSScrollPosition=34

16. 'What is Cochrane?' Accessed at https://www.cochrane.org (2021).

17. Picture credit: Illustration 53. Archie Cochrane in 1949. Courtesy of the Cardiff University Library Cochrane Archive, U. Hospital Llandough.

25. Radiating energy

1. W. Fletcher, 'Sir Samuel Crowe Curran', Biographical Memoirs of Fellows of the Royal Society vol. 45, pp 95-109 (1999). Accessed at https://royalsocietypublishing.org/doi/pdf/10.1098/rsbm.1999.0008

2. W.W. Fletcher, 'Curran, Sir Samuel Crowe (Sam) 1912-1998', Oxford Dictionary of National Biography (2014). Accessed at https://doi.org/10.1093/ref:odnb/69524

3. Bill Fletcher, 'Sir Samuel Crowe Curran', Accessed at https://www.rse.org.uk/wp-content/uploads/2017/11/curran_samuel.pdf

4. 'Joan Stothers [sic] (Lady Curran)', Magnificent Women (2019). Accessed at https://www.magnificentwomen.co.uk/engineer-of-the-week/106-joan-stothers-lady-curran (2021)

5. John Butt, 'John Anderson's Legacy: the University of Strathclyde and its Antecedents 1796-1996', pub. Tuckwell Press Ltd. (1996)

6. Tam Dalyell, 'Obituary: Joan Curran', The Independent, 22nd Oct (2011). Accessed at https://www.independent.co.uk/arts-entertainment/obituary-joan-curran-1071704.html

26. Seeing with sound

1. James Willocks and Wallace Barr, 'Ian Donald – A memoir', pub. RCOG Press (2004).

2. James Willocks, 'Donald, Ian', Oxford Dictionary of National Biography, (2013). Accessed at https://doi.org/10.1093/ref:odnb/40066

3. Geoff Watts, 'John Wild' (Obituary), Br. Med. J. vol. 339, b4428 (2009). Accessed at https://doi.org/10.1136/bmj.b4428

4. J.J. Wild and Donald Neal, 'Use of high-frequency ultrasonic waves for detecting changes of texture in living tissues', The Lancet, Mar. 24th p. 655-657 (1951). Accessed at https://www.sciencedirect.com/science/article/abs/pii/S0140673651924038

5. John J. Wild and John M. Reid, 'Application of Echo-Ranging Techniques to the Determination of Structure of Biological Tissues', Science, vol. 115 pp 226-230 (1952). Accessed at https://science.sciencemag.org/content/115/2983/226

6. Ian Donald, J. MacVicar, T.G. Brown, 'Investigation of abdominal masses by pulsed ultrasound', The Lancet, vol. 271, 7032, pp 1188-1195 (1958). Accessed at https://doi.org/10.1016/S0140-6736(58)91905-6

7. Stuart Campbell, 'An improved method of fetal cephalometry by ultrasound', J. Obstset. Gynaec. Brit. Cwlth. Vol. 75, pp. 568-576 (1968). Accessed at https://doi.org/10.1111/j.1471-0528.1968.tb00161.x

8. Ian Donald, 'Apologia: how and why medical sonar developed', Ann. Roy. Coll. Surg. Eng. vol. 54, pp 132-140 (1974)

9. T.G. Brown, 'Development of ultrasonic scanning techniques in Scotland 1956-1979' and 'Virtual Reality in ultrasonic imaging'. Accessed at https://www.ob-ultrasound.net/brown-on-ultrasound.html (2021)

10. T.G. Brown, 'Ultrasonic detection apparatus', US Patent US3555888A, filed 1968. Accessed at https://patents.google.com/patent/US3555888

11. Alastair S. Macdonald, 'From first concepts to Diasonograph: The role of product design in the first medical obstetric ultrasound machines in 1960s Glasgow', Ultrasound, vol. 28, 3, pp 187-195 (2020). Accessed at https://journals.sagepub.com/doi/pdf/10.1177/1742271X20915226

12. Joseph Woo, 'Obstetric ultrasound history web'. Accessed at https://www.ob-ultrasound.net (2021).

13. Joseph Woo, 'A short history of the developments of ultrasound in obstetrics and gynaecology', Accessed at https://www.creatis.insa-lyon.fr/~cachard/master_is/Ultrasound_history.pdf (2021).

14. 'Nuclear Enterprises (GB)' Grace's Guide to British Industrial History. Accessed at https://www.gracesguide.co.uk/Nuclear_Enterprises_(G.B.) (2021).

15. Picture credit: Illustration 54. Ian Donald. Courtesy of NHS Greater Glasgow and Clyde Medical Illustration Services.

16. Picture credit: Illustration 55. Tom Brown. Courtesy of British Medical Ultrasound Society.

17. Picture credit: Illustration 56. NE 4102 Diasonograph (1973). Courtesy of Technical Museum Nikola Tesla, Zagreb.

18. Picture credit: 57. Illustration Ultrasound image of fetus at four months. Courtesy Centers for Disease Control and Prevention/Jim Gathany.

(2004). Accessed at
https://commons.wikimedia.org/wiki/File:Ultrasound_lores.jpg Public
domain.

27. Blockbusting pharma

1. John Christie McGrath and Richard A. Bond, ' Sir James Whyte Black
    OM', Biographical memoirs of the Royal Society (2020). Accessed at
    https://doi.org/10.1098/rsbm.2019.0047

2. James W. Black, Nobel biographical (1988). Accessed at
    https://www.nobelprize.org/prizes/medicine/1988/black/biographical/

3. A.N. Smith, J.W. Black, E.W. Fisher, 'Inhibitory effect of 5-
    Hydroxytryptophan on Acid Gastric Secretion', Nature, Nov. 23rd, p
    1127 (1957). Accessed at https://www.nature.com/articles/1801127a0

4. Viviane Quirke, 'Putting theory into practice: James Black, Receptor
    Theory and the Development of Beta-Blockers at ICI, 1958-1978', Med.
    Hist. vol. 50, 1, pp 69-92 (2006). Accessed at
    https://dx.doi.org/10.1017/s0025727300009455

5. J.W. Black, W.A.M. Duncan, C.J. Durant, C.R. Ganellin, E.M. Parsons,
    'Definition and antagonism of histamine H2-receptors', Nature, vol. 236,
    5347, pp 385-390, (1972). Accessed at
    https://www.nature.com/articles/236385a0

6. William A.M. Duncan and Michael E. Parsons, ' Reminiscences of the
    Development of Cimetidine', Gastroenterology, vol. 78, pp 620-625,
    (1980). Accessed at https://www.gastrojournal.org/article/0016-
    5085(80)90880-X/fulltext

7. W.A.M. Duncan, 'Some Decisions in the Development of Cimetidine',
    Drug Development Research, vol. 30, 1, pp 18-23 (1993). Accessed at
    https://onlinelibrary.wiley.com/doi/epdf/10.1002/ddr.430300103?saml_
    referrer

8. James W. Black, 'Drugs from emasculated hormones: the principles of
    syntopic antagonism', Nobel Lecture (1988). Accessed at
    https://www.nobelprize.org/prizes/medicine/1988/black/lecture/

9. P. Ranganath Nayak and John M. Ketteringham, 'Tagamet: Instead of
    surgery' in 'Breakthroughs' pp 85-112, pub. Pfeiffer & Company (1994).
    Accessed at http://ww.prnayak.org/sites/default/files/nayak-
    breakthroughs.pdf

10. George Sachs et al., 'Gastric Acid-dependent Diseases: A Twentieth Century Revolution', Digestive Diseases and Sciences, vol. 59, pp1358-1369 (2014). Accessed at https://link.springer.com/article/10.1007/s10620-014-3104-8

11. 'Tagamet: The Discovery of Histamine H2- receptor Antagonists', pub. American Chemical Society National Historic Chemical Landmarks (1997). Accessed at https://www.acs.org/content/acs/en/education/whatischemistry/landmarks/cimetidinetagamet.html (June 2021)

12. D. A. Christie and E.M. Tansey (eds) 'Peptic ulcer: Rise and Fall', Wellcome Witnesses to Twentieth Century Medicine, vol. 14 pub. Wellcome Trust Centre for the History of Medicine at UCL, (2002). Accessed at http://www.histmodbiomed.org/sites/default/files/44836.pdf

13. Picture credit: Illustration 58. Sir James Black, unknown author. Accessed at https://commons.wikimedia.org/wiki/File:James_Black_(pharmacologist).jpg under CC Attribution 4.0 International Licence

28. Work in progress

1. Nobel Organisation, 'The Nobel Prize in Physics 2011'. Accessed at https://www.nobelprize.org/prizes/physics/2011/summary/ (2021)

2. The United Nations Intergovernmental Panel on Climate Change. Accessed at https://www.ipcc.ch/ (2021)

3. 26th UN Climate Change Conference of the Parties (COP 26) Accessed at https://ukcop26.org/ (2021)

29. The origin of life in earth?

1. J.B.S. Haldane, 'The Origin of Life', in the 'Rationalist Annual' vol. 148, pp 3-10 (1929). Accessed at https://www.uv.es/~orilife/textos/Haldane.pdf

2. Stanley L. Miller and Harold C. Urey, 'Organic Compound Synthesis on the Primitive Earth', Science, vol. 130, 3370, pp 245-251 (1959). Accessed at https://science.sciencemag.org/content/130/3370/245

3. A.G. Cairns-Smith, 'The Origin of Life and the Nature of the Primitive Gene', J. Theoret. Biol. vol. 10, 1, pp 53-88 (1966). Accessed at https://doi.org/10.1016/0022-5193(66)90178-0

4. A.G. Cairns-Smith, 'Genetic takeover and the Mineral Origins of Life', Cambridge U. Press (1982)

5. A.G. Cairns-Smith and H. Hartman, 'Clay minerals and the Origin of Life', Cambridge U. Press (1986).

6. A.G. Cairns-Smith, 'Seven clues to the origin of life: a scientific detective story', pub. Cambridge U. Press (1985). Accessed at https://archive.org/details/sevencluestoorig00agca/

7. Richard Dawkins, 'The Blind Watchmaker', pub. Penguin, (2006 ed.)

8. Martha Henriques, 'The idea that life began as clay crystals is 50 years old', BBC Earth (2016). Accessed at http://www.bbc.co.uk/earth/story/20160823

9. A.G. Cairns-Smith, 'Evolving the Mind', pub. Cambridge U. Press (1996)

10. Anne Keleny, ' Obituary: Alexander Graham Cairns-Smith, scientist', The Scotsman, 5th Oct. 2016. Accessed at https://www.scotsman.com/news/obituary-alexander-cairns-smith-scientist-1466822

11. Alison Shaw, 'Obituary – Graham Cairns-Smith, artist, scientist and author of Seven Clues to the Origin of Life', The Herald, 13th Sept 2016. Accessed at https://www.heraldscotland.com/opinion/14738420.obituary---graham-cairns-smith-artist-scientist-author-seven-clues-origin-life/

12. Picture credit: Illustration 59. Scanning electron micrograph image of hexagonal kaolinite clay crystals, courtesy US Geological Survey. Public domain. Accessed at https://commons.wikimedia.org/wiki/File:Kaolinite_-_USGS_bws00008.jpg

13. Picture credit: Illustration 60. Graham Cairns-Smith, courtesy of Set Vivo. Accessed at http://ser-vivo.blogspot.com/2010/09/origen-de-la-vida-en-arcilla.html

30. GCS – the Glasgow Coma Scale

1. 'What is the Glasgow Coma Scale?' Accessed at https://www.glasgowcomascale.org/what-is-gcs/

2. Teasdale G, Jennett B, 'Assessment of coma and impaired consciousness. A practical scale.' The Lancet, 2, pp 81-84 (1974)

3. Bryan Jennett, Fred Plum, 'Persistent Vegetative State After Brain Damage: A Syndrome in Search of a Name', The Lancet, 299, 7753 pp

734-737 (1972). Accessed at https://www.sciencedirect.com/science/article/abs/pii/S0140673672902 425#!

4. Eelco F.M. Wijdicks, 'The transatlantic divide over brain death determination and the debate', Brain - a Journal of Neurology, 135, pp 1321-1331 (2011). Accessed at https://academic.oup.com/brain/article/135/4/1321/356500

5. Paul Brennan, Gordon D. Murray, Graham Teasdale, 'Simplifying the use of prognostic information in traumatic brain injury. Part 1: The GCS-Pupils score: An extended index of clinical severity', J. of Neurosurgery 128, 6, pp 1 -9 (2018). Accessed at https://thejns.org/view/journals/j-neurosurg/128/6/article-p1612.xml

6. Ken Lindsay, 'Bryan Jennett', The Guardian, 19th Mar 2008. Accessed at https://www.theguardian.com/science/2008/mar/19/medicalresearch?g usrc=rss&feed=science

7. Caroline Richmond and Graham Teasdale, ' William Bryan Jennett', BMJ, 336, (7642) p512 (2008). Accessed at https://www.ncbi.nlm.nih.gov/pmc/articles/PMC2258384/

8. Sir Graham Teasdale and Sam Galbraith, 'Bryan Jennett', The Herald, 2nd Feb 2008. Accessed at https://www.pressreader.com/uk/the-herald-1130/20080202/282089157456460

9. Picture credit: Illustration 61. The GCS assessment criteria and scoring.

10. Picture credit: Illustration 62. Lalocolin, 'Escala de Glasgow en niños y lacantes'. Example of the international adoption of the GCS. Accessed at https://commons.wikimedia.org/wiki/File:Escala_de_glasgow_en_niños.gif under CC-BY-SA-3.0 licence

31. Molecular machines

1. Richard P. Feynman, 'Plenty of room at the bottom', transcript of talk given to the American Physical Society in December 1959. Accessed at https://web.pa.msu.edu/people/yang/RFeynman_plentySpace.pdf

2. 'Richard Feynman Introduces the World to Nanotechnology with Two Seminal Lectures (1959 & 1984)'. Accessed at https://www.openculture.com/2013/04/richard_feynman_introduces_th e_world_to_nanotechnology.html

3. P.L. Anelli, N. Spencer and J. Fraser Stoddart, 'A molecular shuttle', J. Am. Chem. Soc. 113, pp 5131-5133 (1991). Accessed at https://pubs.acs.org/doi/pdf/10.1021/ja00013a096

4. Gautam R. Desiraju, 'Chemistry beyond the molecule', Nature, 412, pp 397-400 (2001). Accessed at http://repository.ias.ac.in/10740/1/314.pdf

5. Sir J. Fraser Stoddart, biographical (2016). Accessed at https://www.nobelprize.org/prizes/chemistry/2016/stoddart/biographical/

6. R. Eelkema, …Ben L. Feringa et al., 'Nanomotor rotates microscale objects', Nature, 440, p 163, (2006). Accessed at https://www.nature.com/articles/440163a

7. Bethany Halford, 'A nanocar with four-wheel drive', Chemical & Engineering News, 89,46, (2011). Accessed at https://cen.acs.org/articles/89/i46/Nanocar-Four-Wheel-Drive.html

8. Royal Swedish Academy of Sciences, 'How molecules became machines', (2016). Accessed at https://www.nobelprize.org/uploads/2018/06/popular-chemistryprize2016-1.pdf

9. Royal Swedish Academy of Sciences, 'Molecular machines' (2016). Accessed at https://www.nobelprize.org/uploads/2018/06/advanced-chemistryprize2016-1.pdf

10. The Nobel Prize in Chemistry 2016, Jean-Pierre Sauvage, Sir J. Fraser Stoddart and Bernard L. Feringa, press release. Accessed at https://www.nobelprize.org/prizes/chemistry/2016/press-release/

11. J. Fraser Stoddart, 'Mechanically Interlocked Molecules (MIMs)-molecular shuttles, switches and machines', Nobel lecture, reproduced in Angew. Chem. Int. Ed. 56, pp 11094-11125 (2017). Accessed at https://onlinelibrary.wiley.com/doi/epdf/10.1002/anie.201703216. Video at https://www.nobelprize.org/prizes/chemistry/2016/stoddart/lecture/

12. Northwestern University, 'Stoddart Group' Accessed at https://stoddart.northwestern.edu/ (2020)

13. Picture credit: Illustration 63. An example of a [2]catenane. Generated by M stone from crystal structure data reported by M. Cesario, C. O. Dietrich-Buchecker, J. Guilhem, C. Pascard and J. P. Sauvage in J. Chemical Society, Chemical Communications, pp 244-247 (1985) under GNU Free Documentation Licence, v1.2. Accessed at

https://commons.wikimedia.org/wiki/File:Catenane_ChemComm_244_1985.png

14. Picture credit: Illustration 64. Representation of a [2]rotaxane, M. Stone. Accessed at https://commons.wikimedia.org/wiki/File:Rotaxane_Crystal_Structure_EurJOrgChem_page2565_year1998.png under GNU Free Documentation License, Version 1.2

32. Supernovas – the making of us all

1. NASA, 'Universe 101, 'The life and death of stars'. Accessed at https://map.gsfc.nasa.gov/universe/rel_stars.html (2020)

2. National Geographic, 'Supernovae'. Accessed at https://www.nationalgeographic.com/science/space/universe/supernovae/(2020)

3. S. Chandrasekhar, 'The maximum mass of ideal white dwarfs', Astrophysical Journal, 74, p 81 (1931). Accessed at http://articles.adsabs.harvard.edu/pdf/1931ApJ....74...81C

4. The Nobel Prize in Physics 1983, Subramanyan Chandrasekhar and William A. Fowler, summary. Accessed at https://www.nobelprize.org/prizes/physics/1983/summary/

5. Coddenham Astronomical Observatory, U.K. Accessed at http://www.coddenhamobservatories.org/ (2020)

6. Wikipedia, 'Tom Boles'. Accessed at https://en.wikipedia.org/wiki/Tom_Boles (2020)

7. Q&A with Tom Boles, 'Astronomy and Geophysics', 54, 6, pp 6-9 (2013). Accessed at https://academic.oup.com/astrogeo/article/54/6/6.9/202107

8. The Nobel Prize in Physics 2011, Saul Perlmutter, Brian P. Schmidt and Adam G. Riess, press release. Accessed at https://www.nobelprize.org/prizes/physics/2011/press-release/

9. Picture credit: Illustration 65. D. de Mello, G. Massone, S. Benetti 'Supernova SN 1997D in galaxy NGC 1536'. Public domain. Accessed at https://commons.wikimedia.org/wiki/File:SN_1997D.jpg

10. Picture credit: Illustration 66. Tom Boles, supernova hunter. Courtesy of Tom Boles.

33. Diagnosing and controlling diabetes

1. The Royal Society, 'Ian Shanks biography'. Accessed at https://royalsociety.org/people/ian-shanks-12258/ (2020)

2. Who's Who, 'Shanks, Ian Alexander'. Accessed at https://www.ukwhoswho.com/view/10.1093/ww/9780199540884.001.0001/ww-9780199540884-e-34452/version/5 (2020)

3. Patents by inventor Ian A Shanks. Accessed at https://patents.justia.com/inventor/ian-a-shanks (2020)

4. Ian A. Shanks, Alan M. Smith, and Claes I. Nylander, 'Device for use in chemical test procedures', US patent 5141868 (1992). Accessed at https://patents.google.com/patent/US5141868A

5. Catherine Lee, the IPKat, 'No compensation, no consolation- or no thanks Shanks' (2014). Accessed at https://ipkitten.blogspot.com/2014/05/no-compensation-no-consolation-or-no.html

6. Kiona N Smith, 'Inventor of digital blood glucose meter wins $2.57 million from Unilever in UK court', Forbes (2019). Accessed at https://www.forbes.com/sites/kionasmith/2019/10/26/inventor-of-digital-blood-glucose-meter-wins-257-million-from-unilever-in-uk-court/?sh=4c8d39f63b29#78a8c2d03b29

7. Sam Tobin, 'Ian Shanks: Scientist awarded £2m compensation…' The Independent, 24th Oct (2019). Accessed at https://www.independent.co.uk/news/health/diabetes-uk-test-professor-ian-shanks-compensation-ecfd-a9168761.html

8. Patrick Barkham, 'Professor Ian Shanks: It's nice to have been able to help tens of millions of people around the world in controlling their diabetes', The Guardian, 2nd Dec (2010). Accessed at https://www.theguardian.com/science/2010/dec/02/professor-ian-shanks-diabetes

9. England and Wales Court of Appeal, 'Shanks v. Unilever Plc & Ors' in IIC International Review of Intellectual Property and Competition Law vol. 48, pp 466-467 (2017). Summarised at https://link.springer.com/article/10.1007/s40319-017-0592-zin

10. Supreme Court UK, 'Shanks v Unilever Plc and others', Press summary 23rd Oct (2019). Accessed at https://www.supremecourt.uk/cases/docs/uksc-2017-0032-press-summary.pdf

11. Picture credit: Illustration 67. David-i98: Blood glucose testing, (2007). Accessed at https://commons.wikimedia.org/wiki/File:Blood_Glucose_Testing.JPG under CC Attribution Share Alike 3.0 Unported licence.

34. Looking at life with electrons

1. Tim Paluka, 'Overview of electron microscopy', Caltech history of recent science and technology. Accessed at https://authors.library.caltech.edu/5456/1/hrst.mit.edu/hrs/materials/public/ElectronMicroscope/EM_HistOverview.htm (2020)

2. R. Henderson and P.N.T Unwin, 'Three-dimensional model of purple membrane obtained by electron microscopy', Nature, 257, 5521, pp 28-32 (1975). Accessed at https://www2.mrc-lmb.cam.ac.uk/groups/nu/pdf/nature75.pdf

3. Nobel prize for physics 1986, (Ruska, Binnig, Rohrer) press release. Accessed at https://www.nobelprize.org/prizes/physics/1986/press-release/

4. Nobel prize for chemistry 2017, announcement. Accessed at https://www.nobelprize.org/prizes/chemistry/2017/prize-announcement/

5. Kenneth Chang, 'Nobel prize in chemistry awarded for 3-D views of life's biological machinery', New York Times, Oct 4th (2017). Accessed at https://www.nytimes.com/2017/10/04/science/nobel-prize-chemistry.html

6. Richard Henderson biographical (2017). Accessed at https://www.nobelprize.org/prizes/chemistry/2017/henderson/biographical/

7. Jacques Dubochet biographical (2017). Accessed at https://www.nobelprize.org/prizes/chemistry/2017/dubochet/biographical/

8. 'A curious case of serendipity', EMBL (2017). Accessed at https://www.embl.fr/aboutus/alumni/news/news_2017/20171116_Dubochet-Serendipity/

9. Joachim Frank biographical (2017). Accessed at https://www.nobelprize.org/prizes/chemistry/2017/frank/biographical/

10. Kaspar Mossman, 'Profile of Joachim Frank', PNAS (2007). Accessed at https://www.pnas.org/content/104/50/19668

11. Y. Cheng, R.M. Glaeser and E. Nogales, 'How cryo-EM became hot', Cell, 171,6, pp1229-1231 (2017). Accessed at https://www.ncbi.nlm.nih.gov/pmc/articles/PMC6186021/

12. 'The inside story: A Q&A with cryo-electron microscopist Alasdair McDowall', Caltech Magazine (2018). Accessed at https://magazine.caltech.edu/post/inside-story-alasdair-mcdowall

13. Jim Al-Khalili, 'Richard Henderson zooms in on the molecules of life', The Life Scientific, BBC podcast (2018). Accessed at https://www.bbc.co.uk/sounds/play/b09r4c8f

14. Martin Hannan, "Edinburgh-born Richard Henderson wins Nobel Prize for chemistry", The National, 5th Oct (2017). Accessed at https://www.thenational.scot/news/15576638.edinburgh-born-richard-henderson-wins-nobel-prize-for-chemistry/

15. Picture credit: Illustration 68. Dr Richard Henderson, courtesy of him

16. Picture credit: Illustration 69. Cryo-electron micrograph of molecules of the enzyme pyruvate dehydrogenase (PDH). Courtesy of Richard Henderson.

17. Picture credit: Illustration 70. (Left) electron micrograph of a single 60-unit molecule of PDH with superimposed image of a single sub-unit. Courtesy of Dr Richard Henderson. (Right) image of atomic structure of PDH by Mcn2k10 (2008). Accessed at https://commons.wikimedia.org/wiki/File:PDwhole1.jpg under CC Attribution Share Alike 3.0 licence.

35. Dolly the sheep

1. National Human Genome Research Institute, 'Cloning Fact Sheet' (2020). Accessed at https://www.genome.gov/about-genomics/fact-sheets

2. Sean Cohmer, 'Nuclear transplantation', and Cheryl Lancaster, 'Karl Oskar Illmensee' The Embryo Project Encyclopedia. Accessed at https://embryo.asu.edu (2020)

3. Cloning's historical timeline. Accessed at https://www.drupal.org/files/cloningtimeline.pdf (2020)

4. John Gurdon, 'Journey of a lifetime' lecture, Gurdon Institute (2016). Accessed at https://www.youtube.com/watch?v=c3RuJMTOnE4&t=343

5. '2005 Pioneer Award, Steen M Willadsen', Reproduction, Fertility and Development, 17, xxv (2005). Accessed at https://www.publish.csiro.au/RD/pdf/RDv17n2_PA

6. The Shaw Prize, 'Autobiography of Ian Wilmut', (2008). Accessed at https://www.shawprize.org/prizes-and-laureates/life-science-and-medicine/2008/autobiography-of-ian-wilmut

7. Academy of Achievement, 'Interview with Ian Wilmut', (1998). Accessed at https://web.archive.org/web/20090323173656/http://www.achievement.org/autodoc/page/wil0int-1

8. Roslin Institute, 'Cloning- a life of Dolly'. Accessed at https://web.archive.org/web/20080307083947/http://www.roslin.ac.uk/publicInterest/cloning.php (2020)

9. K.H.S. Campbell, J. McWhir, W.A. Ritchie and I. Wilmut, 'Sheep cloned by nuclear transfer from a cultured cell line', Nature, 380, pp 64 – 65, 7th Mar. 1996. Accessed at https://cbm.msoe.edu/markMyweb/sepaTimeline/assets/17.%20Sheep%20cloned...380064a0.pdf

10. I. Wilmut, A.E.Schnieke, J. McWhir, A.J. Kind and K.H.S. Campbell, 'Viable offspring derived from fetal and adult mammalian cells', Nature, 385, pp 810-813 (1997). Accessed at https://www.nature.com/articles/385810a0

11. BBC news, '1997: Dolly the sheep is cloned'. Accessed at http://news.bbc.co.uk/onthisday/hi/dates/stories/february/22/newsid_4245000/4245877.stm

12. 'Cloning Dolly the sheep', Accessed at http://www.animalresearch.info/en/medical-advances/timeline/cloning-dolly-the-sheep/

13. Zane Bartlett, "Human Factor IX Transgenic Sheep Produced by Transfer of Nuclei from Transfected Fetal Fibroblasts" (1997), by Angelika E. Schnieke, et al." Embryo Project Encyclopedia (2014-08-19). Accessed at http://embryo.asu.edu/handle/10776/8150.

14. K.D. Sinclair et al., 'Healthy ageing of cloned sheep', Nat. Commun., 7, 12359, (2016). Accessed at https://www.ncbi.nlm.nih.gov/pmc/articles/PMC4963533/

15. Sally Lehrman, 'Dolly's Creator Moves Away from Cloning and Embryonic Stem Cells', Scientific American, Aug 1 (2008). Accessed at https://www.scientificamerican.com/article/no-more-cloning-around/

16. BBC news, 'Dolly the sheep's siblings 'healthy'' (2016). Accessed at https://www.bbc.co.uk/news/science-environment-36893506

17. Ian Wilmut, 'Keith Campbell obituary', The Guardian, 16th Oct. 2012. Accessed at https://www.theguardian.com/science/2012/oct/16/keith-campbell

18. David McKittrick, 'Professor Keith Campbell' Obituary, Independent, 12th Oct. 2012. Accessed at https://www.independent.co.uk/news/obituaries/professor-keith-campbell-biologist-who-played-leading-role-cloning-dolly-sheep-8209724.html

19. Picture credit, Illustration 71. 'Dolly the sheep with her firstborn lamb, called Bonnie', photo courtesy of The Roslin Institute, University of Edinburgh UK. Accessed at https://www.ed.ac.uk/roslin/about/dolly/media-links/images

36. His eponymous boson

1. Richard P. Feynman, 'QED: The strange theory of light and matter', pub. Penguin (1990)

2. Jon Butterworth, 'A map of the invisible: journeys into particle physics', pub. William Heinemann (2017)

3. Brian Cox and Jeff Forshaw, 'Why does $E=mc^2$?', pub. Da Capo (2009)

4. Y. Nambu and G. Jona-Lasinio, 'Dynamical model of elementary particles based on an analogy with superconductivity', Phys. Rev. vol. 122, 1, pp 345-358 (1960). Accessed at https://journals.aps.org/pr/pdf/10.1103/PhysRev.122.345

5. Yoichiro Nambu, 'Spontaneous symmetry breaking in particle physics: a case of cross-fertilization', Nobel lecture (2008). Accessed at https://www.nobelprize.org/uploads/2018/06/nambu_lecture.pdf

6. Peter Higgs, 'My life as a boson', based on a talk at King's College London, Nov 24th, 2010. Accessed at https://web.archive.org/web/20140501135924/http://www.kcl.ac.uk/nms/depts/physics/news/events/MyLifeasaBoson.pdf

7. P.W. Higgs, 'Broken symmetries, massless particles and gauge fields', Phys. Lett. vol. 12, pp 132-133 (1964). Accessed at https://lhc-machine-

outreach.web.cern.ch/particle-physics/higgs/1-s2.0-0031916364911369-main.pdf

8. P.W. Higgs, 'Broken symmetries and the masses of gauge bosons', Phys. Rev. Lett. vol 13, 16, pp 508-509, (1964). Accessed at https://journals.aps.org/prl/pdf/10.1103/PhysRevLett.13.508

9. P.W. Higgs, 'Spontaneous symmetry breakdown without massless bosons', Phys. Rev. vol. 145, 4, pp 1156-1163 (1966). Accessed at https://journals.aps.org/pr/pdf/10.1103/PhysRev.145.1156

10. Wikipedia, '1964 PRL symmetry breaking papers'. Accessed at https://en.wikipedia.org/wiki/1964_PRL_symmetry_breaking_papers

11. T.W.B. Kibble, 'History of electroweak symmetry breaking', J. Phys. Conference series 626 012001 (2015). Accessed at https://iopscience.iop.org/article/10.1088/1742-6596/626/1/012001/pdf

12. Arianna Borreli, 'The Weinberg-Salam model of electroweak interactions: Ingenious discovery or lucky hunch?', Annalen der Physik, 530, 1700454, (2018). Accessed at https://onlinelibrary.wiley.com/doi/pdf/10.1002/andp.201700454

13. CERN, 'Short history of particle accelerators', (2006). Accessed at https://cas.web.cern.ch/sites/cas.web.cern.ch/files/lectures/zakopane-2006/tazzari-history.pdf

14. Ian Sample, 'Massive: the Higgs boson and the greatest hunt in science', pub. Virgin Books (2010)

15. Wikipedia, 'Peter Higgs'. Accessed at https://en.wikipedia.org/wiki/Peter_Higgs (2020)

16. U. of Edinburgh, 'Professor Peter Higgs broadcast footage' (2012). Accessed at https://vimeo.com/37175057

17. Peter Higgs, speech at Nobel banquet 2013. Accessed at https://www.youtube.com/watch?v=aBBOTC0xg4s.

18. Symmetry Magazine, 'Scientists search for origin of proton mass'. Accessed at https://www.symmetrymagazine.org/article/scientists-search-for-origin-of-proton-mass (2020)

19. Caltech, 'Dark Matter'. Accessed at https://ned.ipac.caltech.edu/level5/Sept16/Bertone/Bertone1.html (2020)

20. Lord Kelvin, Baltimore Lectures, Lecture XVI, pp 260-278 pub. C.J. Clay & Sons (1904). Accessed at https://archive.org/details/baltimorelecture00kelviala/page/260/

21. Picture credit: Illustration 72. Peter Higgs at chalkboard, by Hans G - Flickr: CC BY-SA 2.0, uploaded by Flaming Ferrari (2013). Accessed at https://commons.wikimedia.org/w/index.php?curid=30213769

37. Magnetic Resonance Imaging

1. I.I. Rabi et al., 'A new method of measuring nuclear magnetic moment', Phys. Rev. vol. 53, 4, p318 (1938). Accessed at https://doi.org/10.1103/PhysRev.53.318

2. Felix Bloch, 'The principle of nuclear induction', Nobel lecture (1952). Accessed at https://www.nobelprize.org/uploads/2018/06/bloch-lecture-1.pdf

3. P.C. Lauterbur, 'Image Formation by Induced Local Interactions: Examples Employing Nuclear Magnetic Resonance', Nature, vol. 242, pp 190-191 (1973). Accessed at https://www.nature.com/articles/242190a0.pdf

4. J.R. Mallard and M. Kent, 'Differences observed between electron spin resonance signals from surviving tumour tissues and from their corresponding normal tissues', Nature vol. 204, p 1192 (1964). Accessed at https://www.nature.com/articles/2041192a0.pdf

5. Paul C. Lauterbur, 'All science is interdisciplinary-from magnetic moments to molecules to men', Nobel lecture, (2003). Accessed at https://www.nobelprize.org/uploads/2018/06/lauterbur-lecture.pdf

6. Sir Peter Mansfield, Biographical, NobelPrize.org. Accessed at https://www.nobelprize.org/prizes/medicine/2003/mansfield/biographical/

7. J.M.S. Hutchison, R.J. Sutherland and J.R. Mallard, 'NMR imaging: image recovery under magnetic fields with large non-uniformities', J. Phys. E: Sci. Instrum. Vol. 11, pp 217-221 (1978). Accessed at https://iopscience.iop.org/article/10.1088/0022-3735/11/3/012/pdf

8. J.M.S. Hutchison, W.A. Edelstein and G. Johnson, ' A whole-body NMR imaging machine', J. Phys. E: Sci. Instrum. vol. 13, 9, pp 947-955, (1980). Accessed at https://iopscience.iop.org/article/10.1088/0022-3735/13/9/013/pdf

9. W.A. Edelstein, J.M.S. Hutchison, G. Johnson and T. Redpath, ' Spin warp NMR imaging and applications to whole-body imaging', Phys. Med. Biol. vol. 25, 751 (1980). Accessed at https://iopscience.iop.org/article/10.1088/0031-9155/25/4/017

10. J. Mallard et al., 'In vivo n.m.r imaging in medicine: the Aberdeen approach, both physical and biological', Phil. Trans. R. Soc. Lond B vol. 289, pp 519-533 (1980). Accessed at https://royalsocietypublishing.org/doi/pdf/10.1098/rstb.1980.0071

11. F.W. Smith, J.M.S. Hutchison, J.R. Mallard, G. Johnson, T.W. Redpath, R.D. Selbie, Anne Reid, C.C. Smith, 'Oesophageal carcinoma demonstrated by whole-body nuclear magnetic resonance imaging', British Medical J. vol. 282, pp 510-512 (1981). Accessed at https://www.ncbi.nlm.nih.gov/pmc/articles/PMC1504319/pdf/bmjcred00645-0012.pdf

12. J.R. Mallard, 'Nuclear magnetic resonance imaging in medicine: medical and biological applications and problems', Proc. R. Soc. Lond B vol. 226, pp 391-419. The Wellcome Foundation Lecture (1984). Accessed at JSTOR www.jstor.org/stable/36203

13. Grampian Hospitals Art Trust, 'Mark-1 The world's first whole-body MRI scanner'. Accessed at https://www.ghat-art.org.uk/mark-1-the-worlds-first-whole-body-mri-scanner/

14. F.W. Smith, 'Magnetic resonance imaging: another Scottish first', The Surgeon, vol. 4, 3, pp 167-173 (2006). Accessed at https://doi.org/10.1016/S1479-666X(06)80088-0

15. Jim Hutchison, Tom Redpath and Glyn Johnson, 'Bill Edelstein in Aberdeen', Obituary, MRPulse, vol. 3, 1, (March 2014). Accessed at https://www.ismrm.org/MRPulse/V3Issue12014/Edelstein.htm

16. Paul A. Bottomley, 'In Memoriam: William A. Edelstein, 1944-2014', Magnetic Resonance in Medicine, vol. 72, pp301-303 (2014). Accessed at https://onlinelibrary.wiley.com/doi/pdf/10.1002/mrm.25296

17. U. of Aberdeen, 'Inventor of first full body MRI machine passes away', Jim Hutchison Obituary, (2018). Accessed at https://www.abdn.ac.uk/news/12225/

18. 'Professor John Mallard', Obituary, The Times, March 1st, (2021)

19. U. of Aberdeen, 'Head of pioneering MRI team passes away', John Mallard Obituary (2021). Accessed at https://www.abdn.ac.uk/news/14707/

20. Picture credit: Illustration 73. John Mallard, Jim Hutchison, and some members of the Aberdeen medical physics group. Accessed at https://www.pressandjournal.co.uk/fp/nostalgia/2372396/highlighting-aberdeens-trailblazing-medical-pioneers-whose-work-helped-millions-of-people/

21. Picture credit: Illustration 74. Jim Hutchison. Accessed at https://mrishistory.org.uk/ Copyright TBD

22. Picture credit: Illustration 75. KeiranMaher, Examples of MRI scans of a human brain using T1, T2 and PD weighting. Accessed at https://commons.wikimedia.org/wiki/File:T1t2PD.jpg. Public domain.

38. Detecting gravitational waves

1. James Overduin, 'Einstein's Spacetime' (2007). Accessed at https://einstein.stanford.edu/SPACETIME/spacetime2.html

2. Daniel Kennefick, 'Einstein versus the Physical Review', Physics Today, vol. 58, 9, pp 43-48, (2005) Accessed at https://physicstoday.scitation.org/doi/10.1063/1.2117822

3. A. Einstein and N. Rosen, 'On gravitational waves', J. of the Franklin Institute, vol. 223, 1, pp 43-54 (1937). Accessed at https://www.sciencedirect.com/science/article/abs/pii/S0016003237905830?via%3-Dihub

4. Galina Weinstein, 'Einstein and Gravitational Waves (1936-1938)' (2016). Accessed at https://arxiv.org/ftp/arxiv/papers/1602/1602.04674.pdf

5. J.J. O'Connor and E.F. Robertson, 'Howard Percy Robertson', MacTutor Maths History (2006). Accessed at https://mathshistory.st-andrews.ac.uk/Biographies/Robertson/

6. Martin Hendry, 'An introduction to General Relativity, Gravitational Waves, and Detection Principles', Second VESF School on Gravitational Waves, Cascina, Italy (2007). Accessed at http://star-www.st-and.ac.uk/~hz4/gr/hendry_GRwaves.pdf

7. Jim Hough, Sheila Rowan and B.S. Sathyaprakash, 'The search for gravitational waves', (2005). Accessed at https://arxiv.org/ftp/gr-qc/papers/0501/0501007.pdf

8. 'What are gravitational waves?', Caltech/LIGO project. Accessed at https://www.ligo.caltech.edu/page/what-are-gw (2020)

9. Royal Society of Edinburgh, 'Ronald William Prest Drever' (2017). Accessed at https://www.rse.org.uk/wp-content/uploads/2019/06/Drever_R.pdf

10. 'The University of Glasgow Story: Ronald Drever'. Accessed at https://web.archive.org/web/20161205233911/http://www.universityst ory.gla.ac.uk/biography/?id=WH26945&type=P (2020)

11. R.W.P. Drever, James Hough et al., 'Gravitational wave detectors', Proc. R. Soc. Lond. A 368, 11-13 (1979). Accessed at https://royalsocietypublishing.org/doi/pdf/10.1098/rspa.1979.0108

12. Sheila Rowan, 'Aspects of Lasers for the Illumination of Interferometric Gravitational Wave Detectors', PhD thesis (1995). Accessed at http://theses.gla.ac.uk/3422/1/1995RowanPhD.pdf

13. 'LIGO' Wikipedia. Accessed at https://en.wikipedia.org/wiki/LIGO

14. Caltech, 'A brief history of LIGO'. Accessed at https://www.ligo.caltech.edu/system/media_files/binaries/313/original/ LIGOHistory.pdf (2020)

15. Nicola Twilley, 'How the first gravitational waves were found', The New Yorker, Feb 11th (2016). Accessed at https://www.newyorker.com/tech/annals-of-technology/gravitational-waves-exist-heres-how-scientists-finally-found-them

16. Davide Castelvecchi and Alexandra Witze, 'Einstein's gravitational waves found at last', Nature News, Feb 11th (2016). Accessed at https://www.nature.com/news/einstein-s-gravitational-waves-found-at-last-1.19361

17. Whitney Clavin, 'Caltech mourns the passing of LIGO co-founder Ronald P.W. Drever', (2017). Accessed at https://www.caltech.edu/about/news/caltech-mourns-passing-ligo-co-founder-ronald-w-drever-54336

18. Rainer Weiss, 'Ronald Drever (1931-2017)', Nature vol. 544, p. 298 (2017). Accessed at https://www.nature.com/articles/544298a

19. Sean Leavey, 'An interview with Sir James Hough', LIGO magazine, Issue 14, pp19-23 (2019). Accessed at https://www.ligo.org/magazine/LIGO-magazine-issue14.pdf

20. Scienceface.org, 'Gravitational Waves: An interview with Prof. Jim Hough of the University of Glasgow', (2016). Accessed at https://www.youtube.com/watch?v=R8eDRYjj3ZQ

21. Scienceface.org, 'Glasgow fibres in the hunt for gravitational waves: An interview with Prof. Sheila Rowan of the University of Glasgow' (2016). Accessed at https://www.youtube.com/watch?v=Qt7LdcN0sgQ

22. Bernard Schutz, 'Sir Jim', The Rumbling Universe (2019). Accessed at https://bfschutz.com/tag/james-hough/

23. Picture credit: Illustration 76. Ronald Drever at the University of Glasgow (2007). Accessed at https://commons.wikimedia.org/wiki/File:Ronald_Drever_Glasgow_2007.jpg under Creative Commons Attribution-Share Alike 4.0 International license.

24. Picture credit: Illustration 77. Professor James Hough (2015). Copyright Institute of Physics. Accessed at https://www.iop.org/news/15/jul/page_65899.html#gref

25. Picture credit: Illustration 78. Professor Sheila Rowan, photo by Duncan Hull (2018). Accessed at https://commons.wikimedia.org/wiki/File:Sheila_Rowan_Royal_Society.jpg under Creative Commons Attribution-Share Alike 4.0 International licence.

39. Cat man

1. 39

40. Last of the summer snow

1. The Royal Society, 'Climate change: evidence and causes', Accessed at https://royalsociety.org/topics-policy/projects/climate-change-evidence-causes (2020)

2. Biography, 'Adam Watson'. Accessed at https://web.archive.org/web/20120214150454/http://www.highlandnaturalists.com/biography/adam-watson?page=0%2C1

3. Adam Watson, 'A snow book, northern Scotland', pub. Paragon (2011). Previewed at https://books.google.co.uk/books?id=oPsiZMM1w38C&lpg=PA4&ots=fjeq4wDH2-&dq

4. A. Watson, R.W. Davison and D.D. French, 'Summer snow patches and climate in northeast Scotland, U.K', Arctic and Alpine Research, 26:2, pp 141-151 (1994). Accessed at

https://www.tandfonline.com/doi/pdf/10.1080/00040851.1994.12003050?needAccess=true

5. Selina Scott, 'Man of the high places', BBC film (1986). Accessed at https://www.youtube.com/watch?v=AYS6UB14F0w

6. Wikipedia, 'Snow patches in Scotland'. Accessed at https://en.wikipedia.org/wiki/Snow_patches_in_Scotland (2020)

7. Iain Cameron, Adam Watson, David Duncan, 'Two Scottish snow patches survive until winter 2011/12', Weather, 67, 6, pp 162-164 (2012) Accessed at https://rmets.onlinelibrary.wiley.com/doi/epdf/10.1002/wea.1918

8. Iain Cameron and Blair Fyffe, 'Scottish snow patches report 2019/2020', Weather, 75, 7, pp 211-213 (2020). Summarised at https://rmets.onlinelibrary.wiley.com/doi/full/10.1002/wea.3709

9. JohnBoy, 'Britain is no country for old men', (2019). Accessed at http://britainisnocountryforoldmen.blogspot.com/2019/01/britain-is-no-longer-country-for-and.html

10. Des Thompson, The Guardian, 'Adam Watson obituary' (2019). Accessed at https://www.theguardian.com/environment/2019/feb/06/adam-watson-obituary

11. Simon Usborne, 'The end is nigh for Britain's last snow', Financial Times, Sept 15th (2017). Accessed at https://www.ft.com/content/cfa3197e-97ab-11e7-8c5c-c8d8fa6961bb

12. Chris Green, 'Meet the 'snow hunter' who tracks the melt on Scotland's mountain peaks – as the climate changes', i news, Aug 2nd (2019). Accessed at https://inews.co.uk/news/scotland/iain-cameron-snow-hunter-scottish-peaks-climate-change-321566

13. Matthew Hay, Everyday Conservation, 'The Sphinx is dead- long live the Sphinx', Oct 20th (2019). Accessed at https://undertheskin.co.uk/journal/the-sphinx-is-dead-long-live-the-sphinx/

14. Iain Cameron, Blair Fyffe, 'One Scottish snow patch survives until winter 2019/2020', Weather, vol. 75, 7, pp 211-213 (2020). Accessed at https://doi.org/10.1002/wea.3709

15. Iain Cameron, Blair Fyffe, Attila Kish, 'Twelve Scottish snow patches survive until winter 2020/21', Weather, vol. 76, 11, pp 380-382 (Nov. 2021) Accessed at https://doi.org/10.1002/wea.3958

16. Iain Cameron, Blair Fyffe, Attila Kish, 'One Scottish snow patch survives until winter 2021/22', Weather, vol. 77, 4, pp 143-145 (Apr 2022) https://doi.org/10.1002/wea.4157

17. Iain Cameron, 'The Vanishing Ice – Diaries of a Scottish snow hunter', pub. Vertebrate Publishing (2022)

18. IPCC, 2021: Summary for Policymakers. In: Climate Change 2021: The Physical Science Basis. Accessed at https://www.ipcc.ch/report/ar6/wg1/downloads/report/IPCC_AR6_WGI_SPM.pdf

19. Picture credit: Illustration 80. Ronofcam, 'Dr. Adam Watson on Glas Maol , Gleann Beag'. Accessed at https://commons.wikimedia.org/wiki/File:Adam_Watson2.jpg. under Creative Commons licence CC BY-SA 3.0

20. Picture credit: Illustration 81. Ronofcam, 'Garbh Choire Mor on Braeriach, showing Scotland's most durable snow patch' (2008). Accessed at https://commons.wikimedia.org/wiki/File:Garbh_Choire_Mor_8th_August_2008.jpg. Public domain.

42

Index

43   Acknowledgements

I am delighted to acknowledge with gratitude the feedback, help and encouragement received from a long list of supporters of the *Scotland's Science* project, including the following:

Iain Logie Baird; Professor Malcolm Baird (McMaster U.); Tom Boles (Royal Astronomical Society); Iain Cameron (Royal Meteorological Society); Professor Sir Iain Chalmers (James Lind Library); Dr Howie Firth (Orkney International Science Festival); Professor Dame Anne Glover (U. of Aberdeen, U. of Strathclyde); Dr Richard Henderson (Medical Research Council Laboratory of Molecular Biology, Cambridge); Professor John R. Hume (U. of Glasgow, U. of St Andrews); Professor John R. Hunter (U. of Birmingham); Dr Phil Judkins (U. of Leeds); Professor David J. Lurie (U. of Aberdeen); Professor Sir David MacMillan (Princeton U.); Graham Murchie (Bawdsey Radar Museum); Professor R. Alan North (U. of Manchester); Professor Sheila Rowan (U. of Glasgow); Professor Ian Shanks (U. of Glasgow); Professor Thomas W. Redpath (U. of Aberdeen); Dr John Shaw-Dunn (U. of Glasgow); Rosemary Soper (Archie Cochrane Library, U. Hospital Llandough); Professor Sir Fraser Stoddart (Northwestern U.); Professor Sir Graham Teasdale (U. of Glasgow); and Dr Robbie Thomson.

Additionally, warmest thanks are due to my patient, principal proof readers – my wife Anthea, and my daughter, Dr Rhiannon Mellis. Any remaining typographical or factual errors are, of course, entirely my own.

What they said about
Scotland's Science...

"An outstanding history of Scottish ingenuity...a well-organised book and a brilliant read...as a fellow Scot I enjoyed it immensely. I like how the history of science was interspersed with other relevant parts of Scottish history. Well done."

Tom Boles, Fellow of the Royal Astronomical Society

"Curated to a calibre I haven't seen in other history books, and I truly admire the work that must have gone in to writing it. I would recommend this book to school and university libraries across Scotland (and the UK more widely...) I can say that this book will sit on my bookshelf proudly, and I would encourage others to do the same – whether you're a student, a teacher, or just someone like me who is fascinated by the great minds of our brilliant wee country."

Jordan Murray, *theGIST* (the Glasgow Insight into Science and Technology)

"Edifying and enjoyable... this is a welcome addition to anyone interested in modern Scottish history and details the biographies of Scottish individuals who fashioned the building blocks of modern science from the late 16th to the early 20th century. The definition of 'science' is elastic and includes engineering, medicine, geology and physics as well as the occasional drift into philosophy and economics – all good grist to understanding the broader cultural landscape of scientific progress. While there are the predictable big names covered – Napier, Watt, Telford, Stevenson, Lister, Kelvin etc - Dr Mellis has ferreted deep into the archives and turned up some lesser known figures whose contribution to science might otherwise have become overlooked...Scotland's Science is a fine piece of biographical research and long overdue given the extraordinary evolution of scientists from such a small country."

John R. Hunter OBE, FSAScot, Emeritus Professor of Ancient History and Archaeology, University of Birmingham, UK

Printed in Great Britain
by Amazon